Ecology of soil animals

A title in the European Animal Biology Series

Consulting Editor

Dr. D. L. Lee
Fellow of Christ's College,
Cambridge

Ecology of
soil animals

John A. Wallwork

Lecturer in Zoology, Westfield College,
University of London

 McGRAW-HILL

London · New York · Sydney · Toronto · Mexico
Johannesburg · Panama

Published by

McGRAW-HILL Publishing Company Limited

MAIDENHEAD · BERKSHIRE · ENGLAND

07 094124 6 (Soft)
07 094125 4 (Hard)

Printed and bound in Great Britain

FOR MICHAEL AND SUSAN
AND ESPECIALLY
FOR JEAN

Preface

The concept of the soil as a biological system is by no means a new one, and this is not the first book to be written about soil animals. It is probably true to say, though, that a discipline begins to come of age when it starts to spawn its own textbooks and, if this is so, then soil biology has only recently reached this stage, although it has been developing towards maturity for the last thirty or forty years. Landmarks in this maturation process include the publication of Kühnelt's *Bodenbiologie,* produced in an English edition in 1961, Kevan's *Soil Animals* which appeared in 1962, and Dunger's *Tiere im Boden* in 1964. These authors have drawn together a considerable amount of information on the general biology of soil animals, and have done much to stimulate interest in this field. Also symptomatic of this interest was the creation, in 1961, of an international journal of soil biology, *Pedobiologia,* which serves as an important medium for the exchange of information between eastern Europe and the rest of the world. Certainly, the last two decades have seen many major developments in the scientific study of soil organisms, and it is appropriate to take stock of what has been learned, from time to time. In 1955, the Proceedings of Nottingham University Easter School were published, under the editorship of Professor Kevan, as a volume entitled *Soil Zoology,* and since this time volumes of research papers and reviews have appeared at frequent intervals. Notable among these have been Murphy's *Progress in Soil Zoology* (1962), *Soil Organisms* (1963) edited by Doeksen and van der Drift, *Soil Biology* (1967) by Burges and Raw, and *Progress in Soil Biology* (1967) by Graff and Satchell. Although these collections of research reports do not qualify as textbooks in the conventional sense, they are extremely valuable reference works, and I have drawn heavily on the information they contain, in this book.

With such literature already available, is there any need to add another title to the list? Obviously, I feel that there is. Considerable progress has recently been made in solving some of the major technical and taxonomic problems that have beset soil biology and restrained its development. Sophisticated methods are now available for collecting representative samples of soil animals, culturing these animals in the laboratory, weighing them, and measuring their rates of assimilation of food material, respiration, and growth. At the present time, there are many more taxonomists interested in soil animals than there were ten or fifteen years ago, with the result that identifications can be carried out more rapidly and more accurately. With these advances, has come a change of emphasis from the purely descriptive ecology, with which the earlier texts were mainly concerned, to a functional or quantitative approach which has many applications in the fields of agriculture, forestry, and conservation.

The economic significance of the soil fauna and flora is becoming increasingly recognized, and courses of instruction in soil biology are being included, more and more, in school and university curricula. This trend will undoubtedly continue, for the soil ecosystem is readily accessible, even in urban and metropolitan areas, and it provides a convenient source of biological material which can be used to illustrate many ecological principles. There are several excellent general ecological texts available at present which, although not concerned exclusively with the soil ecosystem, include it as part of a wider coverage. Notable among these books are Odum's *Fundamentals of Ecology,* Macfadyen's *Animal Ecology,* Southwood's *Ecological Methods,* and Phillipson's *Ecological Energetics.* With these authors, I have tried to provide a text which is basically ecological in its approach, at a level which can be understood by students with a minimum of ecological training. By restricting the subject to one particular ecosystem, however, it has been possible to explore, in some depth, such topics as distribution patterns, population dynamics, feeding behaviour, regulating mechanisms, and energetics. This is a luxury I have particularly enjoyed, and it may not be a vain hope that more advanced students and research workers will find something of interest in what has been written.

As far as the presentation of subject matter is concerned, the book can be divided into three main sections. Chapters 1 and 2 include an account, at a fairly elementary level, of those features of the soil which make it an environment suitable for animal life. The various ways in which the soil fauna can be classified (chapter 3) serve as an introduction to a group-by-group account of the main constituents of this fauna, which is given in chapters 4 to 10 inclusive. In each case, the main features of distribution, population biology, and feeding habits are discussed, along with references to key taxonomic works. In chapters 11, 12, and 13, an attempt has been made to present a synthesis of information, widely scattered in scientific literature, on population and community biology. A final chapter on ecological methods does not really do justice to a topic which has been dealt with much more comprehensively by Professor Southwood, but the simple techniques described here may be useful for teaching and demonstration purposes, and they have been included for this reason.

During the four years in which this book has been in preparation, I have received much needed encouragement and constructive criticism from many colleagues. In particular, I would like to acknowledge the help given by Dr I. Healey of King's College, London, Dr P. Newell and Professor J. Green of West-field College, London, and Dr M. Hadfield recently of Pomona College, California, and now at the University of Hawaii, who have read and criticized various parts of the manuscript. I am also grateful to Drs C. A. Edwards (Rothamsted), P. Lebrun (Nethen, Belgium), J. M. Cherrett (Bangor), W. G. Hale (Liverpool), and W. Dunger (Görlitz) who have made available preprints and reprints of their publications. The list of authors who have generously given permission for the use of published material is too long to be given in full and, instead, acknowledgements are made in the text; I owe a great debt of gratitude to these workers for without their efforts this book could not have been written. In this respect, I would also like to record my appreciation of the facilities extended to me by the editors of *American Zoologist, Annals of Applied Biology, Annual Review of Entomology, Bulletin de la Classe des Sciences, Academie royale de Belgique, Ecological Monographs, Ecology, Entomologists Monthly Magazine, Ibis, Journal of Animal Ecology, Journal of Experimental Biology, Natura Jutlandica, New Zealand Journal of Science and Technology, Oikos, Pedobiologia, Proceedings of the New Zealand Ecological Society, Societas Zoologica Botanica Fennica 'Vanamo',* and to the following publishers: Academic Press, Edward Arnold, Butterworth, VEB Gustav Fischer Verlag (Jena), Franck'sche Verlagshandlung (Stuttgart), The Macmillan Co., North-Holland Publishing Co., Springer Verlag (Berlin), Friedr. Vieweg Verlag (Braunschweig), A. Ziemsen Verlag (Wittenburg Lutherstadt), the Regents of the University of Wisconsin, and the Trustees of the British Museum.

A part of this book was written during a year's stay at Pomona College, California, and I am very pleased to acknowledge the help and cooperation I received from the College authorities and especially from my good friends in the Department of Zoology, Dr Y. Amrein and Mr G. Ott. My thanks are also due to Mrs A. Newman-Coburn of Westfield College for her technical assistance.

A book of this kind can be written in several different ways, depending on the personal inclinations of the author and his impression of what is important and what is not. The choice of themes and examples to go with them has not been a random operation, however, and has been guided by three main considerations. First, the coverage, in a geographical sense, has been made as wide as possible by drawing on information scattered in journals throughout the world. The main limitation here has been the availability of such information, for much more work has been done on the ecology of soil animals in the north temperate region than in other parts of the world. Second, the accessibility of original papers, on which I have relied so heavily for much of the documentation, has influenced the choice. This book is intended for use in schools and universities, both by students and research workers, and although there are few journals which cannot be obtained these days through inter-library loan services, it is the speed with which information can be retrieved that is becoming increasingly important. Finally, although valuable contributions made by pioneer workers in the field of soil ecology have not been neglected, special emphasis has been given to the most recent publications. Even so, the limitations of space have necessitated some curtailment in the list of references cited, and certain topics have not been dealt with in as much detail as I would have liked. Perhaps this is inevitable, but it reminds me forcibly of the truism that an author never finishes a book, he merely abandons it.   John A. Wallwork

Contents

Preface   vii

Chapter
1 THE SOIL ENVIRONMENT   1
   Mineral and Organic Composition of the Soil   1
   Soil Temperature   14
   Soil Moisture   18
   Soil Atmosphere   20
   Light   21
   References   22

2 SOIL-FORMING PROCESSES AND SOIL TYPES   24
   Soil Classification   25
   Calcification   26
   Podzolization   26
   Laterization   27
   Gleization   28
   The Organic Profile   29
   Mull and Mor   29
   Biological Characteristics of Mor and Mull   31
   Biochemical Characteristics of Mor and Mull   34
   Moder   34
   Grassland Soils   35
   Vegetation and Soil Type   36
   References   36

3 CLASSIFICATION OF THE SOIL FAUNA   38
   Body Size   38
   Presence   39
   Habitat Preference   41
   Activity   43
   References   44

4 PROTOZOA, ACOELOMATA, AND PSEUDOCOELOMATA   46
   Protozoa   46
   Platyhelminthes   50
   Nematoda   50
   Rotifera and Gastrotricha   55
   References   57

5	ANNELIDA AND MOLLUSCA	58
	Annelida	58
	Mollusca	70
	References	74

6	ONYCHOPHORA, CRUSTACEA, MYRIAPODA, AND TARDIGRADA	77
	Onychophora	77
	Crustacea	78
	Myriapoda	89
	Tardigrada	100
	References	101

7	INSECTA	104
	Isoptera	104
	Coleoptera	106
	Diptera	116
	Hymenoptera	120
	Lepidoptera	124
	References	125

8	APTERYGOTA	127
	Thysanura	127
	Diplura	127
	Protura	128
	Collembola	130
	References	147

9	ARACHNIDA	150
	Scorpiones and Solifugae	150
	Araneida	150
	Opiliones	153
	Chelonethi	155
	Acari	159
	References	175

10	VERTEBRATES	180
	'Periodic' Vertebrates	180
	Amphibia	183
	Reptilia	183
	Mammalia	184
	References	190

11 THE REGULATION OF POPULATION SIZE 191
 Theory and Practice 191
 Natality 192
 Mortality 196
 Population Regulation 203
 References 205

12 THE CHARACTER OF THE SOIL COMMUNITY 208
 Natural Associations of Species 208
 The Fauna of Grassland Soils 215
 The Fauna of Woodland and Forest Soils 218
 The Fauna of Grassland and Forest Soils Compared 221
 The Effect of Pesticides on the Character of the Soil Fauna 224
 References 225

13 THE FUNCTIONING OF THE SOIL COMMUNITY 228
 The Functional Character of the Community 228
 Primary Production 230
 Nutrient Cycling 231
 Energetics of the Detritivore/Decomposer Food Chain 233
 Energetics of the Detritivore/Carnivore Food Chain 241
 References 245

14 COLLECTION, PRESERVATION, AND IDENTIFICATION OF SOIL ANIMALS 247
 Extraction Techniques 247
 Preservation 256
 Identification of Soil Animals 258
 References 258

Index 260

1. The soil environment

In the central part of southern Idaho, there is a National Monument aptly called the 'Craters of the Moon'. This barren, virtually treeless landscape of some 48 000 acres gives an immediate impression of desolation, bleak and even hostile, with its crisp cinder cones and rolling lava beds. Thousands of years ago, volcanic activity forced extrusions of molten lava through weakened zones and cracks in the earth's crust, and hot cinders rained down on the surrounding countryside, obliterating the existing soil, its vegetation, and the associated fauna. This event, or rather series of events, for the volcanic activity in this region apparently occurred sporadically over a considerable period of geological time, had a devastating effect on the terrestrial communities, an effect still persisting today, 1500 years after the last major eruption. The poverty of flora and fauna, attributable to the absence of soil, provides here a convincing demonstration of the importance of this substance in the development of flourishing terrestrial communities.

So much of the earth's land surface is covered with soil supporting rich and varied biological communities, that sometimes we may take its special features for granted. It is perhaps appropriate to dwell a little on these features at the outset, for living organisms find in the soil an environment providing food, shelter, and concealment from predators.

Mineral and Organic Composition of the Soil

Soil is a decomposition product. Its solid phase has two main constituents, namely mineral material, derived from some parent material by weathering, and organic material. Detailed accounts of the chemical composition and properties of soil-forming rocks can be found in most modern pedology texts (see, for example, Russell, 1961). For our purposes, it is necessary to provide only the basic data given in Tables 1.1 and 1.2. Closely associated with mineral soil is the organic material provided by the vegetation growing in the soil. Both of these components undergo decomposition or transformation under the action of various agents. In the case of parent material, these agents are mainly physico-chemical, although organisms also play a part. The decomposition of organic litter is predominantly influenced by soil organisms, with physico-chemical agents playing a lesser role. Ultimately, these two originally distinct substances become closely integrated as organo-mineral complexes which characterize the mature soil. During this process, the structural and textural qualities of the soil develop, and the characteristic pH is determined.

TABLE 1.1. Classification, characteristics, and mineral composition of the principal soil-forming rocks.

Class	Type	Description	Principal minerals
Igneous Formed by cooling of molten magma	Granite	Usually light in colour, coarse to medium grain	Quartz, feldspar, mica, amphibole, iron oxides
	Diorite	Grey to dark in colour, coarse to medium grain	Feldspar, amphibole, iron oxide, biotite
	Basalt	Dark to black in colour, dense of fine grain	Feldspar, pyroxene, iron oxides, biotite
Metamorphic Formed by change of pre-existing rocks through heat and pressure	Gneiss	With light and dark bands	Much as in granite from which it is formed
	Schist	Foliated structure	Much as in basalt or shale from which it is formed
	Slate	Grey to black in colour, compact and uniform texture	Similar composition to shale from which it is formed
	Quartzite	Light to brown in colour, compact and uniform texture	Similar composition to sandstone from which it is formed
	Marble	Light, red, green, or black in colour, compact, fine to coarse texture	Calcite, dolomite, formed from limestone
Sedimentary Formed by deposition of weathered minerals	Shales	Light to dark in colour, thinly laminated	Clay minerals, quartz
	Sandstone	Light to red in colour, granular and porous	Quartz, clay minerals, iron oxides, calcium carbonate
	Limestone	Light, grey, red, brown, or black in colour, fine grained and compact	Calcite, dolomite, iron oxides, clay minerals

The first thing we learn about the soil is that it has a definite structure; this can be observed in many a fresh road or rail cutting. The vertical profile consists of various zones, one on top of the other, often differing in colour, texture, and thickness. Frequently, these zones are so sharply demarcated from each other, particularly in some forest soils, that we can speak of soil layers or strata. These layers accumulate above the bedrock or parent material over periods of hundreds of years, in a slow developmental sequence. The particular path along which development proceeds is influenced particularly by climate, vegetation type, and

TABLE 1.2. Chemical composition of some common soil minerals.

Mineral	Chemical constitution
Sand and silt minerals[1]	
Quartz	SiO_2
Feldspars	
Orthoclase	$K_2Al_2Si_6O_{16}$
Plagioclase	$NaAlSi_3O_8$
Calcium feldspar	$CaAl_2Si_2O_8$
Micas	
Muscovite	$K(OH)_2Al_2(AlSi_3)O_{10}$
Biotite	K, Mg, Fe, Al silicate
Pyroxene	$(Mg,Fe)SiO_3$
Amphibole	$(Mg\ Fe)_7(Si_4O_{11})_2(OH)_2$
Olivine	$(Mg\ Fe)_2SiO_4$
Iron oxides	
Haematite	Fe_2O_3
Magnetite	Fe_3O_4
Limonite	$FeO(OH).xH_2O$
Clay minerals[1,2]	
Kaolin	$Al_2O_3.2SiO_2.2H_2O$
Montmorillonite	$(Ca,MgO)Al_2O_3.5SiO_2.5H_2O$

[1] These categories are not exclusive, for certain clay minerals occur in sand and silt fractions.
[2] The various clay minerals differ principally from each other in the arrangement of the layer lattices.

the nature of the parent material, and soils can be classified into different structural types, as we will see in the next chapter. This development is not irreversible for if the influencing factors change, an alteration in the soil structure may follow. A succession of vegetation on a given site can modify the soil characteristics, for example, when grassland gives way to forest or when conifers succeed hardwoods. Long-term changes in climate, such as persistently dry conditions replacing alternating wet and dry seasons, may reverse soil development, converting a mature, well-structured soil into a structureless condition akin to an 'embryonic' soil. Many of the soil types recognized and classified are not stable climaxes, but arrested developmental stages, halted by particular environmental conditions operating at a given time, and stable only as long as these conditions persist. This can be illustrated more clearly by tracing the general pattern of soil development under three main headings: decomposition of parent material, decomposition of organic material, and formation of organo-mineral complexes.

Decomposition of Parent Material

The agents promoting weathering of parent material are of three main types: physical, chemical, and biological.

Physical elements are primarily climatic in character, exerting a mechanical effect on the substratum, with the result that fragments are comminuted into

progressively decreasing particle sizes. Little or no chemical alteration occurs
during this process, which is frequently most evident in deserts, in high altitudes
and high latitudes, and in localities with marked topographical relief and sparse
vegetation cover. The agents mainly involved are wind, water, ice, and gravity.

FIGURE 1.1. A quartz monzonite outcrop in the Joshua Tree National Monument, Mojave
Desert, California, showing vertical fracture lines and the rounded contour produced by
abrasive effect of the wind (photo by author).

The fragmenting effect of wind action on bare rock sometimes sculptures
unusual forms, especially when small particles of parent material, carried in air
currents, intensify the abrasive action. An example of this effect is shown in Fig.
1.1. Wind action may also combine with that of water to promote the
weathering of rocky seashores, for example. Wind also brings about temperature
changes in bare rock, usually a cooling effect when combined with the
evaporation of water. It is often suggested that such temperature variations may
produce internal stresses and cracks in rocks with a heterogeneous structure, but
experimental evidence indicates that this is probably not an important method
of physical weathering.

The abrasive effect of water, illustrated in Fig. 1.2, is similar to that of wind.
Water, in the form of frost or ice, is an extremely effective physical agent,
capable of exerting an expansion force of the order of 150 ton/ft^2. The
susceptibility of rocks to this kind of fragmentation varies with the water
content; granite has a relatively low water content and is more resistant than

limestone or sandstone. The effect of ice, in the form of glaciers, is an important factor in soil formation. Glaciers are constantly in motion, advancing and retreating, and the rock over which they move is gradually worn down to produce fine particles which are deposited as drift, or till, when the glacier

FIGURE 1.2. Limestone pavement near Malham Tarn, Yorkshire, showing how percolating ground water has caused erosion along vertical joints and horizontal bedding planes. The deep channels (grykes) between the blocks of limestone are often richly colonized by shade-loving plants (photo by author).

finally retreats. This drift may be derived from bedrock of an entirely different character from that of the rock on which it is finally deposited. Extensive tracts of glacial drift, deposited during the Pleistocene period, cover much of the north temperate region, and good examples are seen in the English Pennines, where clayey drift is laid down over Carboniferous limestone, and in the Great Lakes region of North America, where the drift has a sandy character.

Gravitational action is frequently combined with other agencies, and is most effectively demonstrated by landslides and rock slippages caused by earthquakes and faulting, during which the rock is fragmented by abrasion and the forces of impact. These processes also involve the movement of rock particles from their place of origin to a new site at which the soil will develop. Such a soil is termed a 'transported' soil, in contrast to the soil developing *in situ* above parent bedrock, a 'sedentary' soil. Transported soils may also be produced by windborne deposits, as, for example, the silty loess resulting from dust storms or sanddunes from sandstorms; by iceborne deposits such as glacial drift, till, and moraines; and by waterborne alluvial, lacustrine, and marine deposits.

Sedentary or transported deposits of rock fragments represent an early stage in soil development, and are classified as azonal soils. At this stage in its development, the predominant characteristics of the soil are those inherited from the original material. During subsequent development, the soil will acquire other characteristics under the influence of the prevailing climate and vegetation.

Physical disintegration produces a greater surface area of rock exposed to the effects of chemical weathering agents. Chemical decomposition results in a change in the mineral content of the rock, for, as soil development proceeds, soluble minerals are released into solution and may become adsorbed on the surface of negatively charged colloidal particles, or are removed by leaching, or, again, may participate in the formation of new mineral complexes. Chemical weathering is a complicated process and, in fact, consists of a number of reactions. Of these, oxidation, reduction, carbonation, and hydrolysis are the most important.

Oxidation occurs in well-aerated, well-drained soils; reduction in wet, badly drained, and poorly aerated sites. These two processes frequently occur simultaneously in different parts of a soil and may complement each other. Under certain conditions, elements such as iron and manganese may go into solution (by reduction), and under others may be reprecipitated (by oxidation) in different parts of the soil (Bétrémieux and Hénin, 1965). Hydrolysis is important in the initial stages of several weathering processes and frequently acts in combination with other reactions, such as oxidation/reduction, or carbonation, as in the production of secondary kaolinitic clay minerals from primary orthoclase:

$$K_2Al_2Si_6O_{16} + 2H_2O + CO_2 \longrightarrow Al_2O_3 . 2SiO_2 . 2H_2O + 4SiO_2 + K_2CO_3$$
$$\text{Orthoclase} \qquad\qquad\qquad \text{Kaolin}$$

The release of calcium, magnesium, potassium, sodium, and silicate into the soil solution, as a result of hydrolysis, enhances the availability of these ions to plants. Carbonation is usually associated with later stages in decomposition when higher concentrations of CO_2 in the soil result from the presence of organic material. This process, like hydrolysis to which it is closely linked, increases the solubility of potassium and calcium, a factor of primary importance in the weathering of limestone. The relationship between chemical weathering and the development of soil types is considered in the next chapter.

It must be remembered that, while the surface of bare rock is unsuitable for many forms of life, a number of micro-organisms, lichens, and mosses can gain a foothold (Fig. 1.3). These early colonizers transform the rock into a dynamic system, storing energy and synthesizing organic material (Jacks, 1965). Their activities change the mineral composition as well as the physical structure of the rock. Lichens are present in the initial stages of biological succession, and their growth may cause cracking or flaking, exposing a greater area of rock to further weathering. These algal-fungal associations, together with the mosses that follow them in the successional series, can extract mineral nutrients from the rock, such as phosphorus, sulphur, calcium, magnesium, potassium, sodium, iron, silicon, and aluminium. These elements are combined with organic complexes, and eventually return to the developing soil when the vegetation decomposes. The chemical transformations accompanying this process result in the production of secondary clay minerals and organo-clay complexes. With the accumulation of these important products, the stage is now set for the establishment of a richer, more varied vegetation, and from this point the decomposition of organic matter derived from this vegetation plays an ever-increasing part in soil development. Before turning to this topic, one aspect of geochemical weathering remains to be mentioned.

FIGURE 1.3. Lichen growths on a granitic boulder, Snowdonia National Park, North Wales (photo by author).

We have seen that chemical weathering releases minerals from parent material and, especially in sedimentary rocks which are rich in clay minerals, that this process also results in the formation of secondary minerals. Associated with these changes is the formation of mineral accumulations and, ultimately, concretions. The mechanisms whereby concretions are produced are not fully understood, but it does seem likely, at least in certain cases, that organic agents play an important part. Thus, organic acids promote the conversion of quartz grains into cemented quartzite (Evans, 1965), and, similarly, calcite may be precipitated from $CaCO_3$ solutions.

Decomposition of Organic Material
The fact that living organisms become established very early in the process of decomposition of parent material, means that organic decomposition is also

associated with the early stages in soil formation. During these stages, the organic content of the embryonic soil is not very high, as a general rule, for the vegetation and its associated fauna are not richly developed. Also, the products of organic decomposition frequently occur in combination with those of inorganic decomposition as complexes, not easily separable into component parts in these initial stages. However, as both of these decomposition processes develop side by side and in concert, the size of soil particles, and the spaces between them, become smaller with the result that the water-holding capacity increases. This, together with the increasing amount of plant nutrients and organic material, allows the soil to support higher plant life, such as grasses; the protective covering effect and binding action of root systems so provided, promotes a greater stability of soil structure. These conditions favour the richer development of the soil microflora and microfauna. The amount of organic material accumulating at the surface of the weathered parent material now increases considerably, the soil increases in depth, and the highly organic upper layers become separated from the immediate influence of the parent material by the development of transition zones.

The decomposition of organic material may be considered to progress through two fairly distinct stages. As dead vegetation accumulates on the soil surface, it provides food for a variety of organisms which fragment and chemically degrade it. The end product of this physical and chemical transformation is a complex substance called 'humus'. The production of humus is largely controlled by the soil flora and fauna, although physical and chemical agents also contribute. We may regard the steps leading to the formation of humus as the first phase in organic decomposition, and the slow breakdown of this relatively stable complex as the second (Handley, 1954; Burges, 1965, 1967).

Various workers have reported that decomposition of vegetable material originates with an infection by micro-organisms, and that this occurs before the vegetation is shed from the living plant. The character of the initial infection varies with the pH, fungi being associated with acid conditions, bacteria with more alkaline sites. Many of these pioneers make their first appearance as parasites of the living plant tissue, but persist as saprophytes as the tissue dies and becomes incorporated into the soil; examples of these biphasic forms are the fungi *Rhizoctonia solani, Armillaria mellea, Lophodermium* spp., and *Fusicoccum* spp. (Park, 1967; Burges, 1967). The persistence of these fungi in the soil varies from one species to another and may depend, to some extent at least, on the ability to inhibit, through the production of antibiotic substances, the growth of characteristic soil fungi such as *Penicillium* spp. and members of the *Trichoderma viride* complex. In the case of pine litter, for example, parasitic *Coniosporium* spp. are inactivated when the needles are shed, but *Lophodermium* spp. and *Fusicoccum* spp. may persist for several months after leaf-fall and, in the case of *Fusicoccum* spp., development in the soil is more extensive than in the living plant. As a general rule, however, these pioneer species are largely replaced by characteristic litter and soil species within a short space of time after leaf-fall; this succession is marked by an increase in the rate of decomposition of starch and cellulose in the litter (Burges, 1967).

Phytophagous animals, particularly insect defoliators and herbivorous mammals, will assist in the early stages of decomposition of plant material, although their effects may be localized and of varying intensity over a period of time. Once the vegetation falls to the ground, the breakdown process gathers momentum and comes under the influence of a range of environmental factors. For example, the decomposition rate is affected by the nature of the decomposing material. There is considerable evidence that leaves of most conifers take appreciably longer to decompose completely than leaves of hardwood species (Table 1.3), and herbaceous vegetation breaks down more rapidly than woody

TABLE 1.3. The relationship between speed of decomposition of leaves of various tree species and their C:N ratios (from data provided by Wittich, 1942, 1943).

Tree species	Time, in years, required for major part of decomposition	C:N ratio
Alder	⎤	19:1
Ash	⎬ 1	21:1
Elm	⎦	28:1
Hornbeam	1-2	23:1
Oak	⎤	47:1
Birch	⎬ 2-3	50:1
Poplar	⎦	63:1
Beech	3	51:1
Pine	⎤ 3-5	66:1
Douglas fir	⎦	77:1
Larch	>5	113:1

material. The decomposition rate varies not only with the species, but also with site characteristics. For example, Crossley and Witkamp (1964) showed that leaves of oak and dogwood decomposed more rapidly under oakwood than under pine, although the rate of decomposition of pine needles did not alter markedly in these two sites. The rate of leaf decomposition may be influenced by the original position of the leaves on the tree, for Heath and Arnold (1966) noted that freshly fallen leaves of oak and beech could be classified as 'soft' or 'hard' depending on whether they had occupied shaded or exposed positions on the trees. Measurements of decomposition rates in the field revealed that 'soft' leaves of both species disappeared much more rapidly than 'hard' leaves, and this was particularly noticeable when earthworms were not excluded from the experimental plots. The slower rate of removal of 'hard' leaves was attributed to their higher polyphenol content which rendered them less palatable to soil animals.

Clearly, among the factors affecting decomposition rate, the nature of the plant material and site characteristics are of major importance, although

opinions vary as to which of the two exert a predominant effect. Site
characteristics probably influence decomposition rate mainly in an indirect
manner, through the properties of the soil community, although abiotic effects
which directly determine the speed of chemical reactions may also be important.
Thus, high surface temperatures, such as occur in the tropics and hot deserts,
may speed up the rate of decomposition, provided there is not an excess or
deficiency of moisture. Decomposition frequently proceeds more rapidly in
well-aerated, neutral, or slightly alkaline conditions, but here the effect is
probably achieved through the activities of large saprophages, such as earthworms, which are often abundant under these conditions. Large amounts of
lignin retard decomposition; the rate is also slower in older than in younger
vegetation. Probably the most significant feature of the composition of plant
material, in terms of which many of these other influences may be explained, is
the relative amounts of carbon and nitrogen present, i.e., the C:N ratio. Plant
material with a relatively high C:N ratio decomposes more slowly, other
conditions being equal, than that having a lower C:N ratio, due to the fact that
the initial oxidation of carbon by heterotrophic bacteria, fungi, and actino-
mycetes blocks the nitrification process and humus formation. Wittich (1942,
1943) established this relationship for a number of hard- and softwood species,
as shown in Table 1.3. Expressed in these terms, the decomposition rate is
understandable as a function of soil community activity, for material with a low
C:N ratio will have relatively high amounts of available nitrogen, and will be
broken down more rapidly by decomposer and saprophagous organisms.

Decomposition by micro-organisms cannot, of course, proceed indefinitely,
and as the amount of easily oxidizable carbon decreases, so does their activity.
However, they have brought about radical changes in the appearance and
composition of the organic material and have rendered this more acceptable as
food to such detritus-feeding soil animals as earthworms, enchytraeids, insect
larvae, millipedes, woodlice, collembolans, mites, and protozoans. The inter-
vention of these animals not only accelerates the physical disintegration of the
organic material, but also appears to be necessary for the continued activity of
the micro-organisms (Burges, 1965), possibly by exposing greater areas of
substrate surface, transporting spores, and culling out the older growths of
micro-organisms (Wallwork, 1967).

We can, then, visualize the early stages of organic decomposition as consisting
of an initial infection of microflora which vigorously degrades carbon compounds with the liberation of large quantities of CO_2 and energy. This is
followed and stimulated by the feeding activities of the microfauna, and, as the
amount of oxidizable carbon decreases, there is a reduction in the amount of
CO_2 and energy liberated, and an increase in the amount of nitrification and the
production of humus. The activities of microflora and microfauna are more or
less simultaneous, for detritus-feeding mites and collembolans are often present,
even in the early stages, associated with lichen growths on bare rock. As the soil
develops and more organic material accumulates, the fauna becomes greatly

diversified, and a successional series of forms develops, apparently governed to a large extent by climatic factors (Stebaev, 1963). The growth of mosses and grasses attracts the larger insects, annelids, and myriapods, and much of the organic material ingested by these animals is compacted into faecal pellets, in a finely shredded state. Much of the original character of this material has been lost, but apparently it contains very little humus at this stage (see Kühnelt, 1961). These faeces support a rich microbial growth, and these micro-organisms appear to be the principal agents in the conversion of organic material into humus complexes. Ultimately, these complexes become dispersed through the developing soil profile by physical disintegration of the faecal crumbs. In well-aerated, moderately drained, and neutral or alkaline soils, where this phase of the decomposition process occurs rapidly, humus particles frequently extend to an appreciable depth, for the finely dispersed organic material mixes intimately with the mineral soil. Under conditions of poorer drainage and aeration and lower pH, decomposition occurs more slowly and less completely, and the organic material accumulates in a narrow surface zone. These two types of organic profile, termed 'mull' and 'mor' respectively, are considered further in the next chapter.

The complex community of animals and plants developing in association with these decomposition processes, plays an important part in soil dynamics. Its activity facilitates mixing of organic and mineral materials, improves drainage and aeration, and it engenders conditions suitable for continued microbial activity. This microbial activity is ultimately responsible for the breakdown of humus material, which is phenolic in character (Burges, 1965) and very stable. Degradation to the constituent phenols occurs aerobically through the action of fungi, although the detailed steps involved in this process are largely unknown. The fact that humus can resist decomposition in many soils is of great benefit to the living vegetation, for the relatively high cation exchange capacity of this substance will act to conserve inorganic nutrients, particularly in drier sites. The presence of humus also enhances soil structure through the formation of clay-humus complexes, to which we now turn.

Formation of Organo-mineral Complexes

A fertile soil is one in which the particles are aggregated together in the form of crumbs. These aggregations increase the total pore space in the soil, allowing good aeration and drainage. Soil crumbs are formed in various ways, and we can deal only with some of the more important here. A comprehensive account of crumb formation has been given by Russell (1961).

Basically, we can divide the crumb-forming mechanisms we are going to consider into two types; electro-chemical bonding and cementing. In the former, aggregation of negatively charged colloidal clay and/or humus particles is brought about through electrostatic bondings consisting of bridges of water molecules and metallic ions, particularly calcium (Fig. 1.4). Cementing mechanisms involve the action of substances adsorbed on the surface of soil particles which effectively glue them together. Several different kinds of cements have been defined, and these may be classified into inorganic and organic types. Examples of inorganic cements are common in sandy or silty soils, where

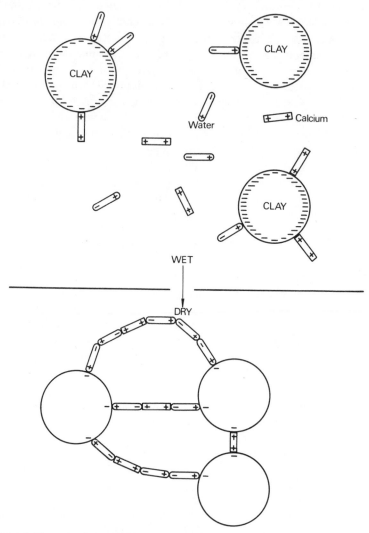

FIGURE 1.4. Electrostatic bonding of clay particles (after Ashby, 1963).

deposits of ferric and aluminium hydroxides coat the surfaces of particles and cause them to stick together. However, it is not always easy to draw a distinction between inorganic and organic cements, for the action of organic substances on mineral particles may cause a partial solution of the mineral, which subsequently recrystallizes to form a secondary cement. One example of this, the conversion of quartz into concreted quartzite, has already been mentioned. Analogous events may also be produced in limestone, with the formation of calcite aggregations. The recrystallization of secondary cements, in these cases, apparently occurs when the organic factor breaks down. Organic substances, in the form of nucleic and amino acids, are common in the soil, particularly where decaying leaf material occurs, around fungal mycelia and plant roots, which are frequently the sites of soil crumbs; it is possible that these acids may be implicated in the formation of complexes between organic and mineral particles. However, the mechanisms responsible for binding humus and clay particles together are not fully understood, and alternative explanations have been advanced to elucidate this problem. For example, Russell (1961) suggested that the negatively charged humus colloids are attracted to positively charged regions on the surface of clay particles in some instances, in others that there is a linkage between the hydroxyl groups of the humus and the silicate surface of the clay particle. It is also known that colloidal humus particles may form gel cements under conditions of partial dehydration. Again, the passage and mixture of organic and mineral material through the gut of the larger detritus-feeders, such as earthworms and slugs, evidently brings into being more stable complexes between the two. Whatever the mechanism, evidently, different kinds or degrees of clay-humus complexes may be formed, depending to a large extent on the type of clay present. Thus, dark-coloured complexes are found with montmorillonite clays, whereas the more weakly charged kaolinitic clays are light in colour, due probably to the less extensive development of the complexes resulting from their relatively low cation adsorption capacity. In soils with adequate calcium and fairly large amounts of clay materials with a high exchange capacity, these complexes are well developed, and are responsible for the fertility of many crumb grassland and forest soils.

In summary, the various stages in soil development may be listed as follows: (a) bare rock or parent material is fractured and particles become progressively smaller in size; (b) basic elements are gradually removed from the particles and are combined into compounds which may go into solution, subsequently to be removed by leaching or retained by adsorption on the surface of colloids; (c) readily decomposed minerals are degraded, leaving a skeleton of resistant compounds, products of mineral decay and resynthesized secondary compounds; (d) colloidal particles accumulate and may aggregate into crumbs or concretions; (e) colloidal humus particles may become associated with mineral particles to form organo-mineral complexes; (f) a characteristic profile develops under the influence of climate, vegetation, parent material, and the activities of the soil community. Such a profile is shown in generalized form in Fig. 1.5. The characteristics of the various strata shown in this figure are discussed in the next chapter with reference to specific soil types. At a more general level, however, we can now turn to the climatic features of this environment which are of primary importance to the organisms making their permanent homes there.

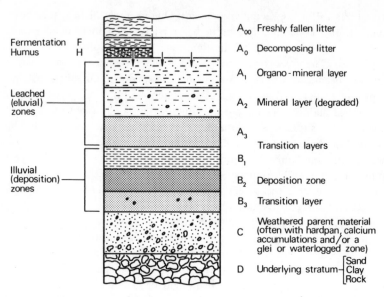

FIGURE 1.5. A generalized soil profile.

Soil Temperature

The amplitude of the temperature wave in the upper layers of the soil is related to the amount of solar radiation falling on the soil surface. How much of this radiation is intercepted, before it reaches the ground, by the surface vegetation will depend, to a large extent, on the angle at which the sun's rays strike the vegetation. This may be governed, in turn, by topographical features of the locality. For example, in the north temperate zone, vegetation growing on a north-facing slope will intercept more solar radiation than vegetation on a south-facing slope, other things being equal, due to the fact that the rays will strike at a more oblique angle, and will be more widely distributed, in the former situation. Further, in these latitudes, the radiation penetrating to the soil surface will be more strongly concentrated over a small area on a south-facing slope, and hence these slopes tend to be warmer than northern slopes.

The heat wave, propagated by radiation striking the soil surface, is considerably dampened in the lower layers, particularly in highly organic soils. As a consequence, there is a time lag between temperature changes at the surface and those in the lower layers (Fig. 1.6). Often, there is a clear correspondence between changes in air temperature and changes in litter temperature, although the latter have a lower amplitude than the former. Temperature changes in the deeper humus and mineral layers are out of phase with those of the air and litter. These deeper layers are still in the process of cooling during the forenoon period, when air and litter temperatures are rising. During late afternoon, when air and litter temperatures drop, the lag effect is such that those of the humus and

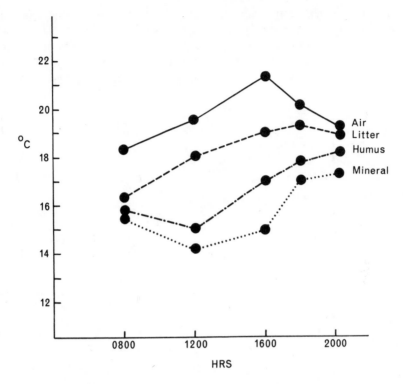

FIGURE 1.6. Diurnal temperature curves in air and floor strata under mixed hemlock and yellow birch forest, Imp Lake, Gogebic Co., Michigan on 15 July 1955.

mineral soil continue to rise, although less sharply as the night approaches. Further, the amplitude of the temperature change in the mineral layer, approximately 8 cm below the surface of the forest floor, is slightly less than that in the humus. Other authors have noted that temperatures in lower depths of the mineral layer do not fluctuate appreciably during the diurnal cycle. Clearly, the soil microclimate offers temperature conditions which show less daily variation than those in the air above, and which decrease progressively in amplitude with increasing depth in the soil. It is known that soil animals, such as the cryptostigmatid mites, show a preference for certain temperature conditions (Wallwork, 1960; Madge, 1961), and that they undergo regular vertical movements during the 24-hour cycle (Tarras-Wahlberg, 1961; Wallwork and Rodriguez, 1961). Such changes in the vertical distribution pattern, may be related to temperature preferenda, at least in part, and may represent a device by which the fauna is able to remain in equable temperature conditions, despite diurnal variations in the temperature profile.

A similar situation can be described for seasonal fluctuations. In temperate zone soils in winter, it is not uncommon to find soil not frozen beneath snow cover, even though the air temperature may be at, or below, freezing. Such an inversion in the temperature profile (Fig. 1.7) is of obvious benefit to soil organisms. Forest soils are generally well protected from extremes of temperature, due to the shelter provided by vegetation and surface accumulation of organic material, although frost pockets may provide local variations where the

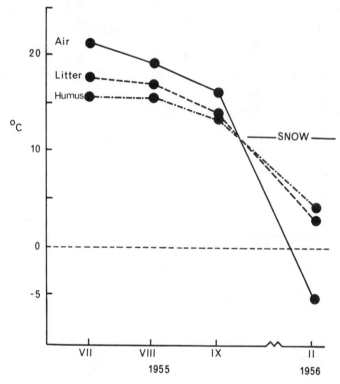

FIGURE 1.7. Temperature curves for air and soil strata under mixed hemlock and yellow birch forest, Imp Lake, Gogebic Co., Michigan, based on mean monthly estimates. Note the inversion of the temperature profile during winter.

topography is irregular. Moist soils show less temperature fluctuation than dry soils, for high moisture content reduces the amplitude of the temperature change in accordance with normal physical principles. In exposed grassland, on the other hand, the little vegetation cover present does not prevent the soil surface from receiving large amounts of direct solar radiation, and temperatures at the air/soil interface may be considerably higher than those of the air above (Fig. 1.8), or in the deeper layers of the soil, during the summer. In winter, exposure to wind may prevent the accumulation of snow and the upper soil layers may become frozen. The activity of the soil fauna may be related to these temperature characteristics; grassland carabid beetles, for example, are generally inactive during the winter and predominantly diurnal during the remainder of the year, whereas their forest counterparts are often active throughout the year, and have symmetrical activity patterns with diurnal and nocturnal components.

There is still much to be learned about the spatial and temporal variability in soil temperature conditions, and the effect of this variability on the distribution and activities of soil organisms, although increasing attention has been paid to the technical problems involved in making accurate measurements of climatic

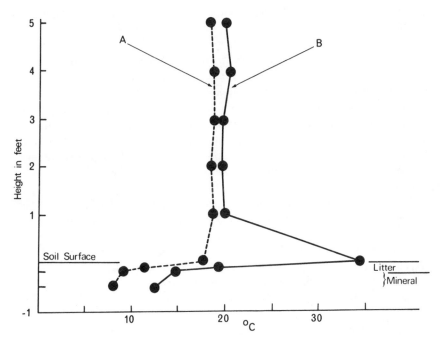

FIGURE 1.8. Temperature profiles taken in November 1966 at Joshua Tree National Monument, Mojave Desert, California. (A) under shade of juniper; (B) unshaded.

factors in the soil. In a recent survey of methods in current use, Macfadyen (1968) suggested that replicated measurements of mean temperatures, obtained by using thermistors or thermocouples, may be more meaningful than a restricted number of continuous recordings carried out with expensive equipment. Thermistors and thermocouples are commercially available as small probes which can be inserted into soil spaces, plant tissue, etc., to make rapid records of temperature changes occurring within a small volume of the environment. Thermistors are semiconductors composed of mixtures of metallic oxides, the resistance of which changes with temperature. Thermocouples are bimetallic loops, made by joining two wires of dissimilar metals, such as copper and constantan, so that an electrical potential difference occurs at the points of contact which provides a measure of the temperature difference across the thermocouple. For a more detailed account of these and other instruments for measuring microclimate, the recent review by Long (1968) should be consulted.

Soil Moisture

Environmental water exists in various forms, such as ice, frost, free water, and water vapour. The roles of ice and frost as agents of physical decomposition have been considered earlier, and we now look briefly at the environmental significance of free water and water vapour.

The free water, comprising the liquid phase of the soil, can be classified into various types, the most important of which are (a) ground, or gravitational, water; (b) capillary water; (c) hygroscopic water. Ground water is that which moves downwards in the profile under the influence of gravity, and either drains out of the soil or collects above an impervious ground layer, its upper level being termed the 'water table'. Generally speaking, soil water present in the larger soil spaces, and being held there at tensions of one-third of an atmosphere or less, will gradually drain out, under suitable conditions, i.e., in the absence of waterlogging, and is considered as ground water. The ecological significance of ground water is twofold; it is instrumental in the leaching of important nutrients and, under conditions of impeded drainage, it interferes with oxidation processes. When all of the ground water has drained from a particular soil layer, this layer is said to be at 'field capacity', or 'maximum capillary capacity', and the water remaining in it is mainly held by capillary forces in the smaller soil channels. This capillary water is extremely important from a biological point of view, for not only does it remain in the soil for a relatively long period of time carrying important nutrients in solution, but its presence also ensures that the soil atmosphere is saturated with water vapour, or nearly so. Many soil microarthropods, for example, perish in a few hours in conditions of low relative humidity, a topic to which we will return in a moment. Obviously, the maximum capillary capacity of a given soil will depend on the number of capillary spaces rather than the total pore volume. Highly organic soils are favoured in this respect, for humus has a relatively high capillary capacity due to the fact that it is a very porous substance and much of the total pore volume is made up of capillary spaces. The capacity of the underlying mineral soil is usually lower than that of humus. Hygroscopic water is of little biological importance, for it is present as a thin film, no more than 15 or 20 layers of water molecules thick, covering the soil particles, and held there by a tension ranging from 31 to 10 000 atmospheres. This water is unavailable and, essentially, in a non-liquid state; its maximum amount in any given soil expressed as a percentage of the dry weight is termed the 'hygroscopic coefficient'. This coefficient varies from soil type to soil type, being low (1-2 per cent) in mineral sites and much higher (60-70 per cent) in those that are highly organic and peaty. The relationships between these various forms of soil water are illustrated in Fig. 1.9.

Several different kinds of soil animals, such as protozoans, nematodes, rotifers, and tardigrades, which have an essentially aquatic existence, depend directly on free water for the maintenance of normal activity. Many more animals, particularly microarthropods, live in the larger spaces between soil particles, and are surrounded by the gaseous phase, the soil atmosphere. This phase will be considered in more detail later, but it is relevant to refer to it at this point, for its water vapour constituent is of considerable biological importance. The moisture content of the atmosphere, expressed as a percentage

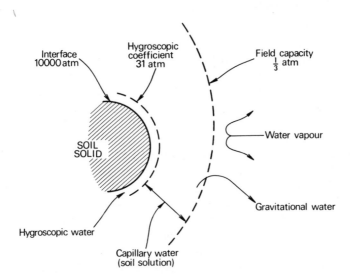

FIGURE 1.9. The relationship between the various types of soil water (redrawn from Lyon *et al.*, 1952).

of the amount that would be needed to saturate the air at the same temperature and pressure, is referred to as the 'relative humidity'. Since the capacity of air to hold water vapour increases with temperature, relative humidity will vary with changing temperature, even though the absolute moisture content may remain the same. Now, the loss of water by living organisms to the surrounding atmosphere is related to the evaporative power of the air, i.e., to its absolute moisture content, rather than to its relative humidity. This evaporative power is commonly expressed in terms of the 'saturation deficit', which is the difference between the actual water vapour pressure and the maximum water vapour pressure, at a given temperature. It is important, biologically, to distinguish between these two concepts, for the drying power of the atmosphere can vary with temperature, even though the relative humidity may remain constant, as emphasized by Cloudsley-Thompson and Chadwick (1964). Experiments carried out on a number of occasions, notably with cryptostigmatid soil mites (Madge 1964a and b; Hayes, 1966), have demonstrated specific differences in the response to, and survival in, a graded series of relative humidities. Information of this kind is difficult to relate to natural behaviour and distribution patterns, for no really accurate method has yet been devised to measure the relative humidity of the soil atmosphere. As already mentioned, if the moisture content of the soil remains above the hygroscopic coefficient, the soil atmosphere is, to all intents and purposes, saturated. However, this may not be a good measure of its drying power, as we have just noted, and it may be more realistic to describe moisture responses in terms of saturation deficit; this is an area of animal ecology which needs much more attention.

Soil Atmosphere

The spaces between soil particles are filled either with water or air, and the characteristic properties of the soil atmosphere are considerably influenced by the water content of the soil. The relative amounts of these two media are variable, depending on a number of factors, including particle size, and thus the diameter of soil spaces, rainfall, lateral and vertical water movements, depth of organic litter and its resistance to decomposition, and the burrowing activities of soil animals. As we have already noted, water is retained for the longest period in capillary spaces and as films surrounding soil particles. However, the larger soil spaces are usually filled with air, except in the case of severe waterlogging. These air channels are the living quarters for many soil animals, and their atmosphere forms an important part of the environment of the fauna. The moisture characteristics of the soil air have been considered above. The oxygen and carbon dioxide components must also be mentioned.

The ground substance of the soil, namely the organic and mineral materials, presents obstacles to the free flow of air between the soil and the atmosphere above it. Coupled with this restriction, is the fact that the metabolic activities of many soil organisms involve the absorption of oxygen and the production of carbon dioxide. As a result, there is the possibility that the concentration of oxygen in the soil air will be gradually lowered, while that of the carbon dioxide will increase. Soil organisms may, therefore, be required to survive in atmospheric conditions characterized by lower oxygen and higher carbon dioxide concentrations than are present in aerial situations (Table 1.4).

TABLE 1.4. Composition of the soil atmosphere in a typical cultivated silt loam at or near optimum moisture content.

	Percentage by volume	
	In soil air	In ordinary air
Oxygen	20·0	21·00
Nitrogen	78·6	78·03
Argon	0·9	0·94
Carbon dioxide	0·5	0·03
	100·0	100·00

Obviously, there is a lower limit to this tolerance and, if the balance is not redressed, the progressive development of anaerobic conditions will result in a strong decrease in the soil fauna. In many soils, however, this does not occur, for there is enough interchange between the soil air and that above ground to maintain suitable conditions for most organisms. There are various ways in which this can be effected. Rain water brings dissolved oxygen into the soil and, by filling up the air spaces, this water expels oxygen-deficient soil air. Fresh air is drawn into these spaces as drainage and evaporation remove some of this water. Changes in atmospheric pressure may cause movements of air into or out of the soil and, in forest sites, tree movements, particularly 'blowdowns', may cause volume changes in the adjacent soil spaces, bringing about expulsion or intake of air. The content of carbon dioxide may also be controlled by the combination of this respiratory product with parent material, for example, limestone, to produce soluble bicarbonate which is removed in drainage water.

Light

The penetration of light into the soil is variable and obviously depends very greatly on local conditions, such as soil type, topographical situation, the amount of vegetation cover, the presence of burrowing animals, and the degree of soil fracture. However, it is fair to say that the dependence of the soil community on the presence of light is most direct during the early stages in soil development, when the community is composed mainly of pioneer species associated with lichens and moss. Of course, even well-developed communities depend ultimately on light for their source of energy, which they obtain through the vegetational part of the ecosystem. On the other hand, confining our attention to the community strictly limited by the physical boundaries of the soil, it is apparent that the various biological processes taking place here, do so in the absence of light. This fact has very important repercussions on the character of the soil community, for it means that herbivorous animals constitute only a small proportion of the consumer organisms, and are represented mainly by root-feeding forms; obviously this is correlated with the absence of green plant material in the soil. Algae, moss, and lichens may occur in local abundance on the uppermost surface of the soil, but in general the primary consumer animals feed on dead and decaying vegetation. Thus, these consumers are essentially saprophagous organisms.

In certain cases, light may be an important factor in triggering the activity patterns of surface-dwelling animals, particularly insects of various kinds, although it is frequently difficult to determine whether light, humidity, or temperature factors are involved separately or in combination. Certainly, many of the true soil animals, for example, the majority of cryptostigmatid mites, do not possess well-developed light-sensitive receptors, and this, in itself, suggests that this factor does not play a direct role of any significance in the lives of these animals. On the other hand, as will be shown in chapter 6, breeding activity of the isopod *Armadillidium vulgare* is correlated with day length, so that this factor cannot be dismissed when the activities of the total soil fauna are being considered.

References

Ashby, M. (1963) *Introduction to plant ecology*, Macmillan, London. x + 249 pp.
Bétrémieux, R. and Hénin, S. (1965) 'Artificial profile development by decomposition of plant material' in Hallsworth, E. G. and Crawford, D. V., eds., *Experimental pedology*, 179-88.
Burges, N. A. (1965) 'Biological processes in the decomposition of organic matter' in Hallsworth, E. G. and Crawford, D. V., eds., *Experimental pedology*, 189-98.
Burges, N. A. (1967) 'The decomposition of organic matter in the soil' in Burges, N. A. and Raw, F., eds., *Soil biology*, 479-92.
Cloudsley-Thompson, J. L. and Chadwick, M. J. (1964) *Life in deserts*, Foulis, London. 218 pp.
Crossley, D. A. and Witkamp, M. (1964) 'Forest soil mites and mineral cycling', *Acarologia*, 6 (fasc. h. s., C. R. Ier Congrès Int. d'Acarologie, Fort Collins, Col., U.S.A., 1963), 137-46.
Evans, W. D. (1965) 'Facets of organic geochemistry' in Hallsworth, E. G. and Crawford, D. V., eds., *Experimental pedology*, 14-28.
Handley, W. R. C. (1954) 'Mull and mor formation in relation to forest soils', *Bull. For. Commn, Lond.*, 23, iv + 115 pp.
Hayes, A. J. (1966) 'Studies on the activity and survival of some phthiracaroid mites (Acari: Cryptostigmata) at different relative humidities', *Pedobiologia*, 6, 281-7.
Heath, G. W. and Arnold, M. K. (1966) 'Studies in leaf-litter breakdown II. Breakdown rate of "sun" and "shade" leaves', *Pedobiologia*, 6, 238-43.
Jacks, G. V. (1965) 'The role of organisms in the early stages of soil formation' in Hallsworth, E. G. and Crawford, D. V., eds., *Experimental pedology*, 219-26.
Kühnelt, W. (1961) *Soil biology with special reference to the animal kingdom* (English edn, trans. Walker, N.), Faber, London. 397 pp.
Long, I. F. (1968) 'Instruments and techniques for measuring the microclimate of crops' in Wadsworth, R. M., ed., *The measurement of environmental factors in terrestrial ecology*, 1-32.
Lyon, T. L., Buckman, H. O., and Brady, N. C. (1952) *The nature and properties of soils* (fifth edn), Macmillan, New York. 591 pp.
Macfadyen, A. (1968) 'The measurement of climate in studies of soil and litter animals' in Wadsworth, R. M., ed., *The measurement of environmental factors in terrestrial ecology*, 59-67.
Madge, D. S. (1961) '"Preferred temperatures" of land arthropods', *Nature, Lond.*, 190, 106-7.
Madge, D. S. (1964a) 'The water relations of *Belba geniculosa* Oudms. and other species of oribatid mites', *Acarologia*, 6, 199-223.
Madge, D. S. (1964b) 'The humidity reactions of oribatid mites', *Acarologia*, 6, 566-91.
Park, D. (1967) 'The importance of antibiotics and inhibiting substances' in Burges, N. A. and Raw, F., eds., *Soil biology*, 435-47.
Russell, E. J. (1961) *Soil conditions and plant growth* (ninth edn, revised Russell, E. W.), Longmans, London. xvi + 688 pp.
Stebaev, I. V. (1963) ['Animal succession in the soil during the course of soil development on rocks and weathered material in forest-grassland sites of the southern Urals.'] (In Russian.) *Pedobiologia*, 2, 265-309.

Tarras-Wahlberg, N. (1961) 'The Oribatei of a central Swedish bog and their environment', *Oikos,* suppl. 4, 56 pp.

Wallwork, J. A. (1960) 'Observations on the behaviour of some oribatid mites in experimentally-controlled temperature gradients', *Proc. zool. Soc. Lond.,* **135,** 619-29.

Wallwork, J. A. (1967) 'Acari' in Burges, N. A. and Raw, F., eds., *Soil biology,* 363-95.

Wallwork, J. A. and Rodriguez, J. G. (1961) 'Ecological studies on oribatid mites with particular reference to their role as intermediate hosts of anoplocephalid cestodes', *J. econ. Ent.,* **54,** 701-5.

Wittich, W. (1942) 'Über die Aktivierung von Auflagehumus extrem ungünstiger Beschaffenheit', *Z. Forst- u. Jagd.,* 718.

Wittich, W. (1943) 'Untersuchungen über den Verlauf der Streuzersetzung auf einem Boden mit Mullzustand II', *Forstarchiv,* **19,** 1-18.

2. Soil-forming processes and soil types

The soil-forming process, described in general terms in the previous chapter, is a very variable phenomenon. Soils show considerable differences in structure and composition from place to place. Development on limestone may produce a different end product from that developed on sand. Quite different soils may occur above the same kind of parent material, under different vegetation types, or in different climatic zones. Again, the character of a soil may change with its age, and it must be emphasized at the outset that the time dimension is most important when considering soil types. It is worth reiterating that a soil profile results from the influence of various factors on the parent material, and its stability is maintained only as long as these factors continue to operate. Changes in the controlling environmental factors frequently bring about alterations in the soil profile. This has been demonstrated, for instance, in the many cases where agricultural practice and land use programmes, such as the development of drainage or irrigation systems, have modified the soil character. Usually, such modifications occur slowly over a long period of time, but less dramatic changes may take place over shorter periods, and many of these differ from long-term changes in that they affect only a part of the profile and are cyclical. A common example of this type of change is provided by those soils in which the level of the ground water is subject to appreciable fluctuations from season to season. Moorland and tropical lateritic soils often show flooding effects in the deeper layers, although this phenomenon is by no means restricted to these types. Waterlogging may be a serious problem as far as the soil fauna is concerned, for in addition to restricting the amount of living space and available oxygen, the reducing conditions which ensue retard organic decomposition, liberate hydrogen sulphide, and affect the mobility of certain ionic species.

So often, soil biologists are concerned with the organic part of the profile only, neglecting the deeper mineral layers which have little direct biological interest. We have already seen, in the previous chapter, that organic and mineral components may combine into complexes having important physical and chemical properties, and it will shortly become evident that the character of the organic material may be influenced directly or indirectly by that of the mineral soil. Accordingly, our attention will continue to be focused on the whole soil profile as we deal, in this chapter, with the structural features of some major soil types and the processes leading to their development.

Soil Classification

Soils may be classified in a number of ways and, for our purposes, we need to consider three of these. In the first instance, the criterion of particle size can be used to distinguish different types. This approach, sometimes called a 'textural classification', recognizes three basic groups of soils, namely, clay, silt, and sand, forming a sequence of increasing particle size. The characteristic particle size range for each of the three groups is commonly held to be:

Clay Below 0·002 mm diameter
Silt 0·002-0·02 mm diameter
Sand 0·02-2·0 mm diameter

Many soils consist of a mixture of particle sizes, and these 'hybrids' are classified under this scheme according to the proportions of the various fractions present. Generally speaking, types having a moderate amount of clay, such as the loam and the clay-loam, are considered to be good agricultural soils.

Soils may also be classified structurally into 'zonal' types, having a well-defined profile reflecting the influences of climate and living organisms, and 'azonal' soils, lacking a well-developed profile. Many of the important grassland and forest soils belong in the former category, freshly deposited sediments and slightly weathered parent material are examples of the latter. A third group, termed 'intrazonal', is also recognized, and includes such types as the alkali and peat soils, in which the profile characteristics are more or less well defined, but the overall character of the type is dominated by some local factor associated with topography, the nature of the parent material, or age. Although we will be concerned with examples from all three of these groups, emphasis will be placed on zonal soils, for their animal associations are richer and more diverse than those of the other two categories. Grassland and forest soils may be distinguished broadly on the basis of their chemical composition, the amount of surface litter, degree of leaching, and, of course, their biological characteristics. However, the terms 'grassland soil' and 'forest soil' have a misleading simplicity, for they conceal a great deal of variability. The chestnut grassland soils are more akin to grey desert soils than to grassland prairie soils which strongly resemble brown forest soils. These intergradations suggest that the various soil types may be considered as a successional series. For example, grassland, forest, heath, moor, and fen soils may be treated, in a rather oversimplified manner, as such a series characterized by the progressive accumulation of surface litter and the increasing intensity of leaching of the upper mineral layers (Fig. 2.1). Under certain natural conditions, this sequence may be simple and linear, for forest may succeed grassland as climatic conditions produce more rainfall; persistent wet conditions may result in waterlogging which restricts forest growth and encourages the accumulation of peat.

However, factors other than rainfall are important, and in discussing these we introduce another method for classifying soils, having as its broad criterion the soil-forming process. Four of these processes will be considered: calcification,

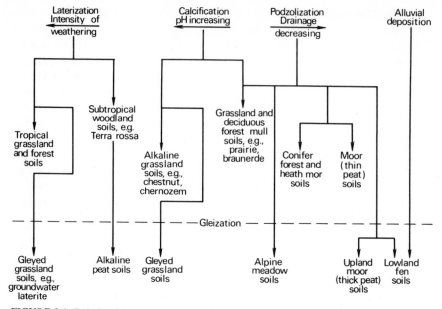

FIGURE 2.1. Relationships between some soil-forming processes and soil types.

podzolization, laterization, and gleization. The processes of salinization and alkalization will not be treated, for little information is available about their effects on soil animals.

Calcification

In its extreme form, this process occurs in areas of moderate to low rainfall, particularly where the parent material is rich in calcium carbonate. The amount of water percolating through the soil in arid regions is insufficient to cause strong leaching of carbonate, and concentrations of calcium near the surface are held by colloidal particles in a high state of base saturation. A definite calcium horizon near the surface is typical of desert soils, and the scarcity of water restricts the growth of vegetation, so that such soils are low in organic material and have a neutral or slightly alkaline pH. In areas with rather higher rainfall, some leaching of calcium carbonate from the surface occurs, and this may be redeposited lower down in the A horizon. Such soils support a moderate growth of grass and have a higher organic content than desert soils. Their surface layers may be slightly acidic as a result. The chernozem, or black earth soils, are examples of this type, as are the weakly leached chestnut soils of more arid regions.

Podzolization

In cool humid regions under forest, podzolization is characterized by strong leaching of bases from the A (eluvial) horizon, and by the deposition of colloidal iron and aluminium in the B (illuvial) zone. Generally, iron accumulates in a distinct region just below the lower limit of the A_2 layer (transition zones between A and B layers are lacking in a true podzol) and just above the zone of aluminium accumulation. The strong leaching of soluble minerals and organic material from the A_2 gives this horizon a bleached appearance, and this layer then consists, essentially, of a strongly weathered mineral skeleton represented mainly by quartz when the podzol is developed on sandy mineral soil, as it frequently is. The illuvial B horizon is darker in colour due to the accumulation of organic material, and may develop a hardpan as metallic ions are concentrated together. It has been suggested that the organic colloids, carried down the profile during leaching, act as agents in the mobilization of iron and aluminium, which are then deposited in varying states of oxidation lower down in the profile. However, Bloomfield (1965) has placed more emphasis on the efficacy of percolating rain water containing soluble polyphenolic substances, leached out from freshly fallen leaves, as the mobilizing agent. Whatever the cause, the effect is clearly seen in the sharp distinctions occurring between the surface layer of unincorporated humus, the leached impoverished A_2, and the darker B horizon giving a strongly structured profile. In a well-developed podzol, there is little mixing of organic and mineral material, and the surface zone of acid, unsaturated humus has a high base exchange capacity (Russell, 1961). Podzols are common in well-drained areas under conifer and heath vegetation which has a low base content, but are not restricted to these conditions: they may also be present in badly-drained moorland, or under deciduous or mixed forest, especially in the tropics.

The podzolization process does not always result in a true podzol profile, for when leaching is less intense, brown podzolic or grey-brown podzolic soils (brown earths) develop, in which the A horizon is more weakly bleached and a transition zone (A_1) may be present between the humus layer and the eluvial A_2. Many of these are the highly fertile mull forest soils (see below). Podzols and podzolic forest soils are characterized by the dominance of iron and aluminium oxides, and for this reason are frequently referred to as 'pedalfers', in contrast to those developing under the process of calcification, the 'pedocals', which usually support grassland. The distinction between these two types is not always easy to make, however, for intermediates formed by the combination of both processes are frequent. These transitional types show moderate leaching, are less acidic, and have surface deposits of calcium compounds, although frequently there is no deeper layer of calcium accumulation, such as occurs in the chernozem. Organic content is high, and the fertile grassland and forest soils of the Braunerde and prairie types may be classified in this category (Fig 2.1).

Laterization

This process is characterized by intense chemical weathering of soil minerals and parent rock, and is largely confined to subtropical and tropical regions. A rapid elimination of soluble bases occurs under these conditions, although oxides of iron and aluminium are retained. The dominance of these compounds is reminiscent of the podzolization process, but laterization differs from this in that it extends much deeper through the soil profile and results in the production of a heavy red, or yellow-brown, resistant soil, which has a neutral or slightly alkaline surface horizon, at least in the early stages. Organic material falling on the soil surface is rapidly broken down or removed by surface run-off during the wet season, and humus compounds may produce only a weakly stained zone at the surface. In later stages of development, particularly in localized areas where the surface relief or the presence of vegetation permit the accumulation of appreciable amounts of surface litter, the humus layers may become more strongly developed and acid conditions occur in the upper regions of the profile. These conditions may favour podzolization and, indeed, podzols and lateritic soils may occur side by side in subtropical and tropical localities. A frequent feature of the laterization process is the presence of mineral concretions which, under certain conditions, may form a hardpan some distance below the surface, or very near the surface. These hardpans are very resistant to further weathering, and may result from, or produce, conditions of impeded drainage. Under these conditions, groundwater laterites and gleisols are developed. Actually, the term 'laterite' includes at least three different products of the laterization process, one of which is the ochrosol developed under savannah vegetation in areas of low to moderate rainfall in the tropics. Less pronounced weathering occurs in subtropical regions, and, in the presence of calcareous material, may give rise to the terra rossa soils of the Mediterranean region.

Gleization

Gleization is associated with waterlogging and, as such, may affect any of the soil types resulting from the processes so far described. The immediate effect of this process is to reduce the amount of oxygen-rich water percolating through the soil profile. The metabolic activities of soil organisms rapidly use up the available oxygen and reducing conditions occur. These anaerobic conditions, in turn, restrict the kinds of soil organisms to those that can tolerate low oxygen levels and high concentrations of ammonia and sulphides. As a consequence, the rate of decomposition of organic material is considerably slowed, and the development of peat ('raw humus') is encouraged. Impeded drainage prevents the leaching of the soluble products of the weathering process, particularly calcium, and the soil layers affected by ground water have a pH which is neutral or only slightly acid. As peat continues to accumulate, the upper parts of the organic layer may become more acid, a phenomenon observed in some fen soils which have a layer of alkaline peat overlaid by acid peat. The development of reducing conditions also promotes the mobilization of iron, which is reduced from the trivalent state to the more soluble divalent condition. Ferrous iron accumulates in the waterlogged, or glei, layer and, if the level of ground water fluctuates appreciably and rapidly enough so that oxidizing conditions may develop, this may result in the precipitation of an ironpan, a common feature of moorland peat soils. However, this does not occur if the soil is permanently waterlogged (Russell, 1961).

The intensity of gleization varies considerably from place to place, and from season to season: it is obviously very closely associated with climatic conditions, particularly the amount of rainfall, and the drainage characteristics of the soil type. These factors will largely control the proportion of the profile affected and, in some cases, this may be restricted to a single layer which is bluish in colour owing to the presence of partly oxidized ferrous hydroxide (Bétrémieux and Hénin, 1965). Gleisols are not restricted to any particular geographical or topographical situation, for their distribution embraces temperate and tropical soils, montane and lowland situations (Fig. 2.1). The main prerequisite is that the locality should receive abundant rainfall for at least some part of the year.

The Organic Profile

The accounts presented above can only touch on the broad categories of soil types and soil-forming processes, for to go into this subject in any greater detail would take us into the realm of geochemistry, and this would require a textbook in itself. Indeed, it would be necessary to qualify many of the remarks made in the preceding sections, to provide a convincing explanation for a great number of the naturally occurring soil types. Climate, vegetation, and the nature of the parent material interact in the production of a particular soil profile: it is not always a simple matter to interpret natural profiles in terms of idealized types. Transitional stages, reflecting the control by one or a few local factors, are common.

On the other hand, a knowledge of the broad outlines of soil-forming processes is important to the biologist for, as we saw in chapter 1, the organic component is an integral part of the soil. Although we still need to learn much more about the reciprocal effects of organic and mineral material in the soil, there are strong indications that these effects may influence directly the composition and activity of the soil community. The characteristics of the organic zone are, then, of primary interest to the biologist. Attention has already been drawn to the fact that the distribution of organic material in the soil profile may vary with the type of decomposition process, and, in addition, the biochemical nature of the resulting humic material is also variable. In strongly structured soils, the organic zone may, itself, have a definite structure or sequence of layers, and may be considered as an organic profile.

Mull and Mor

Many forest soils provide good examples of organic profiles, and the distinction is frequently made between two types, first described by Müller (1879, 1884), namely, the 'mor' and the 'mull'. Mor humus is characteristically rather acid, usually supporting an abundance of fungal growth and low numbers of bacteria. Fungal mycelia may help to bind together particles of humus and decomposing litter into matted layers and in a well developed mor, three such layers can be distinguished, namely a surface litter, or L layer, comprising undecomposed leaves and twigs, below which is the fermentation, or F layer, in which decomposition has proceeded some way towards the development of humus, and beneath this, the humus, or H layer, in which degraded humus fractions accumulate (Fig. 1.5). The binding effect of fungal growths and roots may produce a matted or laminated mor or, in the absence of these, a granular mor may develop. Mor profiles are commonly developed on sandy soils under conifers. The low calcium content of the decomposing vegetation results in the production of an acidic humus; this is also frequently associated with podzolization of the profile. However, mor humus may develop under deciduous stands, such as beech, which have a low calcium content.

Mull humus is neutral or slightly alkaline as a general rule, developing in brown forest soils under tree species having a relatively high calcium content, such as alder, elm, basswood, aspen, and a few conifers, for example, red cedar. In this type of profile, the distinct layering of the mor is lacking, largely because the presence of calcium compounds favour the development of a rich earthworm fauna which promotes a greater mixing of organic and mineral material. Thus, humus is distributed more extensively down the profile, so that there is a broad organic/mineral zone which merges gradually into the region of weathered parent material. Such a profile develops under moderate drainage so that no strong leaching of calcium occurs; it is frequently found where the deeper substratum is clay or silt. The neutral or slightly alkaline conditions favour the growth of nitrifying bacteria, and these probably supplant the fungi, in mull soils, as the primary decomposers.

The difference between mor and mull profiles, as they are commonly defined, which strikes the observer immediately, is the difference in the distribution of organic material, i.e., its restriction to a narrow surface zone in the mor and its more uniform dispersion through the mull profile. This has led to the suggestion that the principal difference between the two types lies in the more rapid rate of decomposition of the mull which prevents its accumulation at the surface. To a certain extent, this may well be true and, moreover, may be expected, for conifer needles usually decompose more slowly than the leaves of hardwood species, and are often associated with mor humus. Rates of litter disappearance over a six-year period in mull and mor profiles on adjoining sites, under mixed hardwood vegetation, were measured and an average disappearance of 338 g/m^2 in mull, compared with 317 g/m^2 in mor, was recorded (van der Drift, 1963, 1965). A progressive accumulation of litter over the period of observation in the mor profile contrasted with no overall accumulation in the mull. Litter production on mull sites was about 6 per cent less than that on mor, and this fact also explained, in part, the differences between litter accumulation in the two profiles. However, this picture is complicated by a number of factors, particularly climate. In years when dry conditions prevailed, litter production on mull sites was more severely curtailed than on mor, and breakdown of the thin surface litter layer in the former case was retarded by desiccation of the organic material. Under these conditions, the actual amount of litter breakdown in mor, which is less subject to desiccation owing to its greater thickness, may be greater than in mull. The rate of litter breakdown obviously varies with climatic conditions, not only from year to year, but also from season to season. Seasonal differences in rate are particularly evident in the tropics, where most of the decomposition occurs during the wet season (Madge, 1965). Again, although we have seen that slowly-decomposing conifer vegetation is usually associated with mor development and the rapidly decaying hardwoods with mull, exceptions to this occur, and particular site characteristics affect rates of decomposition of all species. Gilbert and Bocock (1962) reported that birch and lime leaves disappeared more extensively on a mull site than on acid mor sites, and that attack by larger invertebrates was mainly responsible for this. Crossley and Witkamp (1964) have also shown that beech and pine leaves decompose more rapidly on a beech mull than on acid, pine mor. The pH conditions of the organic layer are clearly important in the decomposition process, and their effect is exerted primarily through the kinds of soil organisms that they encourage. However, the accumulation of organic material in a distinct surface layer does not necessarily mean that there is a greater amount of organic matter in the mor profile, for a similar amount may be present in the mull, uniformly distributed and, therefore, less conspicuous. Indeed, the amount of organic material in the mull frequently exceeds that of the mor. It is also true that some mor humus layers are less acid than mulls and show a greater rate of decomposition.

Biological Characteristics of Mor and Mull

It must now be apparent that measurements of rates of organic decomposition are subject to considerable variation, and for this reason the criterion is unreliable when used as the basis for separating humus types. There is still a good deal of controversy about the way in which mor and mull humus should be defined, and the ways in which they may develop under natural conditions. Although the following account, if anything, is an oversimplification of the problem, there are essentially two schools of thought. The first follows Müller's original view that different kinds of humus result from different kinds of biological activity, and the other suggests that different humus types are formed as a result of chemical variations in the mineral and organic material, and that these create the conditions that determine the biological composition of the humus. It is possible to reconcile these two opposing viewpoints, indeed, it may be necessary to do so, to interpret the variations in profile structure that occur from place to place, which cannot be explained adequately in terms of either of these hypotheses alone.

Much of the available evidence suggests that the various factors influencing decomposition, such as climate and pH conditions, exert their effect through biological activity. Many workers have shown that the mull fauna is characterized by an abundance of the larger invertebrates, such as earthworms, slugs, millipedes, and insect larvae, in addition to the bacterial component, and that comparable niches in mor profiles are filled by the much smaller mites and Collembola which are frequently associated with flourishing fungal colonies. The pH of mor humus is generally too acid for the larger invertebrates, such as earthworms, which feed on organic material containing an appreciable amount of calcium, although apparently the distribution of these animals is limited by pH conditions rather than by the actual calcium content of the litter (Satchell, 1955). The smaller microarthropods, which form the numerically dominant component of the fauna of mor humus, apparently can tolerate the lower pH conditions found there, and this factor does not appear to be limiting over the range normally occurring in most soils. Thus, we may distinguish mull and mor types on the basis of their biological composition. This distinction becomes even more significant when we consider the results of biological activity, especially feeding habit, in the two types. To do this, it is necessary to differentiate between the effects of soil animals and those of the soil microflora.

The larger invertebrates characteristic of mull modify their environment in several ways by their feeding habits. Earthworms, molluscs, and termites are well known for their ability to remove large litter fragments from the surface, and to carry these down through their burrows to be consumed immediately or stored, in any event to become more intimately and more uniformly mixed with mineral soil. The amount of organic material ingested in this way is considerable and may be of the order of several tons per acre each year (Guild, 1955). During its passage through the animal gut, the litter material is physically comminuted until much of its original character is lost, and parts of it are digested and assimilated. For example, the millipede *Glomeris marginata* will assimilate appreciable amounts of holocellulose, crude fat, and soluble carbohydrate from ash leaf litter under experimental conditions (Table 2.1). These digestive

TABLE 2.1. Changes in the chemical composition of ash litter during its passage through the gut of *Glomeris* (from Bocock, 1963).

Test material	% crude fat	% soluble carbohydrates	% holocellulose	% lignin	% ash
Control	3·1	4·6	34	32	11·4
Food	3·6	4·6	30	34	12·0
Uneaten food	3·3	4·4	33	34	10·6
Faecal pellets	1·7	4·0	27	34	14·4

processes also release nitrogen from organic material, principally in the form of ammonia, and render this more readily available to the rest of the ecosystem (Satchell, 1963; d'Aguilar and Bessard, 1963; Heath, 1965). The faecal pellets produced as a result of this activity contain minute fragments of organic material closely mixed with particles of mineral soil. These faecal crumbs, which are more resistant to dispersion by water action than untreated soil (Guild, 1955), may occur extensively in or on the surface of the soil, particularly where earthworms are active, and may play an important part in improving the soil structure and texture.

As a general rule, the enzyme systems of the larger invertebrates are apparently incapable of attacking lignin, cellulose, and the phenolic complexes which are the sources of much of the humus material, although exceptions to this are found among some species of slugs which can produce cellulase. It is difficult to analyse the role of the soil fauna in humus formation for there is still a lot to be learned about the digestive processes of these animals, and the composition and methods of formation of humus. It has not been clearly established, for example, whether the digestive system of the soil animal is responsible for the crumblike structure of the faecal pellet and the release of nitrogen from the organic material, or whether these effects are the result of the activity of the gut microflora. These bacteria and fungi are probably more important as agents in the decomposition of lignin and cellulose, and it may be that this decomposition is not only uninterrupted, but also intensified, as the material passes through the gut of the animal. All the evidence seems to indicate that whatever changes occur during this passage render the faecal material more susceptible to attack by micro-organisms (Table 2.2; Dunger, 1963; Ghilarov,

TABLE 2.2. Comparison between the number of bacteria (in thousands/g) in earthworm castings and in surrounding soil under three different types of plant cover (from Ghilarov, 1963).

	Thousands/g		
	Oak forest	Rye field	Grasses
Earthworm castings	740	3430	3940
Surrounding soil	450	2530	2000

1968). In mull soils, bacteria are frequently the main micro-organisms, and these are capable of decomposing cellulose under aerobic conditions (Russell, 1961).

In mor soils, the immediate effect of the absence of the larger burrowing invertebrates is shown by the more restricted distribution of organic material, the lower degree of organo-mineral mixing, and the much lower amount of crumb formation. The feeding habits of small invertebrates, such as mites and Collembola, have a much less marked effect upon the physical structure of the soil than do those of the larger invertebrates in mull. Nevertheless, recent micromorphological studies of mor profiles suggest that this effect may closely parallel that in mull (Jongerius, 1963). There is also no reason to suppose that chemical changes in the organic material during its passage through the gut of a microarthropod are radically different from those occurring in the gut of an earthworm or millipede, although here again much more information is needed.

Biochemical Characteristics of Mor and Mull

The differences between mull and mor, with respect to the chemical environment and biological characteristics, are reflected in differences in the properties of the kinds of humus produced. Mull humus differs from mor in having larger amounts of ammonium and nitrate nitrogen which, according to Handley (1954), is less resistant to mobilization by biological agencies than that in mor. It also has a lower fulvic acid fraction, a higher concentration of calcium, and a humic acid fraction with higher base exchange capacity (Russell, 1961). In mor humus, the organic material may be less completely degraded, as evidenced by greater amounts of lignin and hemicellulose. These substances give the humus a fibrous quality and are particularly characteristic of the extreme form known as 'peat'.

In summary, we may distinguish between mull and mor humus on the basis of differences in biochemical composition, at least as far as idealized types are concerned. This criterion emphasizes that the *type* of decomposition process and, to a lesser extent, the *rate* of breakdown are important. We may also reconcile the two viewpoints regarding the methods of humus formation by recognizing that the chemical environment, provided by the weathering of parent mineral and organic material, and reflected by pH conditions and mineral composition, may, on the one hand, determine the major features of the soil community, and, on the other, be modified by biological activity. Thus, the larger soil invertebrates, such as the millipedes and earthworms, may counteract acid conditions in humus by producing faeces with a higher pH than the food ingested. Physical disintegration of organic material, and its subsequent distribution through the profile as crumbs or finely dispersed particles, is effected mainly by soil animals; differences in the extent to which these processes occur reflect differences in the species composition of the fauna. Chemical degradation is carried out mainly by fungi and bacteria, and, here again, differences in the chemical products may be correlated with differences in the microfloral composition. How can we say that one set of factors is more important than another in determining the development of a mature soil, when both are necessary? Such a soil could not develop in the absence of soil organisms any more than it could in the absence of parent material.

Moder

Mull and mor types are easier to differentiate in theory than in practice, for under natural conditions many intermediates exist, definable on the basis of their biological composition (Kubiena, 1955). One of the commoner transition forms is the 'moder', originally described as a 'mull-like mor'. This type resembles a mor in that there is a sharp distinction between organic and mineral layers, but differs in that the microarthropod fauna is supplemented with a stronger representation of insects, particularly by larvae of the dipteran Bibionidae and Tipulidae, and by Diplopoda. The earthworm fauna is impoverished and consists mainly of acid-tolerant species, such as *Bimastos eiseni* and *Dendrobaena* spp.

The effect of this increased proportion of larger arthropods is seen in the greater abundance of faecal material in the organic layer, compared with that in a mor.

The moder grades into another transitional type strongly resembling the mull, designated 'mull-like moder' (Kubiena, 1955). In this type, insects are to some extent supplanted by Myriapoda and Isopoda, and there is also a greater representation of earthworms. In the true mull, as we have seen, the activities of

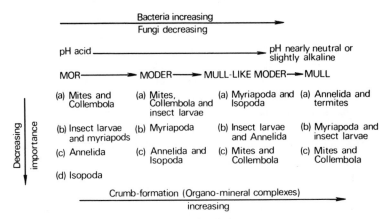

FIGURE 2.2. Sequence of humus types and related phenomena.

the earthworms dominate those of other faunal groups, although in the tropics similar effects may be produced by the activities of termites. The successional series from mor to mull is then characterized by a progressive increase in the dispersion and chemical degradation of organic material, paralleled by a biological succession in which mites, Collembola, and Enchytraeidae are replaced by insect larvae, nematodes, myriapods, isopods, lumbricids and termites. In illustrating these sequences in Fig. 2.2, it must be remembered that it is difficult, in practice, to separate cause from effect or to be dogmatic about the faunal characteristics of any particular humus type, for these characteristics are determined by a whole range of environmental factors. For example, it has been suggested (Kubiena, 1955; Russell, 1961) that the preponderance of insect larvae, myriapods, and isopods over earthworms in shallow limestone rendzina soils is due to the fact that these soils are not deep enough to provide suitable conditions for the deep-burrowing species of Lumbricidae. Thus, these and other 'thin' soils, such as heathlands, typically develop a humus of the mor or moder type.

Grassland Soils

The concepts of mull and mor as humus types were developed originally in regard to forest soils. However, we have seen that they can be extended to the interpretation of other types, for instance, moorland, heathland, fenland, and rendzina soils. However, the classification of grassland soils presents some difficulties, for these are frequently subject to human modification. Under natural conditions, grasslands develop in regions too dry for the development of forest. The soil profile under this type of vegetation is weakly structured, possibly due to a more rapid rate of organic turnover. The prairie grassland soils are, however, frequently referred to the mull type; they resemble the brown forest soils in a number of respects (Russell, 1961). Organic material is finely dispersed as organo-mineral complexes to an appreciable depth in these soils, and their biological characteristics are closer to mull forest soils than to mor types. The main differences between grassland and forest mull appear to be: (a) In the former, most of the organic material in the profile is derived from the decomposition, *in situ*, of the root systems of the vegetation; in the latter, leaf-fall also provides an important source of organic material. (b) A more pronounced circulation of silica is probably characteristic of grasslands, for this vegetation has a higher concentration of silicon than leaves of tree species. (c) A greater annual circulation of organic material may occur in grassland, possibly due to the more rapid growth and decomposition of herbaceous vegetation compared with that of tree species.

Vegetation and Soil Type

To conclude this chapter, we may briefly summarize the relationships between soil types and vegetation. Forest soils are broadly divided into the podzols and the brown earths, the former being characterized by a surface accumulation of mor humus, a strongly leached profile, and a vegetation consisting predominantly of conifers; the latter have a mull type organic profile, less intense leaching of the A_2 horizon, and support hardwood or mixed forest types. Heath soils usually develop a mor or moder humus type as a relatively thin layer over the parent material; these may be referred to the podzol class. Moorland and fen soils are characterized by an extreme form of mor humus, commonly called 'peat'. Grassland soils in temperate regions may be identifiable with the mull type; in more arid regions, these soils grade into desert soils. However, it must be stressed that transitional stages may be more in evidence than idealized types.

References

Bétrémieux, R. and Hénin, S. (1965) 'Artificial profile development by decomposition of plant material' in Hallsworth, E. G. and Crawford, D. V., eds., *Experimental pedology*, 179-88.

Bloomfield. C. (1965) 'Organic matter and soil dynamics' in Hallsworth, E. G. and Crawford, D. V., eds., *Experimental pedology*, 257-66.

Bocock, K. L. (1963) 'The digestion and assimilation of food by *Glomeris*' in Doeksen, J. and Drift, J. van der, eds., *Soil organisms*, 85-91.

Crossley, D. A. and Witkamp, M. (1964) 'Forest soil mites and mineral cycling', *Acarologia*, 6 (fasc. h. s., C. R. Ier Congrès Int. d'Acarologie, Fort Collins, Col., U.S.A., 1963), 137-46.

D'Aguilar, J. and Bessard, A. (1963) 'Activité biologique des larves de *Bibio* dans divers composts', in Doeksen, J. and Drift, J. van der, *Soil organisms*, 103-8.

Drift. J. van der (1963) 'The disappearance of litter in mull and mor in connection with weather conditions and the activity of the macrofauna' in Doeksen, J. and Drift, J. van der, eds., *Soil organisms,* 125-33.

Drift, J. van der (1965) 'The effects of animal activity in the litter layer', in Hallsworth, E. G. and Crawford, D. V., eds., *Experimental pedology,* 227-35.

Dunger, W. (1963) 'Leistungsspezifität bei Streuzersetzern' in Doeksen J. and Drift, J. van der, eds., *Soil organisms,* 92-102.

Ghilarov, M. S. (1963) 'On the interrelations between soil dwelling invertebrates and soil microorganisms' in Doeksen, J. and Drift, J. van der, eds., *Soil organisms,* 255-9.

Ghilarov, M. S. (1968) 'Soil stratum of terrestrial biocenoses', *Pedobiologia,* 8, 82-96.

Gilbert, O. J. and Bocock, K. L. (1962) 'Some methods of studying the disappearance and decomposition of leaf litter' in Murphy, P. W., ed., *Progress in soil zoology,* 348-52.

Guild, W. J. McL. (1955) 'Earthworms and soil structure' in Kevan, D. K. McE., ed., *Soil zoology,* 83-98.

Handley, W. R. C. (1954) 'Mull and mor formation in relation to forest soils', *Bull. For. Commn. Lond.,* 23, iv + 115 pp.

Heath, G. W. (1965) 'The part played by animals in soil formation' in Hallsworth, E. G. and Crawford, D. V., eds., *Experimental pedology,* 236-43.

Jongerius, A. (1963) 'Optic-volumetric measurements on some humus forms' in Doeksen J. and Drift, J. van der, eds., *Soil organisms,* 137-48.

Kubiena, W. L. (1955) 'Animal activity in soils as a decisive factor in establishment of humus forms' in Kevan, D. K. McE., ed., *Soil zoology,* 73-82.

Madge, D. S. (1965) 'Leaf fall and litter disappearance in a tropical forest', *Pedobiologia,* 5, 273-88.

Müller, P. E. (1879) 'Studier over Skovjord, som Bidrag til Skovdyrkningens Theori. I. Om Bøgemuld og Bogemor paa Sand og Ler', *Tidsskr. Skovbr.,* 3, 1-124.

Müller, P. E. (1884) *idem.* 'II. Om Muld og Mor i Egeskove og paa Heder', *ibid.,* 7, 1-232.

Russell, E. J. (1961) *Soil conditions and plant growth* (ninth edn, revised Russell, E. W.), Longmans, London. xvi + 688 pp.

Satchell, J. E. (1955) 'Some aspects of earthworm ecology' in Kevan, D. K. McE., ed., *Soil zoology,* 180-201.

Satchell, J. E. (1963) 'Nitrogen turnover by a woodland population of *Lumbricus terrestris*' in Doeksen, J. and Drift, J. van der, eds., *Soil organisms,* 60-6.

3. Classification of the soil fauna

The definition of a soil animal as one that lives in the soil carries with it little intrinsic significance, for most of the major phyla have representatives which spend at least a part of their life cycle in the soil. Not all of these animals have an equally close association with this environment, and some, such as sea birds which nest in the soil burrows and many arthropods which seek only a temporary refuge in the soil, can be considered, at most, only marginal members of this community, for although their effect on a particular soil may be considerable, it is often localized and temporary. These examples serve to highlight the difficulty of determining what exactly constitutes a true soil-dweller, and it may be of some value, in introducing this section, to review some of the criteria used in defining the various components of the soil fauna.

Of the various methods that can be, and have been, used to classify the different elements of the soil fauna, four major groupings are most widely adopted, namely, those based on body size, presence in the soil, habitat preference, and activity.

Body Size
The range of body size shown by soil animals is considerable, extending from about 20μ to more than 200 mm. The various taxonomic groups occupy fairly distinct positions within this range, such that we can define the following categories:

Microfauna
Body size within the range 20μ to 200μ. Only one group is entirely contained within this range, the Protozoa, although the smallest mites, nematodes, rotifers, tardigrades, and copepod Crustacea may be included near the upper limit.

Mesofauna
Body size within the range 200μ to 1 cm. The microarthropod Acari (mites) and Collembola (springtails) are important members of this group which also includes the larger nematodes, rotifers, and tardigrades, together with most of the Araneida (spiders), Chelonethi (pseudoscorpions), Opiliones (harvestmen), Enchytraeidae (pot-worms), insect larvae, and the smaller millipedes and isopods.

Macrofauna

Body size greater than 1 cm. Here belong the majority of the Lumbricidae, the Mollusca, the largest insects and arachnids, and the soil-dwelling vertebrates.

The arrangement of the various groups of soil animals, according to this criterion, is shown in Fig. 3.1. The limits of the various categories are rather

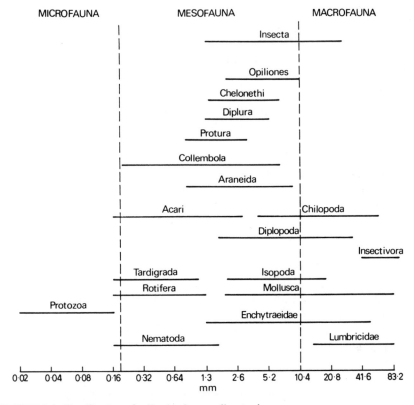

FIGURE 3.1. Classification of soil animals according to size.

arbitrarily defined, and modifications of this basic arrangement have been proposed from time to time. For example, the size limits defining the mesofauna are sometimes placed at 200 μ to 2 mm, those for the macrofauna, at 2 mm and 20 mm; and a fourth grouping, the megafauna, is added to accommodate those animals with body size exceeding 20 mm (van der Drift, 1951). Some authors prefer to use the term 'meiofauna', instead of 'mesofauna' (e.g., Murphy, 1953).

Presence

A distinction can be made between temporary and permanent members of the soil fauna. To the former category belong insects that enter the soil as adults to escape unfavourable conditions above the ground, as, for example, the hibernating Coleoptera, Thysanoptera (thrips), and Heteroptera. Also included in this temporary fauna are the insects which undergo part of their development, usually as eggs and larvae, in the soil. Diptera larvae are important members of this group. Both of these groups of temporary soil animals have been designated as 'geophiles' (Jacot, 1940), although it is probably important to distinguish between the inactive geophiles and those groups that are active members of the soil fauna, at least for part of their life.

Inactive geophiles include many adult insects which seek the shelter afforded by loose leaf litter and decaying logs lying on, or partly embedded in, the surface of the soil. For example, females of flower and grass thrips, such as *Limothrips cerealium,* often descend into the leaf litter at the end of an English summer, to overwinter there. A similar behaviour pattern is adopted by the adults of various plant bugs, for example, aphids, pentatomids, leaf hoppers, and coreids. Sometimes these invasions reach remarkable proportions, as in the case of overwintering adults of the Coleoptera Coccinellidae, the ladybirds. In the vicinity of citrus orchards in southern California, adult males and females of the coccinellid, *Hippodamia convergens,* a predator of the citrus aphid, can be found in leaf litter, under stones, and on fallen logs, in aggregations comprising several thousand quiescent individuals, during the cooler winter months. Many phytophagous beetles, particularly those belonging to the Chrysomelidae, overwinter as adults, and may be encountered from time to time in soil and litter samples. Because of their relative inactivity, these temporary members of the soil fauna make only a slight contribution, at the most, to the soil ecosystem.

Many insects pass through a distinct stage or stages of development in the soil, eventually to emerge as winged, aerial adults, and thus have a closer association with the soil than those just discussed. These forms may properly be classed as active geophiles. For the most part, these insects belong to one of three major Orders, namely, the Diptera, Coleoptera, and Lepidoptera, and since they are all holometabolous, the developmental stages concerned are the larvae and pupae. Insect pupae play little or no part in the soil ecosystem, for they are relatively inactive. Insect larvae, on the other hand, are often of considerable importance as detritus-feeders or carnivores, particularly where they occur locally in high densities.

These insect larvae occupy a special position in the soil community, for they are well adapted in body form, methods of locomotion, and feeding habits to life in the soil, and yet they are transients because many of them will pupate and eventually leave the soil as adults with entirely different adaptations to aerial life. Ecologically speaking, the main distinction between these geophiles and the permanent soil fauna is that, in the former case, immigration (as eggs laid in the soil) and emigration (as adult emergence) make a much greater contribution to population changes than they do in the latter. This is particularly true of those species that oviposit and emerge as adults at restricted times of the year.

Kevan's (1962) classification separates the inactive geophiles ('transients') from the active ones which are further grouped into 'periodic' and 'temporary' categories, depending on degree of presence in the soil. The permanent elements of the soil fauna, sometimes referred to as 'geobionts', develop through the whole of their life cycle in the soil, and include the protozoans, nematodes, annelids, myriapods, isopods, mites, the various apterygote groups including the Collembola, together with some insects and molluscs. Figure 3.2 illustrates the basic differences between these various divisions.

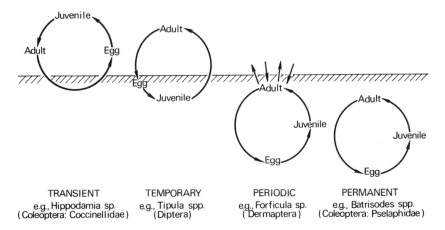

TRANSIENT	TEMPORARY	PERIODIC	PERMANENT
e.g., Hippodamia sp.	e.g., Tipula spp.	e.g., Forficula sp.	e.g., Batrisodes spp.
(Coleoptera: Coccinellidae)	(Diptera)	(Dermaptera)	(Coleoptera: Pselaphidae)

FIGURE 3.2. Categories of soil animals defined according to degree of presence in the soil, as illustrated by some insect groups.

Habitat Preference

The soil provides a variety of microhabitats, and it is not surprising that several different classifications based on habitat preference have been devised. A distinction can be made, for example, between the aquatic fauna living in water-filled spaces and surface films covering soil particles, and the terrestrial element. To the former grouping belong the protozoans, rotifers, tardigrades, copepod crustaceans, and certain nematodes, while the bulk of the meso- and macrofauna belong to the latter.

The vertical stratification of the soil environment provides a convenient, if somewhat arbitrary, framework for the classification of soil animals according to habitat preference. As we have already noted, the profile of an undisturbed, mature soil is divisible into a number of layers or strata: these are most clearly identifiable in rather acid forest soils where there is a sharp separation between the surface organic layers and the underlying mineral soil. Ecologists recognize the distinction between these two zones by designating them 'hemiedaphon' and 'euedaphon' respectively, and since this scheme of classification can logically be extended to include the vegetation layer above the soil surface, a third zone is defined to include this: the 'epigeon' or 'atmobios'.

The properties of these zones vary from one soil or vegetation type to the next, and also geographically. From the point of view of the soil fauna, one of the most important variables is the soil moisture content, and since this is liable to greater fluctuation in the surface organic layer than in the deeper mineral soil, the hemiedaphon has been further subdivided on the basis of its moisture status. In an attempt to relate species composition of the fauna to microhabitat, Gisin (1943) proposed to define hemiedaphic Collembola as: (a) hydrophile (living on the surface of free water), (b) mesophile (living in moist organic litter on the soil surface), or (c) xerophile (living in drier, more exposed sites, such as moss, lichens, and tree bark). This system has been extended to other soil arthropods, notably the cryptostigmatid mites (Strenzke, 1952; Klima, 1956; Tarras-Wahlberg, 1961), with arguable success, and forms the basis for the definition of 'life forms' (*Lebensformtypen*), an example of which is provided in Table 3.1.

TABLE 3.1. Some Collembolan life forms (from Christiansen, 1964).

Category	Characteristics	Normal ecological distribution
Epigeon	Eight eyes, well pigmented; antennae and furcula long	Plant growth
Hemiedaphon	Antennae moderately long, eyes and pigment well developed	
Hydrophile	Lamellate mucra; modified unquis	Water surface
Mesophile	Normal mucro; few clavate or pointed tenent hairs	Surface, ground litter
Xerophile	Normal mucro; cuticle often rigid, many clavate tenent hairs	Moss, bark lichens
Euedaphon	Eyes reduced; antennae short; pigment absent or limited to eyes	Deep soil layers, caves
Troglomorphs	Eyes and pigment absent; antennae long; unquis modified	Caves
Synoecomorphs	Eyes and pigment absent; mouth-parts modified, furcula and legs well developed; with unusual scales and setae	Ant and termite nests

It may be pointed out that the fauna of the epigeon includes a large number of species which do not normally occur in the soil, as, for example, many of the phytophagous insects. Nevertheless, there is a certain amount of overlap between the epigeal and hemiedaphic fauna, for some phytophagous species move down into the hemiedaphon temporarily, as we have seen. Conversely, many isopods, molluscs, arachnids, and Collembola exhibit seasonal, or diurnal, vertical movements that take them out of the litter layer into the aerial vegetation. Such movements also occur between the hemiedaphon and the euedaphon, and underline the difficulty of applying a rigid classification to soil animals based on stratigraphical relationships.

Activity

Two main activities, feeding and locomotion, have been used in the classification of soil animals. Both of these are treated in some detail in later chapters under the appropriate animal groups; it is sufficient at this stage, therefore, to draw attention only to the major subdivisions of these two criteria. In terms of feeding activity we can define:

1. *Carnivores* which may be subdivided into:
   (a) Predators, e.g., carabid, pselaphid, scydmaenid, and some staphylinid beetles, many mesostigmatid and prostigmatid mites, the spiders, harvestmen, pseudoscorpions, scorpions, sun-spiders, centipedes, and some nematodes and molluscs.
   (b) Animal parasites, e.g., ichneumonids, some staphylinid beetles, parasitic Diptera, and some nematodes.
2. *Phytophages* feeding on:
   (a) Green plant material above ground, e.g., molluscs and lepidopteran larvae.
   (b) Root systems, e.g., nematode plant parasites, symphylids, larvae of some Diptera, scarabaeid Coleoptera and Lepidoptera, molluscs, and burrowing Orthoptera.
   (c) Woody material, e.g., some termites, beetle larvae, and phthiracaroid mites.
3. *Saprophages* which feed on dead and decaying organic material include, for example, the lumbricids, enchytraeids, isopods, millipedes, and some of the hemiedaphic mites, Collembola, and insects. Some of these forms are also probably faecal-feeders (*coprophages*), wood-feeders (*xylophages*), and carrion-feeders (*necrophages*), and are often variously referred to as *scavengers, debris-feeders,* or *detritivores.*
4. *Microphytic-feeders* comprise those animals feeding on fungal hyphae and spores, algae, lichens, and bacteria. Many of the saprophagous mites and Collembola may also be included here, together with fungus-feeding insects, such as ants, termites, dipteran Mycetophilidae and coleopteran Nitidulidae, nematodes, and certain molluscs and protozoans.
5. *Miscellaneous feeders.* Many of the groups of soil animals considered above are not so restricted in their feeding habits as to fit easily into one or other of the preceding classes. Species that will accept a range of food material, plant or animal, fresh or decaying, woody or herbaceous, macrophyte or microphyte, are to be found particularly among the nematodes, cryptostigmatid mites, Collembola, and the larvae of Diptera and Coleoptera. The diet of these miscellaneous feeders usually varies from site to site, depending on what is available in the way of food.

This essentially descriptive classification can be used as the basis for an alternative, but complementary, scheme that emphasizes the functional relationships between different groups of animals linked together in a common food chain. The starting point for such a chain is the material and energy provided by green plants, the 'primary producers', which are supplied to the soil ecosystem as dead and decaying leaves, fruits, woody stems, and roots. This organic material provides food for 'primary consumers' which, in the soil, are the saprophagous animals, and, above ground, the phytophages or herbivores. These primary consumers, in turn, form the prey of the 'secondary consumers' or carnivores. The larger carnivores which prey on the secondary consumers are termed 'tertiary consumers'. This distinction between carnivore levels is, to some extent, artificial, for many predators apparently do not distinguish between the lower trophic levels with the same facility that the ecologist does. Thus, a pseudo-scorpion may be a 'secondary consumer', feeding on Collembola, at one point in time, and a 'tertiary consumer', feeding on macrochelid mites or other pseudo-scorpions, at the next.

With regard to locomotion, we can distinguish between burrowing animals and those which move through the soil by making use of existing pore spaces, cavities, or channels. The distribution of burrowing species is largely independent of the cavity structure of the soil, and there is little relationship between body size and depth distribution, although burrowing is obviously easier in loose, as opposed to compacted, soils. This grouping is here considered to include many lumbricids, which eat their way through the soil, together with groups which may be considered more properly as 'excavators'. The latter dig burrow systems, and include the fossorial Coleoptera and Orthoptera among the insects, the iuloid millipedes, certain isopods such as the desert-dwelling *Hemilepistus*, and burrowing vertebrates, such as the mole *Talpa* and the kangaroo-rat *Dipodomys*. The non-burrowers are generally of small body size, and can utilize existing soil spaces. Examples of this group are the micro-arthropod mites and Collembola, the soil-water fauna, enchytraeids, and symphylids. Larger animals, such as the polydesmoid millipedes, centipedes, isopods, and certain lumbricids, are morphologically adapted to squeeze through existing soil spaces, and, since this activity may enlarge preexisting channels, these non-burrowers are difficult to distinguish from the burrowers.

The schemes of classification discussed in this chapter are not intended to be all-inclusive, but have been presented because they give some idea of the different ways in which the members of the soil fauna can be considered. It is obvious that none of the criteria employed is wholly satisfactory, nor would we expect this to be so for all of the classes defined are, to some extent, artificial. More detailed classifications have been proposed along lines similar to the above, for example by Kevan (1962).

References

Christiansen, K. (1964) 'Bionomics of Collembola', *A. Rev. Ent.*, **9**, 147-78.

Drift, J. van der (1951) 'Analysis of the animal community in a beech forest floor', *Tijdschr. Ent.*, **94**, 1-168.

Gisin, H. (1943) 'Ökologie und Lebensgemeinschaften der Collembolen in schweizerischen Excursionsgebiet Basels', *Rev. suisse Zool.*, **50**, 131-224.

Jacot, A. P. (1940) 'The fauna of the soil', *Quart. Rev. Biol.*, **15**, 28-58.

Kevan, D. K. McE. (1962) *Soil animals*, Philosophical Library, New York. xv + 237 pp.

Klima, J. (1956) 'Strukturklassen und Lebensformen der Oribatiden (Acari)', *Oikos*, **7**, 227-42.

Murphy, P. W. (1953) 'The biology of forest soils with special reference to the mesofauna or meiofauna', *J. Soil. Sci.*, **4**, 155-93.

Strenzke, K. (1952) 'Untersuchungen über die Tiergemeinschaften des Bodens: Die Oribatiden und ihre Synusien in den Böden Norddeutschlands', *Zoologica*, **37**, 1-167.

Tarras-Wahlberg, N. (1961) 'The Oribatei of a central Swedish bog and their environment', *Oikos*, suppl. 4, 56 pp.

4. Protozoa, Acoelomata, and Pseudocoelomata

Although much of this chapter is devoted to two major groups of soil animals, the protozoans and the nematodes, mention will also be made of some aspects of the biology of three other groups of lesser importance in the soil: the Platyhelminthes, Rotifera, and Gastrotricha.

Protozoa

This group, which has been the subject of a comprehensive review by Stout and Heal (1967), is represented in the soil mainly by rhizopods, ciliates, and flagellates.

Composition of the Fauna

Amoeboid forms belonging to the genera *Amoeba* and *Naegleria*, ciliates, such as the common *Colpoda steinii*, and flagellates belonging to the Zoomastigina, such as *Bodo* and *Oicomonas* species, are often common near the surface in several soil types. Thecamoebae, or Testacea, of the genera *Centropyxis, Nebela, Plagiopyxis, Heleopora, Phryganella, Difflugiella, Euglypha, Trinema,* and *Corythion* have a wide distribution, although some of these forms appear to show geographical zonation. For example, the genus *Nebela* is more common than the Centropyxidae in beechwood soils in New Zealand, whereas the reverse is the case in European beechwoods (Stout and Heal, 1967). Green flagellates have little significance in the soil community, and are generally restricted to the upper layers of the litter.

Horizontal Distribution

The relative abundance and species diversity of the protozoan fauna are influenced in a general way by soil type. This is well illustrated by a study of distribution in three beechwood soils in the English Chiltern Hills (Stout, 1963). A total of 34 species of rhizopod was recorded from the three sites, of which 28 species occurred in an acid mor, 23 in an acid mull, and 19 in a calcareous mull. The naked amoebae showed little preference for any one of the three sites, but the testacean groups generally favoured acid sites. In contrast, 40 species of ciliates were better represented in calcareous mull (35) than in acid mull (30) and mor (21) (Fig. 4.1). Extending these comparisons to include the protozoan fauna of Danish and German beechwoods, Stout (1968) was able to make the following general conclusions. Firstly, that the distribution of amoebae differs little with site characteristics, and that this group is best represented in the upper horizons of the soil profile. Secondly, that the richest ciliate fauna occurs in

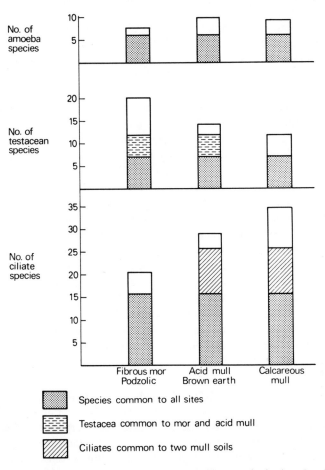

FIGURE 4.1. Distribution of amoeba, testacean, and ciliate species in three beechwood soils on the Chiltern Hills, England (from Stout and Heal, 1967).

calcareous soils. This group shows a preference for mull soils with a high base status and, to a lesser extent, deep, moist mor profiles provided these are not too acid. Thirdly, that the Testacea are most richly represented in the highly organic strata of mor profiles, both on acid and calcareous sites, and, although many species belonging to this group are distributed rather widely in mull and mor alike, certain groups—of which members of the genera *Arcella, Nebela, Heleopora, Hyalosphenia,* and *Trigonopyxis* are examples—occur with greater regularity in mor profiles. Differences in species composition and abundance within these broad associations reflect different tolerances to environmental factors. Among the Testacea, the degree of tolerance of variations in soil moisture content may be indicated by the shape and the size of the shell. Within the genera *Plagiopyxis, Centropyxis,* and *Paracentropyxis,* there is a tendency for the shell aperture to become reduced in relation to the size of the entire shell and, in some cases, this process culminates in the formation of an outer chamber, or vestibule, which provides some protection from the desiccating effect of the external environment. Further, species with large, pyriform shells, such as *Nebela, Hyalosphenia,* and *Difflugia,* are more demanding in their moisture requirements, and, therefore, are more commonly encountered in moist, highly organic mor profiles than those species possessing flattened shells, such as the Centropyxidae; the latter are common in mull soils, and evidently have a greater tolerance of variations in the environmental moisture content.

In the case of ciliates, ecological tolerance is related to the efficiency of the encystment mechanism (Stout and Heal, 1967). For example, a gradient of decreasing tolerance can be proposed for the series: *Colpoda steinii–Chilodonella gouraudi–Blepharisma* and *Frontonia* spp., the first two groups, which are morphologically simple and show a wide tolerance of environmental factors, being common in a range of New Zealand grasslands while the third, more specialized and less efficient at encysting, is more strongly restricted to base-rich soil. Faunal differences may also occur between uncultivated grassland and cultivated soils, but these differences are often in numbers rather than in species composition. Cultivation may have a detrimental effect on populations of Testacea, although when manure treatment is applied to stimulate greater plant yield, the enhancement of root growth and exudates apparently stimulates the growth of protozoan populations, particularly amoebae.

Vertical Distribution

The effects of microhabitat factors on protozoan populations can also be illustrated by considering vertical distribution patterns. For example, Heal (1962) noted a well-defined vertical distribution of 30 species of Testacea in *Sphagnum,* with *Hyalosphenia papilio* and *Amphitrema flavum* largely restricted to the upper six centimetres of the plant, a distribution possibly associated with the presence of zoochlorellae in these two species, and the majority of the remainder (25 species) most abundant in the lower levels, where mineral materials necessary for the construction of the shell were in good supply. In forest soils, amoebae, testaceans, and ciliates are usually more richly represented, in terms of numbers of species, in organic layers compared with the mineral soil, a distribution which apparently reflects the effects of pore space, thickness of the water film, distribution of shell-building materials, in the case of the Testacea, as well as the ability of different protozoan species to withstand desiccation (Stout and Heal, 1967).

The diameter of soil spaces is an important factor in the distribution of various Testacea; groups with large, spherical, or pyriform shells, such as members of the genera *Nebela* and *Heleopora,* are more or less restricted to surface organic layers in which the cavity size is relatively large, whereas groups with smaller shells, such as members of the Centropyxidae, also occur in the deeper mineral layers of the profile where pore spaces are smaller in size.

Population Sizes

Although the accuracy with which estimates of population size can be made varies with the different groups, direct counts of testaceans provide figures of the order of millions per square metre. For example, Heal (1962) estimated 16 millions/m^2 in a *Sphagnum* sward, and much larger populations have been recorded more recently from a variety of sites (see Stout and Heal, 1967). Population estimates, expressed as numbers per gram of wet soil, are often quoted in the literature (see Table 4.1); in temperate soils these range from less than 10^3/g wet soil for ciliates in grassland sites to more than 10^6/g wet soil for amoebae.

TABLE 4.1. Numbers and estimated biomass of Protozoa in a Rothamsted soil (from Stout and Heal, 1967, after Singh, 1946).

	Flagellates	Amoebae	Ciliates
No./g wet soil	70 500	41 400	377
Est. biomass g/m^2	0·35	1·6	0·12

Seasonal changes in the size of protozoan populations have been recorded, and the general pattern consists of a summer decline in numbers followed by an increase in autumn. For example, Stout (1962) found that testacean populations in New Zealand beech (*Nothofagus*) forest soil varied from a summer minimum of about 1 million/m^2 to a winter maximum of 20 million/m^2. The rapidly reproducing Protozoa resemble many other groups of soil animals in this respect. This period of population increase coincides with the period of maximum biological activity in the organic layers of the soil, stimulated, no doubt, by the abundance of food and moisture. In arid sites, these favourable conditions occur after the winter rains when the soil temperature rises and, consequently, population peaks occur in February, March, and April in the northern hemisphere.

Feeding Habits

In general, Protozoa are regarded as bacterial-feeders, and it has even been suggested (Cutler *et al.,* 1922) that the inverse relationship existing between populations of amoebae and bacteria, under natural conditions, is a result of protozoan predation. Apparently, no such correlations have been demonstrated between flagellates and bacteria, but, as Stout and Heal (1967) point out, this is hardly surprising for there is strong evidence of food selection by protozoans at the specific level. Thus, although many testaceans are bacterial-feeders, some, at least, ingest organic litter and fungi, and may be able to digest cellulose.

The relationships between soil Protozoa and bacteria are of considerable interest, for the latter are important decomposer organisms, and predation by these animals may contribute significantly to the turnover of available nutrients and the enhancement of biochemical activity in the soil (Stout and Heal, 1967).

Platyhelminthes

Flatworms are represented in the soil by terricolous Tricladida (planarians), the Rhabdocoelida, and the Alloeocoela. With few exceptions, notably *Rhyncho-demus terrestris* which may attain a length of 12 mm or more, these forms are small is size and are more frequently found in highly organic forest soils than elsewhere. The richest development of the land-dwelling planarian fauna occurs in the warm, moist litter layers of tropical and subtropical forests, for example, in South Africa and South America. Perhaps the best-known representative of the terricolous Tricladida is *Bipalium kewense,* a species which has become widely distributed around the world through human agencies, although the genus to which it belongs is probably indigenous only in the Oriental region and Madagascar (Lawrence, 1953).

Planarians are predators or carrion feeders, digesting their food extracellularly before imbibing the liquified products through the muscular, eversible pharynx. Lawrence (1953) noted that the triclad *Artiocotylus* is often found with the onychophoran *Peripatopsis* in decaying wood in South African forests, although he could find no evidence that the former was a predator of the latter. Both of these groups show cannibalistic behaviour in cultures.

The eggs of terrestrial planarians number between 4 and 20 per batch and are enclosed in a large cocoon which, in *Artiocotylus,* is black in colour and shiny in appearance. After a period of development, usually 4 to 8 weeks, immature stages emerge which are similar in general appearance to the adult, and progress to adulthood without any subsequent metamorphosis.

Nematoda

The taxonomy of the soil nematodes is still far from complete, and identification is often difficult. A most useful text for this purpose is provided by Goodey (1963). The ecology of the group is complicated by the fact that the line between parasitic and free-living species is not always easy to draw. For example, members of the genera *Rhabditis* and *Strongyloides* may be facultative parasites, phoretic, or free-living forms, depending on environmental conditions.

Composition of the Fauna

The nematodes inhabiting soil and decaying organic material, essentially, can be classified into four Orders: the Rhabditida, Tylenchida, Chromadorida, and Enoplida, including about 30 genera of which the most common are listed in Table 4.2. In addition to these free-living groups, the soil also harbours the eggs and free-living larval stages of other nematodes which are parasites as adults in vertebrates or invertebrates. Examples of these forms are found among the Strongylina.

TABLE 4.2. Some representative genera of nematodes commonly encountered in soil samples (from Peters (1955)).

Order	Genera	Length (mm)
Rhabditida	*Rhabditis*	1·2
	Diplogaster	1·0
	Cephalobus	0·9
Tylenchida	*Tylenchus*	1·0
	Heterodera	0·7
	Aphelenchoides	0·7
Chromadorida	*Plectus*	1·0
	Monhystera	0·9
	Prismatolaimus	0·7
Enoplida	*Tripyla*	1·4
	Mononchus	1·4
	Dorylaimus	4·5

Horizontal Distribution

Taken as a group, the nematodes are ubiquitous, occurring not only as animal and plant parasites, but also free-living in the sea, fresh water, and soil (Fig. 4.2). There is a strong similarity between the nematode fauna of fresh water and soil,

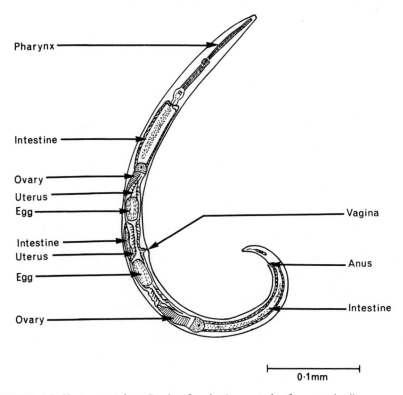

FIGURE 4.2. *Plectus granulosus* Bastian, female. A nematode of moss and soil.

many species or genera being common to both habitats. This is, perhaps, not surprising when we recall that terrestrial, free-living nematodes belong to the soilwater fauna.

Relatively few nematode species are restricted in their general distribution to one particular soil type. Thus, Nielsen (1949) recorded a large group of species, including *Dorylaimus obtusicaudatus, D. carteri, Prismatolaimus dolichurus, Aphelenchoides parietinus, Tylenchus filiformis, Monhystera vulgaris,* and *Plectus* spp., common to sand, clay, raw humus, and peaty soils. Species with a distribution largely limited to sandy soil included *Tripyla setifera, Acrobeles ciliatus,* and *Tylencholaimus mirabilis,* whereas *Acrobeles vexilliger, Wilsonema otophorum,* and *Bunonema reticulatum* were typical of raw humus, although not restricted to this soil type. Similarly, *Plectus rhizophilus* was found to be numerically more important in the nematode fauna of moss cushions than in the soil. This detailed study also showed that there was a close correspondence between the fauna of sandy and clay soils, and a detailed comparison of the species composition in sand, raw humus, and peat revealed the presence of two faunal components in each case, namely, a eurytopic group, able to colonize a variety of habitats, and a stenotopic group, much more strongly restricted in its distribution. The relative importance of these two groups differed in the various soil types, the eurytopic species constituting 95 per cent of the total weight of the nematode fauna in sandy soil and raw humus, only 25 per cent of this weight in permanently moist soils, such as peat.

Between 100 and 200 species of nematode are known to be parasites of plant roots, either internally, as in *Heterodera* spp., or externally, as in *Tylenchus* spp., and the association between host plant and parasite is sometimes fairly specific, for example, in the case of the potato root eelworm, *Heterodera rostochiensis.* The extent of this specificity obviously governs the distribution of the nematode. In many cases, this association appears to be facultative rather than obligatory, although soil nematodes in general are usually concentrated around the rooting systems of plants, as the analysis of vertical distribution patterns clearly shows.

Vertical Distribution

In the large majority of soils examined to date, the nematode fauna is concentrated within the top 10 cm of the profile. However, there are exceptions to this general statement, for Nielsen (1949) showed that the pattern of vertical distribution varied somewhat with the character of the habitat. The fauna of undisturbed soils followed the general rule, irrespective of the kind of vegetation cover and the moisture content of the soil (Fig. 4.3a). It is within these upper layers of the profile that the greatest abundance of plant roots and their exudates occurs, along with decaying organic matter and a wide variety of soil animals, all potential food sources for nematodes (see below). The most important factor influencing the vertical distribution pattern, in this case, would appear to be the distribution of food. On the other hand, in open areas, where vegetation is scarce or absent, the nematode fauna is concentrated at a depth of about 5 cm, and decreases in abundance upwards and downwards from this level (Fig. 4.3c). The scarcity of nematodes in the upper 5 cm in this site may reflect the inability of these animals to tolerate the desiccation to which the surface of these exposed soils is subject. In cultivated soils, there was a more even distribution of the fauna down to a depth of about 20 cm (Fig. 4.3b) attributable to the mixing effects of ploughing.

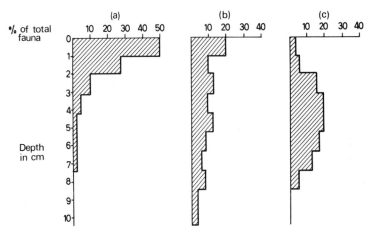

FIGURE 4.3. Three patterns of vertical distribution of nematodes. (a) Permanent pasture; (b) cultivated soil; (c) bare *Corynephorus* slopes (from Nielsen, 1949).

That nematodes can undertake vertical migrations, is suggested by the observations of Nielsen (1967) on the moss-inhabiting *Plectus rhizophilus.* This species moves up and down moss stems, being concentrated in the canopy of the moss during the night or during periods of rain. During the driest times of the day, numbers are greatest lower down in the base of the moss cushion. More information is required on the extent of such migrations among the soil nematodes, particularly in relation to the changes in moisture content of the surface litter layers. However, it is unlikely that such movements would alter appreciably the picture of vertical distribution given above, if, indeed, they occur, for in temperate regions desiccation rarely proceeds further than the uppermost surface of the organic layer. In any event, the nematode species inhabiting the topmost levels of the soil profile may be capable of surviving drought in an anabiotic condition.

Population Sizes

Absolute restriction to specific sites is rare among soil nematodes, horizontal and vertical differences in the fauna being quantitative rather than qualitative. Population densities are usually highest in grassland soils where estimates of the order of 20 million/m² have been recorded (Table 4.3). Densities in raw humus soils are lower, usually within the range 1-3 million/m², while estimates from heathland and moorland soils are variable, sometimes exceeding 5 million/m², but more often being less than 1 million (see page 218). Although any given population size is undoubtedly the result of an interaction between various environmental factors, such as food, temperature, moisture, and the intrinsic reproductive rate of the species, it seems reasonable to conclude from the evidence available that the density of nematodes is related to the amount of vegetation cover and root material present in the soil.

TABLE 4.3. Some estimates for population size of soil nematodes (from Banage, 1963).

Habitat	Sample depth	Biomass g/m² fresh wt	Numbers 10^6/m²	Author
Grassland	15 cm	5·0		Stöckli (1946)
Grassland	5 cm	6·0-17·8	4-20	Nielsen (1949)
Raw humus	5 cm	1·5-4·5	1·2-2·7	Nielsen (1949)
Beech floor	25 cm	4·1	12·1	Volz (1951)
Oak floor	25 cm	15·2	29·8	Volz (1951)
Peat moor	6 cm	0·48-0·75	1·9-3·1	Banage (1960)

Fluctuations in population sizes of soil nematodes do not appear to conform to any regular cyclical pattern, to judge from the information available. For example, Nielsen (1949) concluded, from his study of the fauna of permanent pasture in Denmark, that no marked seasonal variation in numbers occurred in mineral grassland soils. However, if fluctuations do occur it is likely that the timescale of these changes is relatively short, and that they would not be detected by a monthly sampling programme. Under laboratory conditions at 15-16°C, nematodes representing about a dozen different species completed their life cycle, egg to egg, in a period of two or three weeks (Nielsen, 1949). Even allowing for a slower development time in the field, a conservative estimate for the number of generations per year would be five or six. Moreover, unless these were synchronized, at least for the numerically important species, and restricted to a short period of the year, well-marked density peaks would not be expected. However, much more information is required on this point.

Feeding Habits

This very common group of soil animals is characterized by a variety of feeding habits. Species of *Rhabditis,* for instance, found commonly in decaying organic matter such as humus, dung, and compost, ingest liquefied decomposition products, plant or animal, although the actual source of nutriment may be the bacteria associated with this material. Other saprophagous, fungivorous, or bacterial-feeding species belong to the genera *Plectus, Acrobeles, Cephalobus, Chiloplacus, Acrobeloides, Diplogaster, Bunonema, Tripyla, Prismatolaimus,* and

Monhystera. Nematodes are frequently found in association with the faecal masses of wood-boring phthiracaroid mites, and are probably bacterial-feeders or fungivores in this situation. They are also common in the galleries of wood-boring beetles (see Goodey, 1963). However, the most familiar soil-inhabiting nematodes are those which feed on the root systems of cultivated crops. Examples of these plant parasites are *Tylenchus* spp. and *Dorylaimus* spp. which feed from the outside by inserting the buccal apparatus into the host tissue, and *Heterodera* spp. which are truly endoparasitic and may cause extensive lesions in the roots of the host.

Several authors, notably Nielsen (1949) and Banage (1963), have proposed classifications of feeding habits of nematodes, and it is evident that these habits are not clearly defined in all cases. Banage, for example, defined plant feeders, microbial feeders, predators, and miscellaneous feeders. The latter group includes species of *Dorylaimus, Aporcelaimus, Tylencholaimus,* and *Enchodelus* among others, which, apparently, can adapt to what is readily available in the form of food, whether of plant, animal, or microbial origin. Some species of *Dorylaimus, Monhystera, Mononchus, Trilobus, Prionchulus Anatonchus, Iotonchus, Miconchus,* and *Choanolaimus* appear basically to be predatory forms. These carnivores find abundant food in the soil provided by other nematodes, small earthworms, rotifers, protozoans, and mites. It is often only a short ecological step from this type of feeding behaviour to the parasitic one, and many nematodes parasitize other animals, externally or internally. Favourite hosts include insects, particularly beetles, earthworms, and slugs. Various species of the common genus *Rhabditis* may be found associated with each of these groups.

The general concensus of opinion (see, for example, Nielsen, 1949; Banage, 1963) is that the feeding activity of soil nematodes does not contribute significantly to the decomposition of organic material or the formation of humus in the soil. However, since many species feed on bacteria, their effects on these decomposer organisms merit further study. The Nematoda also provide an important source of food for other members of the soil community. Culture experiments have demonstrated that macrochelid mites will feed on nematodes (Rodriguez *et al.,* 1962), as will the cryptostigmatid mite *Pergalumna omniphagous* (Rockett and Woodring, 1966), while examples of predaceous fungi feeding on nematodes have been described on a number of occasions (for example, Duddington, 1955).

Rotifera and Gastrotricha

The Rotifera, often referred to as 'wheel animalcules', is a richly varied group of microscopic forms, rarely exceeding 2 mm in length and often considerably smaller than this. Rotifers have achieved their greatest radiation in freshwater habitats, and those members of the group that have succeeded in colonizing the soil belong to the soilwater fauna. According to Donner (1966), 94·5 per cent of the hitherto recorded species of soil rotifer belong to the Order Bdelloidea, representatives of which often abound in damp moss. Commonly occurring soil Bdelloids belonging to the genera *Philodina, Habrotrocha, Macrotrachela,* and *Mniobia* (Fig. 4.4) are creeping forms, moving over the substratum in a looping action, in which the suctorial rostral cilia and the adhesive foot participate. The foot of soil-inhabiting rotifers is well adapted for this mode of progression, for it is supplied with toes, spurs, and mucous glands.

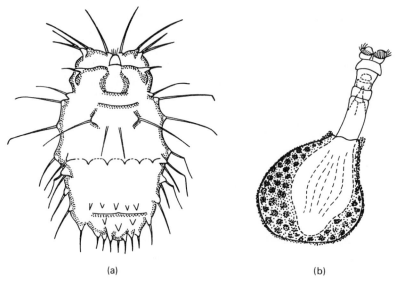

(a)   (b)

FIGURE 4.4. Two common soil rotifers: (a) *Macrotrachela spinosa,* contracted; (b) *Habrotrocha tridens excedens,* partly emerged from its nest of mucus, faeces, and dirt (after Donner, 1966).

Although rotifers are active only when adequate moisture is present, they have various devices to protect them against desiccation. Soil-inhabiting Bdelloids, for example, often construct shells from a body secretion to which may be added particles of debris and faecal material, as is the case with *Habrotrocha tridens excedens*; some rotifers make use of the protection afforded by empty shells of Testacea (Donner, 1966), from which they can emerge from time to time. During periods of drought, Bdelloid rotifers assume an anabiotic state, i.e., they become shrivelled and inert and able to withstand temperature conditions ranging from −200°C to +110°C in this condition (Donner, 1966). In this dried state, many of these animals are dispersed by wind currents. Anabiosis also tends to prolong the lifespan which, in the Bdelloidea, is a matter of a few months at the most, to a period of several years. Reproduction in the soil-inhabiting Bdelloidea is parthenogenetic: males do not occur.

The Bdelloidea are vortex feeders, creating currents in the surrounding water by the beating action of the cilia on the wheel organs; in this way, particles of organic material of plant or animal origin are conveyed to the mouth and ingested. The importance of these organisms in the processes of organic decomposition has not yet been evaluated, although it is probably greater in moist, organic soils, where densities up to and exceeding 100 000/m² may occur.

Mention may also be made at this point of another little-known group of the soilwater fauna, the Gastrotricha, which resemble the Rotifera in some respects. These minute animals, rarely exceeding 1 mm in length, of which the aquatic *Chaetonotus* spp. are common examples, may be identified by their spiny appearance and creeping habit. They are predatory forms and feed on other members of the soilwater fauna.

References

Banage, W. B. (1960) *Studies on the nematode fauna of moorland soils.* Ph. D. Thesis, Durham University.

Banage, W. B. (1963) 'The ecological importance of free-living soil nematodes with special reference to those of moorland soil', *J. Anim. Ecol.,* **32,** 133-40.

Cutler, D. W., Crump, L. M., and Sandon, H. (1922) 'A quantitative investigation of the bacterial and protozoal population of the soil, with an account of the protozoan fauna', *Phil. Trans. R. Soc.,* B **211,** 317-50.

Donner, J. (1966) *Rotifers* (English edn, trans. Wright, H. G. S.), Warne, London. xii + 80 pp.

Duddington, C. L. (1955) 'Inter-relations between soil micro-flora and soil nematodes' in Kevan, D. K. McE., ed., *Soil zoology,* 284-301.

Goodey, T. (1963) *Soil and freshwater nematodes* (second edn), Methuen, London.

Heal, O. W. (1962) 'The abundance and microdistribution of testate Amoebae (Rhizopoda, Testacea) in Sphagnum', *Oikos,* **13,** 35-47.

Lawrence, R. F. (1953) *The biology of the cryptic fauna of forests,* Balkema, Cape Town, Amsterdam. 408 pp.

Nielsen, C. O. (1949) 'Studies on the soil microfauna II. The soil-inhabiting nematodes', *Natura jutl.,* **2,** 1-131.

Nielsen, C. O. (1967) 'Nematoda' in Burges, N. A. and Raw, F., eds., *Soil biology,* 197-211.

Peters, B. G. (1955) 'Soil-inhabiting nematodes' in Kevan, D. K. McE., ed., *Soil zoology,* 44-54.

Rockett, C. L. and Woodring, J. P. (1966) 'Biological investigations on a new species of *Ceratozetes* and of *Pergalumna* (Acarina: Cryptostigmata)', *Acarologia,* **8,** 511-20.

Rodriguez, J. G., Wade, C. F., and Wells, C. N. (1962) 'Nematodes as a natural food for *Macrocheles muscaedomesticae* (Acarina: Macrochelidae), a predator of the house fly egg', *Ann. ent. Soc. Am.,* **55,** 507-11.

Schönborn, W. (1965) 'Untersuchungen über die Ernährung bodenbewohnender Testaceen', *Pedobiologia,* **5,** 205-10.

Singh, B. N. (1946) 'A method of estimating the numbers of soil Protozoa, especially amoebae, based on their differential feeding on bacteria', *Ann. appl. Biol.,* **33,** 112-19.

Stöckli, A. (1946) 'Der Boden als Lebensraum', *Vjschr. naturf. Ges. Zürich,* **91,** 1-18.

Stout, J. D. (1962) 'An estimation of microfaunal populations in soils and forest litter', *J. Soil Sci.,* **13,** 314-20.

Stout, J. D. (1963) 'Some observations on the Protozoa of some beechwood soil on the Chiltern Hills', *J. Anim. Ecol.,* **32,** 281-87.

Stout, J. D. (1968) 'The significance of the protozoan fauna in distinguishing mull and mor of beech (*Fagus silvatica* L.)', *Pedobiologia,* **8,** 387-400.

Stout, J. D. and Heal, O. W. (1967) 'Protozoa' in Burges, N. A. and Raw, F., eds., *Soil biology,* 149-95.

Volz, P. (1951) 'Untersuchungen über die Microfauna des waldboden', *Zool. Jb. (Syst.),* **79,** 514-66.

5. Annelida and Mollusca

In this chapter, we consider two groups of large-sized soil animals which have in common the tendency to be more abundant in neutral or slightly alkaline soils, at least in the northern hemisphere. The two groups differ ecologically in a number of respects, for the annelids are generally subterranean, whereas the molluscs are mainly surface-dwellers; the former are probably more important than the latter in the decomposition processes occurring in the soil. Their grouping together in a single chapter is largely a matter of convenience.

Annelida

Soil annelids are Oligochaeta belonging, in Europe, to two families, the Lumbricidae, the familiar earthworms or 'night-crawlers', and the Enchytraeidae, the lesser-known pot-worms. Outside the Palaearctic region, lumbricids are less common, and earthworms belonging to other families achieve greater prominence. For example, Khalaf El Duweini and Ghabbour (1967) recorded six families of Oligochaetes from the muddy banks of the Nile and from irrigated land in Egypt, in a list that included representatives of the Aeolosomatidae, Naididae, Tubificidae, Megascolecidae, and Glossoscolecidae, in addition to the Lumbricidae. Many of these forms must be regarded as aquatic rather than terrestrial, although the Megascolecidae includes truly terrestrial members, such as those belonging to the now widely distributed genus *Pheretima*, and the Australian *Megascolides* species which may attain a length of several feet. The ecology of these south temperate and tropical forms has received little attention although some, at least, may be important in promoting soil aeration and mixing. Madge's (1969) work on the eudrilids *Hyperiodrilus africanus* and *Eudrilus eugeniae*, a group restricted to tropical and subtropical Africa, showed that both species produced surface casts during the wet season, the funnel-shaped casts of *H. africanus* predominating in the soils of forest and shaded grassland, whereas the mound-shaped casts of *E. eugeniae* were more abundant in open grassland. In South Africa, earthworms of the family Microchaetidae have been studied by Ljungström and Reinecke (1969). These are large earthworms, usually exceeding 20 cm, and sometimes more than 1 m in length; the (unconfirmed) record for this group is held by a worm 6·78 m long and 8 cm thick. The distribution of the microchaetids is apparently correlated with a high water table, and they rarely emerge on the surface, except after rain. The surface castings of these worms are deposited in the form of bowls, called *kommetjies*, which may be a metre in diameter, and it has been estimated that a population of 300 000 per acre, with a biomass of 315 kg, can produce 20 000 kg of castings each year.

Much more study has been devoted to the ecology of the lumbricids and enchytraeids, and it is with these groups that we are particularly concerned in this chapter.

Lumbricidae

Earthworms have been considered to have a marked effect on the structure and properties of the soil, and they are undoubtedly the best known of all soil animals. Their influence on the decomposition processes in organic material and the formation of organo-mineral complexes has been studied since the time of Darwin, and a considerable amount of literature relating to the group has accumulated over the years (see, for example, the recent accounts by Satchell, 1955, 1963, 1967; Gerard, 1967). Even so, there is still much to be learned about their ecology, particularly since modern sampling and experimental techniques now permit a critical evaluation of their natural distribution patterns and activity.

Composition of the Fauna

Nineteen of the more than 200 species comprising this family are commonly distributed in Europe. In Britain, where about 25 species belonging to seven genera occur, representatives of the genera *Lumbricus, Allolobophora* and *Dendrobaena* are commonly encountered in soil samples. Keys to the identification of British lumbricids have been compiled by Cernosvitov and Evans (1947) and revised by Gerard (1964).

Horizontal Distribution

The general distribution of the lumbricids is mainly governed by pH conditions of the soil for, as we have noted, the majority of species occur in neutral, slightly alkaline or, at the most, slightly acid conditions. However, tolerance of pH conditions varies with the species (Satchell, 1955; Reynoldson, 1955). For example, *Allolobophora caliginosa, A. longa, A. nocturna, A. chlorotica,* and *Eisenia rosea* prefer neutral or alkaline mull soils, whereas a greater tolerance of more acid conditions is reflected in the wider distribution of *Lumbricus terrestris, L. rubellus* and *Octolasium cyaneum* (Fig. 5.1). *Bimastos eiseni* and *Dendrobaena* spp. can tolerate acid conditions better than most, and are the characteristic species of earthworm in highly organic mor soils, along with *Lumbricus rubellus*. In extreme mor conditions, *L. rubellus* and *Dendrobaena rubida* may be absent (Cragg, 1961; Satchell, 1967).

In his study of the Lumbricidae of a cattle-grazed maritime grassland in Scotland, Boyd (1958) demonstrated that local conditions may influence the distribution patterns of some acid-tolerant species. For example, dungpats formed a microhabitat clearly distinct from that of open soil during April, and, at this time, populations of *Dendrobaena octaedra* and *Lumbricus rubellus*

showed significant aggregations beneath them, whereas *Allolobophora caliginosa*
populations did not. As the dungpats decayed through the summer, their effect
became less marked, and populations of *D. octaedra* and *L. rubellus* were more
strongly dispersed. Attraction to dungpats, apparently, is more strongly
developed in pigmented species, such as *L. rubellus, L. castaneus, L. festivus, D.*

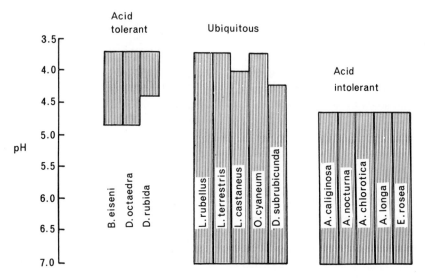

FIGURE 5.1. Classification of earthworm species according to pH of litter or soil in which
they are found (from Satchell, 1955).

octaedra, D. rubida, and *B. eiseni,* than in the non-pigmented *Allolobophora*
species, according to Svendsen (1957a and b), who also noted that different
dung-inhabiting species were associated with different soils in English moorland.
For example, *D. octaedra* and *B. eiseni* were found to be typical of peat habitats,
while *D. rubida* and *L. rubellus* preferred mineral soil.

The aggregated distribution pattern of earthworms cannot always be
explained in terms of the heterogeneity of the habitat, however, as Satchell's
(1955) study of populations of *E. rosea* and *L. castaneus* in a grassland soil
showed. Aggregations of these species occurred even in relatively uniform sites
where manuring and stock grazing had been excluded; one possible explanation
for these is provided by the relationship between reproductive and dispersion
rates. When reproduction occurs more rapidly than the offspring can disperse,
family aggregations result.

The limiting effects of variations in soil moisture content on distribution
patterns are most strongly felt in surface-dwelling species. This is to be expected,
for, except in the dry desert soils, where earthworms are entirely lacking, it is
only the surface layer of the profile which is subject to desiccation. A

comparison between the earthworm populations of irrigated and non-irrigated sites on Lower Greensand in Bedfordshire, showed a marked decline in numbers of surface-dwelling *Allolobophora caliginosa, A. chlorotica* and *Eisenia rosea* in the drier plots. Populations of the deep-burrowing *Lumbricus terrestris* were not affected by these treatments, since their burrow systems extended down into permanently moist soil in both instances (Gerard, 1960). Different tolerances to soil moisture may be shown at the subspecific level in the widely distributed *A. chlorotica* which occurs in two colour varieties, green and pink. The green morph is mainly restricted to wet sites, the pink one to drier sites; no physiological explanation has yet been proposed for this difference (see Satchell, 1967).

It is perhaps well to remember that not all lumbricids are terrestrial forms, some are typically aquatic and others, such as *A. chlorotica,* although occurring in soil, can also live quite happily submerged in lakes. On the other hand, certain species, such as *L. terrestris* and *Bimastos eiseni,* are restricted to soil and may show a preference for drier sites, despite the fact that all of them can survive long periods immersed in aerated water. The restriction of these species to relatively dry habitats is, then, not due to an inability to tolerate submergence, but is either a reflection of intolerance to low oxygen tensions occurring in permanently wet sites, such as moorland soils (Satchell, 1967), or is due to an ability to aestivate during dry conditions. There is no experimental evidence to suggest which, if either, of these two interpretations is the more likely.

Vertical Distribution

The extent to which different species of lumbricids can penetrate the soil varies, consequently, differences in vertical distribution occur. In Britain, *Lumbricus terrestris* and *Allolobophora nocturna* may burrow to depths of several feet (Evans and Guild, 1947), and other deep-burrowing species include *Allolobophora longa, Octolasium cynaeum* and sometimes *O. lacteum* (Guild, 1955). Figure 5.2 shows the relationship between the distribution of these deep-burrowers and surface-dwelling species. Among the latter, are species that produce a burrow system, for example, *Allolobophora caliginosa, A. chlorotica,* and *Eisenia rosea,* and forms that do not, such as *Lumbricus rubellus* and *L. castaneus,* although members of the latter category probably enlarge existing soil spaces by their activity. Although the ability to penetrate down the soil profile is generally better developed in the large-sized species than in those of small size, the character of the soil may have an important effect, for species that normally live in the top 5 to 7 cm in undisturbed grassland often penetrate deeper into the profile in cultivated soil, where ploughing renders the soil easily workable to a depth of 15-22 cm. In addition, populations of surface-dwellers often undergo vertical migrations down the profile during the summer season, possibly in response to increased temperatures and the drying out of the surface organic layer. This behaviour is considered in the next section in relation to the changes in age structure of earthworm populations during the seasonal cycle.

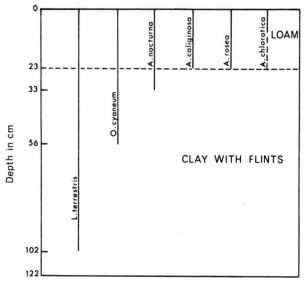

FIGURE 5.2. Vertical distribution of earthworms in a Rothamsted pasture (from Satchell, 1953, 1967).

Population Sizes

There is considerable variation in the size of earthworm populations from one site to another, maximum densities generally occurring in base-rich grassland soils and mull woodland soils, and minimum in acid moorland and raw humus. Densities in cultivated soil usually fall between these two extremes (Table 5.1). The estimates of numerical density and biomass given in the table are adequate for general comparisons between habitats, but they are unsatisfactory in certain respects, particularly because they do not take into account the considerable fluctuations occurring seasonally. The timing of peak densities, which coincide with large numbers of juvenile forms, may vary from species to species as the rate of development varies, and from site to site as local conditions—particularly soil temperature, moisture, and the availability of food—affect fecundity, the length of the incubation period, and the extent of juvenile mortality (see chapter 11). Nevertheless, these effects often are synchronized so that well-defined population peaks occur in spring and early summer, sometimes extending into autumn or early winter, at least in Britain. In order to interpret the behaviour of populations over a yearly cycle, it is necessary to refer to the reproductive biology of these animals, and we digress briefly, at this point, to consider some of the more important aspects of this.

Cross-fertilization occurs in the majority of British members of the genera *Allolobophora* and *Lumbricus,* while in other groups parthenogenesis is not uncommon, being facultative or obligate in *Dendrobaena,* and obligate in *Octolasium, Eiseniella,* and *Allolobophora rosea* (Satchell, 1967). Eggs are

TABLE 5.1. Numbers and biomass of earthworms in various habitats (from Satchell, 1967, after various authors).

Site	No./m^2	g/m^2	Locality
Eriophorum moor[1]	0·01		Westmorland
Calluna moor[1]	0·1-0·5		Westmorland
Raw humus:			
Picea[2]	18-31	0·9-1·5	Denmark
Fagus[2]	23-81	1·2-5·4	Denmark
Pseudotsuga[3]	14	4·7	North Wales
Mull:			
Picea[2,3]	101	5·1	Denmark
Fagus[2,3]	73-177	5·9-54	Denmark
Quercus[2,3]	122	61	Denmark
Mixed wood[3]	157	40	North Wales
Mixed wood[4]	78-493	148-162	Lake District
Apple orchard/grass[3]	25-500	11-122	Holland
Apple orchard/grass[3,4]	848	287	Cambridgeshire
Apple orchard/arable[3]	13-30	11-23	Holland
Apple orchard/arable[3,4]	196	153	Cambridgeshire
Arable[5]	220	48	Germany
Arable[3]	287	76	Bardsey, N. Wales
Arable[3]	146	50	North Wales
Arable[4]		50-106	Rothamsted
Base-rich grassland[3]	389-470	52-110	Westmorland
Base-rich grassland[3]	390	56	Bardsey, N. Wales
Base-rich grassland[3]	481-524	112-120	North Wales

[1]Dung-baiting. [2]Tullgren funnels. [3]Hand-sorting. [4]Formaldehyde. [5]Wet sieving.

deposited in cocoons, and, although several ova may be present in a cocoon, it is usual for only one of these to hatch. Evans and Guild (1948) noted that there was a relationship between fecundity and the severity of the environmental factors to which different species are exposed. Deep-burrowers, such as *Allolobophora nocturna, A. longa, Octolasium cyaneum,* and *Lumbricus terrestris,* which are not usually subjected to desiccation, produce a small number (3-13) of cocoons each year in laboratory cultures, whereas surface-dwellers, such as *Lumbricus rubellus, L. castaneus,* and *Dendrobaena subrubicunda,* produce between 42 and 106 per year (Table 5.2). The immature

TABLE 5.2. The relationship between depth distribution and fecundity in laboratory cultures of some British Lumbricidae (adapted from Evans and Guild, 1948).

Depth distribution	Species	No. of cocoons/worm/yr
0-102 cm	*Lumbricus terrestris*	3-13
0-56 cm	*Octolasium cyaneum*	3-13
0-33 cm	*Allolobophora nocturna:*	3-13
0-23 cm	*Allolobophora caliginosa*	27
0-23 cm	*Allolobophora chlorotica*	25-27
<23 cm	*Lumbricus rubellus*	79-106
<23 cm	*Lumbricus castaneus*	65
<23 cm	*Dendrobaena subrubicunda*	42

worms differ from adults in lacking a clitellum and tubercula pubertatis, development being associated with a gradual increase in body size, the various categories of immatures being defined as 'small', 'medium', and 'large'.

Reproduction apparently occurs throughout the year in many Lumbricidae (Evans and Guild, 1948; Satchell, 1967) if conditions are favourable, although van der Drift (1951) suggested that breeding was restricted to the autumn season

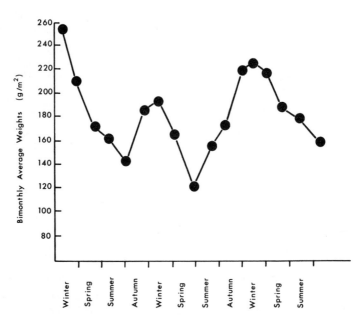

FIGURE 5.3. Seasonal variations in biomass of New Zealand populations of *Allolobophora caligiuosa* (from Satchell, 1967, after Waters, 1955).

in the case of a population of *Dendrobaena octaedra* inhabiting a beech forest floor. Gerard (1967) noted that cocoons of *Allolobophora chlorotica* and *A. caliginosa* were deposited mainly during the winter and spring in a permanent pasture at Rothamsted, and reached a peak density in May and June. The emergence of immature worms started to increase in May, but many of these early juveniles died during the early part of the summer. Those hatching later, in July, probably survived by moving downward in the soil to avoid the dry conditions at the surface. This movement, which evidently took the worms down to a depth greater than that sampled, is probably responsible for the apparent population decline at this time. These survivors became adults in December, the calculated maturation period for *A. caliginosa* being 25 weeks, compared with 21 weeks in *A. chlorotica*. A slight difference between the two species was the persistence of a large number of early immature forms of *A. chlorotica* into October. This suggests that the summer drought retarded the early development of this species. The length of the developmental period is undoubtedly influenced by environmental factors: varying times of development from hatching to maturity have been quoted for *A. chlorotica,* ranging from 13 weeks at 18°C, to 29-42 weeks in an unheated cellar (see Satchell, 1967).

There appears to be a general tendency, among lumbricids in Britain and New Zealand, at least, for the main period of population decline to occur in the late winter, when the predominant age class present is the adult. Consequently, it is not surprising to find that this period of numerical decline coincides with a peak in biomass (Fig. 5.3). The reproductive life of the adult is generally short, spanning a few months at the most, although individual instances have been recorded in which adult longevity extended over several years. Long-term studies on *Lumbricus terrestris* revealed that the mortality rate of adults was nearly constant over a number of years, and although the exact causes of death are not known, fungal infections may play a part (Satchell, 1967).

Feeding Habits

That earthworms ingest decaying organic material and mineral soil is, of course, well known. However, recent studies have shown that there is a good deal of selectivity in the kind of plant material accepted, for *Lumbricus terrestris, L. rubellus, Allolobophora longa, A. caliginosa, A. rosea, Eisenia foetida,* and *Dendrobaena octaedra,* at least, can discriminate between different litter materials (see Satchell, 1967). There is a direct relationship between the palatability and the nitrogen and sugar content of the food material; leaves rich in these nutrients, such as those of dog's mercury, nettle, wood-sorrel, hawthorn, ash, elm, alder, birch, hornbeam, and sycamore, are more acceptable than those of oak, beech, pine, spruce, and larch. Palatability is also increased by organic decomposition which may result in the degradation of distasteful polyphenols.

The immediate effect on the soil of the feeding activities of earthworms, and this applies particularly to burrowing species, is to comminute litter fragments and mix them thoroughly with mineral soil. The pH of the organic matter may also be raised slightly, possibly due to the secretion of calcium compounds from the worm's calciferous glands (Arthur, 1963). Nitrogen bound in organic complexes is converted to the more readily 'available' ammonia, nitrites, and nitrates, a process known as 'mineralization' (see Heath, 1965). The fine, unassimilated particles passing out of the gut as faeces are bound together in a crumblike cast which is less susceptible to water action than the original soil. In view of these effects, lumbricids have long been considered as important agents in promoting the redistribution of organic debris, soil drainage, and fertility, the availability of plant nutrients, and a stable soil structure. However, it is possible to overemphasize the significance of these processes, as Satchell (1967) points out. For example, the crumb structure of surface casts may be stable for only a short period of time and, accordingly, is of little importance as far as soil structure is concerned. The mechanics of crumb formation are incompletely known, although various agencies have been suggested, of which the binding action of fungal hyphae and the cementing effect of bacterial products are probably the most important (see chapter 1). To what extent these effects are enhanced by the passage of material through the earthworm gut is not yet clear. It is likely that the growth and binding action of plant roots are equally significant in promoting soil stability, particularly in grassland soils. Hence, it is important to view the activities of the earthworms within the context of the totality of factors which may promote good soil structure and fertility.

Enchytraeidae

These worms are less conspicuous than the lumbricids for they are considerably smaller in size, the range for adult length being of the order of 1 mm to 5 cm. They are white in colour and relatively uniform in their external appearance. Biological investigations on the group have been hampered until recently by a lack of easily-worked taxonomic keys. However, Nielsen and Christensen (1959) and O'Connor (1967) have compiled keys to European genera.

Composition of the Fauna

O'Connor's key recognizes 21 genera, of which 13 are small, in terms of the number of constituent species. The remaining eight, which are commonly distributed in general, are *Fridericia, Lumbricillus, Marionina, Enchytraeus, Mesenchytraeus, Achaeta, Henlea,* and *Cognettia.*

Distribution

Enchytraeid distribution contrasts with that of the lumbricids in that they are generally more abundant in highly organic forest and moorland soils than in alluvial and sandy grassland (Table 5.3). Nielsen (1955a) estimated that population densities in the latter varied between 1000 and 100 000/m², compared with peak densities of over 200 000/m² in the more acid soils of heathland and conifer forest. On the other hand, Springett (1963) reported higher total population density and greater species representation in a grassland

TABLE 5.3. Annual mean density of Enchytraeidae in different habitats (from O'Connor, 1967).

Site	Numbers (10³/m²)	Author and region
Sandy permanent pasture (3 sites)		
1	44	Nielsen, Denmark
2	30	Nielsen, Denmark
3	74	Nielsen, Denmark
Conifer soil	134·3	O'Connor, N. Wales
Alluvial grass	10-25	Peachey, Pennine moor
Juncus moor	130-290	Peachey, Pennine moor
Nardus grass	37-200	Peachey, Pennine moor
Eroded peat	12-50	Peachey, Pennine moor

soil than in two different forest sites. While it appears to be generally true that permanently damp soils with a high content of organic matter offer the most suitable conditions, enchytraeid populations can survive in drier situations; this may be due, in part, to the habit shown by certain species, such as members of the genera *Enchytraeus, Fridericia,* and *Henlea,* of covering the cocoons with soil particles embedded in mucus (O'Connor, 1967). However, the influence of various environmental factors on the macro- and microdistribution of these worms is not clearly understood. For example, O'Connor (1967) noted that different species under different environmental conditions showed similar patterns of clumping, suggesting that aggregation resulted from some intrinsic behaviour pattern of the group as a whole.

Despite the wide distribution of many species, some general points may be made about the distribution of generic groups (O'Connor, 1967). For instance, *Lumbricillus, Mesenchytraeus,* and *Cognettia* show a preference for very wet sites, the first-named in the marine littoral, the other two in bogs and fens. The greater tolerance to a range of environmental moisture may be shown by the genera *Marionina, Henlea, Enchytraeus,* and *Fridericia,* as already noted, for they occur in habitats ranging from fresh water to dry sandy soil. Quantitative differences at the species level may, however, be useful as indicators of certain environmental conditions. For example, O'Connor (1967) noted that the genera *Cognettia, Marionina,* and *Achaeta* occurred in three moder humus sites, but that *Cognettia* was most abundant in the litter layer, *Marionina* in the humus layer, and *Achaeta* in the mineral soil. Furthermore, two of these three genera were represented by different species in the three sites (Table 5.4).

TABLE 5.4. Species of Enchytraeidae in three sites (from O'Connor, 1967).

Site	*Cognettia*	*Marionina*	*Achaeta*
Douglas fir	*cognettii* (Issel)	*cambrensis* (O'Connor)	*eiseni* (Vejdovsky)
Oak	*glandulosa* (Michaelsen)	*cambrensis*	*camerani* (Cognetti)
Beech	*sphagnetorum* (Vejdovsky)	*cambrensis*	*bohemica* (Vejdovsky)

Population Fluctuations

Rather violent changes in the size of populations of enchytraeids have been recorded (Nielsen, 1955a), the occurrence of peaks and declines during the seasonal cycle depending on the temperature and moisture conditions of the habitat, at least in some cases. For example, in the permanently moist soils of coniferous woodland and moorland, maximum densities have been recorded in summer and minimum in late winter (O'Connor, 1957, 1958, 1967; Peachey, 1962, 1963), as shown in Fig. 5.4a and b. The summer peak consists predominantly of juvenile forms which hatch from overwintering cocoons during the spring. A gradual winter decline in population size may be the result of a high death rate among adults following the deposition of cocoons, although this mortality is evidently not temperature-induced. In these moist situations, population numbers are regulated, apparently by the effect of temperature on reproductive activity, the timing of the summer peak probably being influenced by the duration of the previous winter. Thus, when the winter is long and the spring late, as in Pennine moorland, the density peak occurs late in the summer

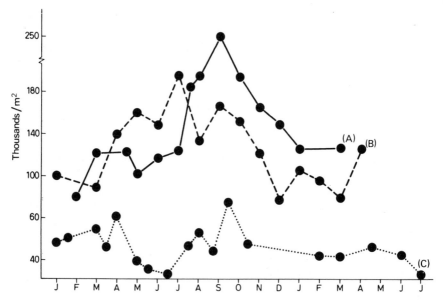

FIGURE 5.4. Population fluctuations of Enchytraeidae in three different soil habitats. (a) *Juncus* moorland; (b) conifer woodland; (c) permanent pasture (after O'Connor, 1967).

or in the autumn, whereas an early spring season advances the density peak to midsummer (Fig. 5.4a). In contrast to this pattern, Huhta *et al.* (1967) noted spring and autumn maxima, and summer and winter minima, in Finnish populations inhabiting a coniferous soil. These authors attribute the summer decline to the effects of drought, and the winter trough to the effects of frost.

A characteristic phenological pattern occurring in habitats subjected to summer drought has a well-defined density peak in autumn, and a minimum in spring or early summer (Fig. 5.4c). Nielsen (1955a and b) detected this decline and the subsequent autumnal increase in six different sampling stations in Denmark, although the extent of the fluctuation varied with the locality. The heavy spring/early summer mortality accounted for as much as 99 per cent of the population and apparently was caused, at least in part, by desiccation. This explanation is confirmed by the observations that a spring density peak is allowed to develop, if the onset of drought is delayed until the beginning of summer (O'Connor, 1967). However, the Danish work showed that a high mortality in spring/early summer also occurred in some permanently moist habitats where desiccation would not be a factor. In these cases, it is possible, although not established, that post-reproductive mortality in adults increases markedly in spring and early summer. The sharp increase in population size which produces the autumn peak is caused by mass hatching from cocoons that have survived the summer drought, and it is of interest to recall that there is a differential ability of cocoons of different species to survive drought conditions. Evidently, the phenological pattern, in dry localities, is influenced not only by the duration of drought, but also by the species composition of the fauna.

Although much valuable information on the biology of the Enchytraeidae has been accumulated in the studies described above, a number of areas still remain to be investigated. Little is known about the rate of cocoon production, duration of the reproductive period in the field, the length of the life cycle in many species, and the influence of downward migration on the apparent summer decline in numbers, in dry habitats. In addition, it is worth noting that the number of sexually mature worms is usually small in comparison to the number of juveniles. As O'Connor (1958) pointed out, the low overall percentage maturity suggests that most of the population never reaches this condition. The factor, or factors, responsible for this have not been determined.

Feeding Habits

The feeding habits of the enchytraeids have been reviewed recently by O'Connor (1967) and, although much has still to be learned, the information obtained so

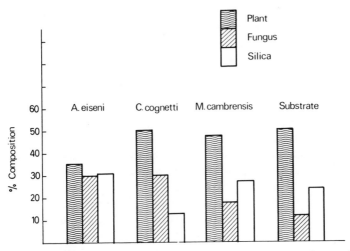

FIGURE 5.5. Feeding preferences, as indicated by gut content analyses, of humus populations of *Achaeta eiseni, Cognettia cognetti,* and *Marionina cambrensis* from coniferous forest soil (after O'Connor, 1967).

far allows a preliminary assessment of the role of these worms in the decomposition processes occurring in the soil. Gut content analyses have shown that plant fragments, fungus, and silica grains are ingested in proportions that vary with the species (Fig. 5.5) and with the availability of these materials. *Achaeta eiseni* and *Marionina cambrensis* ingest appreciable amounts of siliceous material with the organic food, and may make a significant contribution to the production of stable organo-mineral complexes in the soil. Some enchytraeids, for example, *A. eiseni* and *Cognettia cognetti*, may feed selectively on fungi, but there is no evidence that any of the organic material ingested is chemically decomposed to form humus compounds. It is possible that bacteria, ingested along with the plant material, may also provide a source of food, but confirmation of this must await further investigations.

Mollusca

In temperate regions, terrestrial molluscs are mainly pulmonate Gastropoda of the Order Stylommatophora, readily divisible into 'slugs' and 'snails'. These land-dwelling representatives of a predominantly marine phylum have often attracted the interest of the agriculturalist on account of their destructive effects on cultivated crops. However, the group is often neglected by the soil zoologist, due to its sparse occurrence in many mature acid soils, and also because many of its representatives belong to the fauna of the vegetation layer above the soil. A key to the identification of British slugs has been provided by Quick (1960), and one for snails by Janus (1965).

Distribution

Land pulmonates occur only sporadically in strongly structured soils supporting sparse herbaceous cover. For example, van der Drift (1951) could record only *Arion subfuscus, A. intermedius, Limax tenellus,* and the predatory *Hyalinia* sp. in his survey of the animals of a beech forest floor, and of these, only the first-named occurred in appreciable numbers. Pulmonates occur more frequently in localities which have exposed rock surfaces intermixed with a field layer of vegetation; in many cases, species distribution is related, either directly or indirectly, to the nature of the rock material. Lozek (1962) found *Abida secale, Cochlodina commutata, Delima ornata, Helicigona cingulella, Neostyriaca corynodes,* and *Orcula doliolum* commonly associated with calcareous rock formations in central Europe, whereas *Balea perversa, Clausilia parvula, C. dubia, Laciniaria nitidosa,* and *Vertigo alpestris* were not so strongly restricted, and occurred on basic silicate rocks. Environmental moisture may also have an influence on distribution, characteristic species associated with wet soils include *Succinea* spp., *Vertigo* spp., *Zonitoides nitidus, Carychium minimum, Deroceras laeve* (= *Agriolimax laevis*), and species of the predominantly freshwater genera *Anisus, Limnaea,* and *Pisidium.* A preference for humid surroundings is also apparent in the distribution of *Acicula parcelineata, Carychium tridentatum, Eucobresia nivalis,* and other inhabitants of decaying wood.

It is generally accepted that the distribution of snails is governed, to a large extent, by the presence of calcium carbonate or calcium ions in food plants (Newell, 1967), although different degrees of tolerance are shown by different species. In Lozek's study, mentioned above, it was noted that some steppe and woodland species could tolerate conditions of low calcium content, to judge from their distribution. These included members of the genera *Laciniaria, Pupilla, Caecilioides, Eucobresia, Cepaea, Acicula, Ena, Euomphalia, Fruticicola, Iphigena, Vitrea,* and *Isognomostoma* among others. Thus, the molluscan fauna of a particular type of vegetation, such as steppe or forest, is often a composite of several different ecological groups characterized by their dependence on the calcium content of the soil or rock (Table 5.5).

Many molluscs, for example, the common *Agriolimax reticulatus* (Fig. 5.6), live on the soil surface or in crevices, but others, such as *Caecilioides petitiana, C. acicula, Oxychilus inopinatus,* and adults and immatures of species of *Limax, Milax, Arion, Vitrina,* and *Daudebardia,* are among those that may be encountered below the surface. In an ecological study of arable soil populations of three species of garden slug common in Britain, namely, *Agriolimax reticulatus, Arion hortensis,* and *Milax budapestensis,* Hunter (1966) found differences in depth distribution between species (Fig. 5.7a), and also showed

TABLE 5.5. Species of Gastropoda occurring in steppe and forest soils in central Europe (adapted from Lozek, 1962).

Habitat		Ecological grouping	
	Calcicole	Calciphile	Tolerant of low calcium content
Steppe (a) Compact stony soils	*Alopia clathrata* *Chondrina avenacea* *Chondrina clienta* *Chondrina tatrica* *Pyramidula rupestris* *Spelaeodiscus tatricus*	*Clausilia grimmeri* *Pupilla sterri* *Truncatellina claustralis* *Truncatellina strobeli*	*Laciniaria biplicata* *Pupilla triplicata*
(b) Loose soils		*Caecilioides petitiana* *Helicella neglecta* *Helicella obvia* *Oxychilus inopinatus* *Zebrina detrita*	*Caecilioides acicula* *Chondrula tridens* *Helicella itala* *Helicella striata* *Helicella unifasciata*
Forest		*Discus perspectivus* *Helicigona rossmässleri* *Helicondonta obvoluta* *Orcula doliolum* *Pagodulina pagodula*	*Acicula polita* *Cepaea hortensis* *Ena obscura* *Eucobresia diaphana* *Euomphalia strigella* *Fruticicola fruticum* *Helix pomatia* *Helicigona, Iphigena, Laciniaria* spp., and many others

FIGURE 5.6. *Agriolimax reticulatus,* the common British garden slug (photo by A. Newman-Coburn).

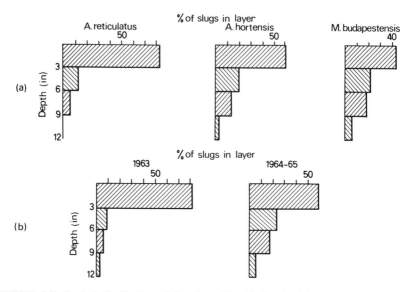

FIGURE 5.7. Vertical distribution of slugs in arable soil, showing (a) a comparison between *Agriolimax reticulatus, Arion hortensis,* and *Milax budapestensis*; and (b) the effect of ploughing after the 1963 season (three species combined) (from Hunter, 1966).

that winter frost and summer drought, affecting the surface soil, caused populations of all three species to move down the profile to a depth of 15-22 cm. There was also an increase of populations of all three species combined in the lower layers after ploughing to a depth of 32 cm had loosened the soil (Fig. 5.7b). Subterranean forms often show a nocturnal activity pattern, emerging periodically to forage at the surface. Subsequently, they may return to their original point of emergence, in a homing behaviour pattern which has been described in the slugs *Limax maximus, L. flavus,* and *Agriolimax reticulatus.* A fuller discussion of this activity is given by South (1965) and Newell (1967).

Population Sizes

The size of mollusc populations inhabiting mature podzol and brown earth soils is generally small, often about a few thousands per acre. However, where the soil is calcareous and loosely packed, and where surface vegetation provides abundant food, remarkably large populations are able to flourish, and the estimates available (Table 5.6) indicate that these run to tens or hundreds of thousands of individuals per acre. Densities of this order of magnitude present a serious problem to the growers of cultivated crops, and necessitate chemical control methods, such as those used in the citrus orchards of southern California, where huge mounds of shells of *Helix aspersa* can be found under every tree. In this locality, fluctuations in estimates of the snail population occur between summer and winter, higher densities being recorded in the former season, as shown in Table 5.6. Characteristically, molluscs are less active during cold and dry weather, and it is important, in applying control methods and assessing their effects, to distinguish between a decline in activity and a decline in numbers of individuals. Much of the available evidence suggests that adult and egg stages can tolerate low temperatures, and this resistance, coupled with the fact that many slugs and snails lay their eggs in the top 15 cm of soil (Hunter,

TABLE 5.6. Population sizes of some groups of terrestrial Gastropoda (based on Newell, 1967).

Group	Population size	Locality	Author
Achatina	7500/acre	Hawaii	Weber (1953)
Helix aspersa	9-9·5 x 10⁴/acre	Citrus orchard in summer	Lewis and La Follette (1942)
Helix aspersa	4·65-5 x 10⁴/acre	Citrus orchard in winter	
Agriolimax reticulatus	600 000/acre	Wheat crop	Thomas (1944)
Agriolimax reticulatus	72 000± 25 000/acre	Barley/grass and clover	Newell (1967)
Arion subfuscus	5600/acre	Beech forest	van der Drift (1951)

1966), suggests that cold-induced mortality has no appreciable effect on these age classes (Newell, 1967). On the other hand, Hunter (1966) attributed the winter declines in numbers of immature *Agriolimax reticulatus*, and *Arion hortensis* to the effects of frost, although this author points out that the most important density regulating factor was the severity of the winter season and its effect on the rate of maturation of individuals in their first year, and on the timing of the following spring breeding season. This topic is considered in more detail in chapter 11.

Feeding Habits

A wide variety of organic material serves as food for land molluscs, although several broad categories of feeding habit can be defined. Slugs of the genera *Arion, Limax, Agriolimax,* and *Milax* are herbivorous, feeding on the aerial parts of garden and farm crops, and on the underground roots and tubers of, for example, potatoes and carrots. Species of the genus *Caecilioides,* and various slugs, appear to be mainly fungivorous, whereas *Helix aspersa, Cepaea nemoralis, Arion ater, Limax maximus,* and species belonging to the genera *Zonites, Zonitoides, Vitrea, Pupilla, Clausilia,* and *Vertigo* are detritus-feeders, ingesting mainly leaf litter and, in some cases, carrion. Some soil-inhabiting molluscs are predators; species of *Testacella, Glandina,* and *Vitrina* feeding mainly on earthworms, may be cited as examples.

The fact that many molluscs feed on surface vegetation and then move down into the subsurface layers of the soil, suggests that they may have an important function in the incorporation of organic material into the mineral structure of the soil. This activity achieves a special significance when we realize that some species, at least, produce cellulases, and are therefore able to effect a marked chemical degradation of their food material. In addition, the mucus, which they produce in great quantities, may serve to promote the development of water-stable soil crumbs which not only contribute to a good soil structure, but may also provide a suitable substrate for the development of soil microflora. As yet, we can only speculate on the importance of these effects, but, since molluscs are more often associated with immature or disturbed soils, they probably achieve their greatest significance in the early stages of soil formation.

References

Arthur, D. R. (1963) 'The post-pharyngeal gut of the earthworm *Lumbricus terrestris'*, *Proc. zool. Soc. Lond.,* **141,** 663-75.

Boyd, J. M. (1958) 'The ecology of earthworms in cattle-grazed machair in Tiree, Argyll', *J. Anim. Ecol.,* **27,** 147-57.

Cernosvitov, L. and Evans, A. C. (1947) See Gerard, B. M. (1964).

Cragg, J. B. (1961) 'Some aspects of the ecology of moorland animals', *J. Anim. Ecol.,* **30,** 205-34.

Drift, J. van der (1951) 'Analysis of the animal community in a beech forest floor', *Tijdschr. Ent.,* **94,** 1-168.

Evans, A. C. and Guild, W. J. McL. (1947) 'Studies on the relationships between earthworms and soil fertility. I. Biological studies in the field', *Ann. appl. Biol.,* **34,** 307-30.

Evans, A. C. and Guild, W. J. McL. (1948) *idem.* 'IV. On the life cycles of some British Lumbricidae', *ibid.,* **35,** 471-84.

Gerard, B. M. (1960) *The biology of certain British earthworms in relation to environmental conditions.* Ph.D. Thesis, University of London.

Gerard, B. M. (1964) The Linnean Society of London Synopses of the British Fauna, no 6, 'Lumbricidae (Annelida)'.

Gerard, B. M. (1967) 'Factors affecting earthworms in pastures', *J. Anim. Ecol.,* **36,** 235-52.

Guild, W. J. McL. (1955) 'Earthworms and soil structure' in Kevan, D. K. McE., ed., *Soil zoology,* 83-98.

Heath, G. W. (1965) 'The part played by animals in soil formation', in Hallsworth, E. G. and Crawford, D. V., eds., *Experimental pedology,* 236-43.

Huhta, V., Karppinen, E., Nurminen, M., and Valpas, A. (1967) 'Effect of silvicultural practices upon arthropod, annelid and nematode populations in coniferous forest soil', *Ann. Zool. Fenn.,* **4,** 87-143.

Hunter, P. J. (1966) 'The distribution and abundance of slugs on an arable plot in Northumberland', *J. Anim. Ecol.,* **35,** 543-57.

Janus, H. (1965) *Land and freshwater molluscs,* Burke, London.

Khalaf El Duweini and Ghabbour, S. (1967) 'Records of Oligochaeta in Egypt', *Pedobiologia,* **7,** 135-41.

Lewis, H. C. and LaFollette, J. R. (1942) 'Control of the brown snail in citrus orchards', *J. econ. Ent.,* **35,** 359-62.

Ljungström, P. O. and Reinecke, A. J. (1969) 'Ecology and natural history of the microchaetid earthworms of South Africa', *Pedobiologia,* **9,** 152-7.

Lozek, V. (1962) 'Soil conditions and their influence on terrestrial Gasteropoda in central Europe' in Murphy, P. W., ed., *Progress in soil zoology,* 334-42.

Madge, D. S. (1969) 'Field and laboratory studies on the activities of two species of tropical earthworms', *Pedobiologia,* **9,** 188-214.

Newell, P. F. (1967) 'Mollusca' in Burges, N. A. and Raw, F., eds., *Soil biology,* 413-33.

Nielsen, C. O. (1955a) 'Survey of a year's results obtained by a recent method for the extraction of soil-inhabiting enchytraeid worms' in Kevan, D. K. McE., ed., *Soil zoology,* 202-14.

Nielsen, C. O. (1955b) 'Studies on the Enchytraeidae. 2. Field studies', *Natura jutl.,* **4,** 1-58.

Nielsen, C. O. and Christensen, B. (1959) 'The Enchytraeidae. Critical revision and taxonomy of European species (Studies on Enchytraeidae VII)', *Natura jutl.,* **8/9,** 1-160.

O'Connor, F. B. (1957) 'An ecological study of the enchytraeid worm population of a coniferous forest soil', *Oikos,* **8,** 161-99.

O'Connor, F. B. (1958) 'Age class composition and sexual maturity in the enchytraeid worm population of a coniferous forest soil', *Oikos,* **9,** 272-81.

O'Connor, F. B. (1967) 'The Enchytraeidae' in Burges, N. A. and Raw, F., eds., *Soil biology,* 213-57.

Peachey, J. E. (1962) 'A comparison of two techniques for extracting Enchytraeidae from moorland soils' in Murphy, P. W., ed., *Progress in soil zoology,* 286-93.

Peachey, J. E. (1963) 'Studies on the Enchytraeidae (Oligochaeta) of moorland soil', *Pedobiologia,* **2,** 81-95.

Quick, H. E. (1960) 'British slugs', *Bull. Br. Mus. nat. Hist.,* **6,** 103-226.

Reynoldson, T. B. (1955) 'Observations on the earthworms of North Wales', *NWest. Nat.,* **3,** 291-304.

Satchell, J. E. (1953) *Studies on earthworms and their relation to soil fertility.* Ph.D. Thesis, University of London.

Satchell, J. E. (1955) 'Some aspects of earthworm ecology' in Kevan, D. K. McE., ed., *Soil zoology,* 180-201.

Satchell, J. E. (1963) 'Nitrogen turnover by a woodland population of *Lumbricus terrestris'* in Doeksen, J. and Drift, J. van der, eds., *Soil organisms,* 60-6.

Satchell, J. E. (1967) 'Lumbricidae' in Burges, N. A. and Raw, F., eds., *Soil biology,* 259-322.

South, A. (1965) 'Biology and ecology of *Agriolimax reticulatus* (Müll.) and other slugs: Spatial distribution', *J. Anim. Ecol.,* 34, 403-17.

Springett, J. A. (1963) 'The distribution of three species of Enchytraeidae in different soils' in Doeksen, J. and Drift, J. van der, eds., *Soil organisms,* 414-19.

Svendsen, J. A. (1957a) 'The distribution of Lumbricidae in an area of Pennine moorland', *J. Anim. Ecol.,* 26, 411-21.

Svendsen, J. A. (1957b) 'The behaviour of lumbricids under moorland conditions', *J. Anim. Ecol.,* 26, 423-39.

Thomas, D. C. (1944) 'Discussion on slugs. II. Field sampling for slugs', *Ann. appl. Biol.,* 31, 163-4.

Waters, R. A. S. (1955) 'Numbers and weights of earthworms under a highly productive pasture', *N.Z. Jl Sci. Technol.,* 36, (A), 516-25.

Weber, P. W. (1953) 'Studies on the giant African snail', *Proc. Hawaii. ent. Soc.,* 15, 363-67.

6. Onychophora, Crustacea, Myriapoda, and Tardigrada

This chapter and the three following are devoted to the Arthropoda, a phylum whose members are always a conspicuous and important part of the soil community. In numbers of individuals and species, arthropods frequently dominate all other groups of the soil meso- and macrofauna, and representatives of almost all of the major subdivisions of the phylum have been found in, or associated with, the soil. At the same time, it must be pointed out that many forms use the soil for concealment and shelter only, and do not exhibit the features typical of true soil-dwelling species. The majority of the larger arthropods, including the Onychophora, and many adult insects and arachnids, are predominantly surface-dwellers, living in the loose upper litter layers or in crevices under bark or in rocks. On the other hand, many insects, Collembola, and mites live deeper in the soil and have important roles in soil development and the maintenance of soil fertility. The survey presented in this and the following chapters can touch on but a few selected examples of this rich and diverse fauna. First, we consider four Classes which are grouped together in a single chapter very largely as a matter of convenience. Two of these Classes, the Onychophora and Tardigrada, do not qualify in every respect as arthropods, and their systematic position is uncertain. However, it is convenient to include them at this point.

Onychophora

These so-called 'primitive' arthropods, distinguished by their elongate, wormlike form, occur most commonly in the leaf litter and decaying logs in South Africa (*Peripatopsis* and *Opisthopatus*) and Australasia (*Peripatus* and *Peripatoides*), where they prey on a variety of soft-bodied invertebrates.

Onychophorans occupy a similar ecological niche to the terrestrial triclad planarians, and may possibly compete directly with the latter for food, for, in South African forests, *Peripatopsis* sp. is often found in the proximity of the triclad *Artiocotylus* sp. in decaying wood (Lawrence, 1953). Both of these groups feed in a similar manner, secreting digestive enzymes into the prey and sucking out the liquefied tissues, and both have been observed to be cannibalistic in culture.

In South Africa, at least, the distribution of Onychophora is not uniform, for they are less numerous in the northern forests than in the Cape Peninsula

(Lawrence, 1964). The genera *Peripatopsis* and *Opisthopatus* are separated geographically, to some extent, the former predominating in the western part, the latter in the east, and, whereas the species *Opisthopatus cinctipes* ranges from sea level to 3000 m, *Peripatopsis* is most abundant below 1350 m.

Onychophorans share with the scorpions a characteristic unusual among soil animals, namely, viviparity. Sperm transfer is by means of flask-shaped spermatophores which contain a coiled sperm reservoir in *Peripatus* (Lawrence, 1953). In the genus *Peripatopsis*, males become sexually mature at the age of 9-11 months, and, although mating may occur with females of the same age, young are not produced until the females are 2 years old; births continue thereafter throughout the life span of the adult. The young onychophorans emerge covered in an envelope of mucus, and moult immediately after birth. They resemble the adults in general form, although smaller and paler in colour, and progress towards maturity through 18-22 moults. Members of the genus *Peripatopsis* have a life span of 6-7 years, attaining maximum size after 4 years. Of the South African representatives of this genus, *P. balfouri* is the smallest (maximum size about 40 mm), *P. moseleyi* is the largest (maximum size about 75 mm), and *P. capensis* is intermediate between these two (maximum size 60 mm). These species show interesting colour variations, the common forms being dark green or brick red, to which may be added a white collar.

Crustacea

This Class is represented in the soil by members of the Ostracoda, Copepoda, and the malacostracan Amphipoda, Decapoda, and Isopoda. Of these, only the Isopoda are usually regarded as being successful colonizers of terrestrial habitats, although, as Hurley (1959, 1968) has pointed out, amphipods belonging to the family Talitridae are adapted behaviourally and, to a lesser extent, morphologically to life on land. Members of this family are common in the debris which collects at high water mark along the seashore; in Britain, some species have extended their range for considerable distances away from the sea into habitats provided by damp soil and rock crevices—examples of such partly terrestrial forms are *Orchestia bottae* and *Talitroides dorrieni* (Reid, 1947). However, most of the true soil-dwelling Talitridae are not endemic to Europe and North America. The distribution of these land amphipods is widespread in the Indo-Pacific region, and they have also been recorded, apparently as endemics, from North and West Africa, the Mediterranean region, the Canary Islands, the Azores, the West Indies and Central America. In these tropical and south temperate regions, species of the genera *Talitrus, Talorchestia,* and *Orchestia,* which have probably evolved independently from supralittoral stocks, favour damp forest or woodland litter where populations numbering several thousand per square metre may be developed. Many of these species apparently cannot survive outside the saturated environment provided by moist leaf litter, but there are occasional exceptions to this. For example, in New Zealand, *Talitrus sylvaticus* has been encountered, in company with the isopod *Porcellio scaber,* under rocks on dry ground several hundred feet above sea level (Hurley, 1968), and a species of *Orchestia* is adapted to the habitat provided by grassland soil to the extent that it can burrow in the soil to evade drought conditions, and climb into the vegetation to avoid flooding. For the most part, however, soil Amphipoda are less tolerant of desiccation than the Isopoda and consequently less successful in colonizing dry habitats. In the soil, as on the seashore, Amphipoda feed mainly on decomposing plant material.

Reports of Ostracoda living in the soil are few but, nevertheless, reliable in the sense that they do not refer to accidental introductions from aquatic sources. Lawrence (1953) collected 25 specimens of an ostracod, subsequently described as *Mesocypris terrestris,* from forest humus at an elevation of 300 m above sea level at Knysna, South Africa. This has proved to be a unique record, for the species has not been found in any other part of South Africa to date. Kühnelt (1961) reported the occurrence of *Cypridopsis* sp. from organic litter bordering a brackish pond in Egypt, and *Heterocypris brevicaudata* from leaf litter under woodland near Glasgow. Little is known of the ecology of these crustaceans, which is not surprising in view of their very sporadic occurrence.

Harpacticoid copepods are more frequently encountered than ostracods in the soil, and although this crustacean group is not richly represented in terms of numbers of species in the soil community, the few species that are present may occur in large numbers in damp soils, particularly in the litter layer under tropical and subtropical forests. In Britain, large numbers of *Bryocamptus pygmaeus* (Fig. 6.1) have been recovered from litter material collected under beech stands

FIGURE. 6.1. *Bryocamptus pygmaeus* (Crustacea, Copepoda) from beech litter, Chiltern Hills, England (photo by author).

in the Chiltern Hills, and such populations deserve further study to determine the extent to which these animals contribute to the decomposition processes occurring in the soil.

Soil-dwelling decapods comprise the burrowing crabs and crayfish which, again, are usually restricted to very damp soils. North American crayfish are noted for their ability to leave rivers and streams to construct burrows in the earth along the banks. Land crabs are commonly encountered on various Pacific islands, where their local effect may be quite considerable under certain circumstances. Niering (1963) noted that land and hermit crabs, such as *Cardisoma rotundum, Gecarcoidea lalandei, Geograpsus crinipes, G. grayii, Metasesarma aubryi, Coenobita brevimanus, C. perlatus,* and *Sesarma rotundatum,* were abundant in forest floor debris on the Micronesian atoll of Kapingamarangi, consuming and transporting underground large quantities of litter. This author estimated that 230 acres of cultivated plantation housed 118 450 individuals of these groups of crabs.

With the exception of a few of the Amphipoda, none of the crustacean groups so far mentioned has been able to become truly terrestrial, for, in their morphology, physiology, and behaviour, they have retained the characteristics associated with an aquatic mode of life. In contrast, the Isopoda have not only been able to establish themselves as truly terrestrial forms, but have also been able to show some degree of adaptive radiation on land; it is to this group that we now turn our attention.

Isopoda

The 'woodlice' are familiar animals, and so much is known about their biology that it is possible to touch on just a few aspects. The wide distribution of certain species in various parts of the world may be a reflection of dispersal through human agency. Species common in Europe, such as *Armadillidium vulgare, Trichoniscus pusillus, Oniscus asellus,* and *Porcellio scaber* (Fig. 6.2), are also widespread in North America (Hatchett, 1947; Palmén, 1951; Edney, 1953). The family Porcellionidae is particularly well represented throughout the world, and includes over 500 species. Isopods have successfully colonized a variety of terrestrial habitats, ranging from humid litter in tropical and subtropical forests, where they are often abundant, to the hot, dry soils of North African and North American deserts. Comprehensive reviews of the biology of the group have been given by Edney (1954a, 1968); this author also provides a key to the identification of British species (Edney, 1954b).

Distribution

Of the various factors which may influence distribution, environmental moisture is of considerable importance in view of the fact that the isopod cuticle is, to a large extent, permeable. Certainly, these crustaceans lose water under non-saturated conditions at a more rapid rate than do the insects, and until recently it has been believed that a waterproofing mechanism is lacking in isopods. This

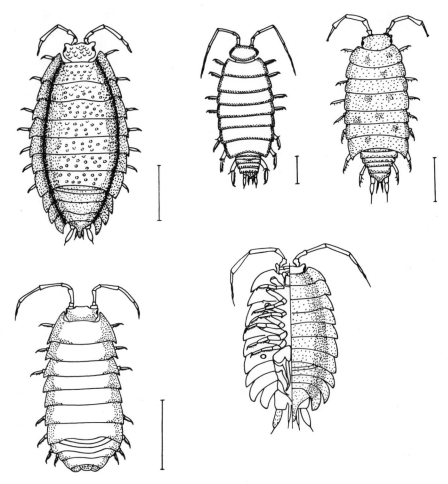

FIGURE 6.2. Some common British Isopoda (Top row, left to right: *Porcellio scaber, Philoscia muscorum, Trichoniscus pusillus*; bottom row: *Armadillidium vulgare, Oniscus asellus* (scale in mm).

belief was based on observations which suggested that the permeability of the isopod cuticle is not affected by temperatures within the biological range, that cuticular transpiration is directly proportional to the vapour pressure of the external atmosphere, and that variations in permeability occurred from one iso-pod group to another in a manner inversely related to the dryness of the habitat (Edney, 1954a). The ability of some groups to tolerate non-saturated conditions better than others has led to the definition of a family sequence: Ligiidae-Trichoniscidae-Oniscidae-Porcellionidae-Armadillidiidae, which can be correlated with an increasing capacity to withstand desiccation. This sequence is reflected in the comparison of transpiration rates presented in Table 6.1, from which it

TABLE 6.1. Transpiration rates of various isopod species measured in dry air at temperatures between 19° and 30°C (from Edney, 1968).

Species (and family)	Rate of transpiration (mg/cm^2/hr/mmHg $\times$ 10^3)	Habitat
Ligia oceanica (Ligiidae)	220	Wet
Philoscia muscorum (Oniscidae)	180	
Oniscus asellus (Oniscidae)	165	
Cylisticus convexus (Cylisticidae)	125	
Porcellio scaber (Porcellionidae)	110	Moist
Porcellio dilatatus (Porcellionidae)	104	
Armadillidium vulgare (Armadillidiidae)	85	
Hemilepistus reaumuri (Porcellionidae)	23	
Venezillo arizonicus (Armadillidae)	15	Dry

may be noted that desert-dwelling forms, such as the African *Hemilepistus reaumuri* and the American *Venezillo arizonicus*, have lower permeabilities than species of Oniscidae inhabiting moist sites.

Recently, however, evidence has been presented which strongly suggests that some type of waterproofing mechanism is present in the cuticle of land isopods. Measurements of transpiration rates of several species at various temperatures, within the range 5-45°C, have demonstrated that the rate per unit saturation deficit generally falls with increasing temperature over the lower part of the range, but then rises sharply, at least in *Oniscus asellus, Porcellio dilatatus,* and *Venezillo arizonicus* (Bursell, 1955; Warburg, 1965; Edney, 1968). The point at which this increased permeability of the cuticle occurs, the transition temperature, is at about 28°C in *O. asellus* and *P. dilatatus,* and at 35°C in *V. arizonicus,* and this phenomenon suggests that a waterproofing barrier is being destroyed at these temperatures. Evidently, the barrier is less efficient than the epicuticular lipid layer of insects, for the rise in transpiration rate above the transition temperature is not as steep in these isopods as it is, for example, in the roach *Blatella germanica* (Edney, 1968). The nature and location of the barrier in the isopod cuticle have not been fully elucidated, although Bursell (1955) has suggested the presence of a lipid layer deep in the endocuticle of *Oniscus* and *Porcellio,* since (a) abrasion of the epicuticle does not result in a marked increase in transpiration rate, and (b) rates are higher in newly moulted animals which probably possess a complete epicuticle, but only an incompletely developed endocuticle. On the other hand, Warburg (1965) has shown that the waterproofing mechanism in *Venezillo arizonicus* is destroyed by treatment with warm chloroform, as is the case with the epicuticular barrier of the insects.

The ability to limit the amount of water lost by transpiration through the cuticle clearly varies with the species and is better developed in those isopods, such as *Hemilepistus reaumuri, Venezillo arizonicus,* and *Armadillidium vulgare,* which inhabit arid regions. However, this adaptation to a terrestrial existence is far from perfect, and its significance lies not in conferring independence of saturated conditions, but rather in enabling isopods to survive for periods of time in non-saturated air. This ability is further enhanced by the unique type of respiratory system possessed by some land isopods; the pseudotracheal system. Pseudotracheae are invaginations of the pleopods which are the primary respiratory structures in the Isopoda. This system permits the rate of oxygen uptake in dry air to be maintained at only a slightly lower level (90-94 per cent) than that in moist air, at least in the case of *Porcellio scaber* and *Armadillidium vulgare* (Edney and Spencer, 1955). In *Oniscus asellus* and *Ligia oceanica,* which do not possess pseudotracheae, oxygen uptake falls drastically in dry air to 33 per cent and 13 per cent, respectively, of the rate in moist air, and ultimately death ensues due to oxygen starvation. Thus, the adaptive value of pseudo-tracheae is demonstrated, but, as Edney (1968) points out, the mechanism involved is not fully understood for no spiracular closing devices have been identified with this system. This author suggests that closure may be effected by the apposition of the pleopods to another surface, and in this regard the characteristic habit of isopods to aggregate in large clumps, one on top of the other, may be of considerable significance. Despite these adaptations, land isopods cannot survive indefinitely in dry air, and they tend to congregate in moist cavities under rocks and decaying vegetation, even in arid regions. For example, Paris (1963) was able to show that aggregations of *Armadillidium vulgare,* containing significant proportions of young forms, occurred in damp areas around the bases of *Brassica campestris* plants in Californian grassland (Table 6.2). Evidently, these damp areas, produced by the precipitation of water

TABLE 6.2. Numbers of *Armadillidium vulgare* in samples with and without *Brassica* stems (from Paris, 1963).

Isopod numbers	
Samples with stems	Samples without stems
77	1
16	0
20	2
9	0
78	0
5	0
43	1
71	3
6	0

on the aerial parts of the vegetation, provided suitable conditions for the survival of the young during periods of drought.

The relationship between distribution and environmental temperature follows a pattern very similar to that just described for moisture. Thus, the desert-dwelling *Venezillo arizonicus* has a lethal temperature of 42°C, at 100 per cent RH, compared with 34°C in *Oniscus asellus* under the same humidity conditions (Edney, 1968). Some isopod species, at least, have the ability, admittedly very limited, to regulate body temperature by evaporative cooling, and the permeability of the cuticle may be very important in this process. Edney (1967) observed that the burrowing isopod, *Hemilepistus reaumuri*, of the Sahara can lower its body temperature by about 3°C by evaporative cooling if it wanders away from its shelter during the daytime. This device obviously cannot be used for any length of time, in view of the loss of water involved, but it may enable the animal to avoid immediate immobilization in the event of a rapid increase in the environmental temperature, and perhaps would allow the isopod to reach its burrow.

Among other factors that influence distribution, the nature of the substratum must be considered briefly. J. van der Drift (1962) found that the Isopoda, as a group, was more prevalent on acid mull (moder) sites than on calcareous mull soils of a Dutch oak woodland. *Armadillidium vulgare* is exceptional in this respect, showing a preference for calcareous soils and being rare or absent in woodland habitats (Brereton, 1957). According to this author, the common woodland isopods of north-west Europe are *Trichoniscus pusillus, Philoscia muscorum, Oniscus asellus,* and *Porcellio scaber.* Differing habitat preferences are shown by these species, although overlapping patterns of distribution are, not uncommon. Thus, *P. muscorum* was common under stones and litter in oak-ash-sycamore woodland at all times of the year, and also occurred frequently in an adjoining *Brachypodium* grassland in association with *A. vulgare. T. pusillus* and *O. asellus* overwintered under stones, moving out into the litter and, in the latter case, on to trees during the summer. *P. scaber* overwintered in moss at the base of trees and underwent a vertical migration into the upper parts during the summer, at which time its distribution overlapped with that of *O. asellus.*

Seasonal vertical migration is a characteristic feature of the Californian grassland population of *Armadillidium vulgare* studied by Paris (1963). During the wet season, the bulk of this population was concentrated in the top 4 cm of the soil profile, but as the dry season set in there was a general movement down the profile through fissures and rodent burrows, and aggregations of individuals were found at depths of 15-25 cm. Superimposed on this seasonal activity pattern, was a pattern of a much shorter period, for even during the dry season these isopods emerged at night to feed on the surface. Circadian rhythms in isopods have been studied in some detail and we may now consider some of the more important findings.

Circadian Rhythms

Terrestrial isopods are essentially nocturnal animals. Restricted during the day to sheltered, moist habitats, they emerge at night to crawl over the surfaces of stones, bare ground, and tree bark. In a series of experimental studies, Cloudsley-Thompson (1952) demonstrated a locomotory activity pattern in *Oniscus asellus* which was a combination of an inherent rhythm and a direct response to environmental changes. These investigations showed that activity was correlated with alternating light and dark periods, rather than with fluctuating temperature and humidity. The photonegative response of these animals increased during darkness, ensuring a return to sheltered conditions before daybreak. However, if drying conditions persisted, the woodlice became photopositive enabling them to move to other, damper sites where they again became photonegative. The nocturnal activity which takes the woodlice to drier, more exposed sites than they would occupy during the day is not inhibited in non-desiccated animals by the lower humidity conditions, for these experiments also showed that humidity responses decreased in intensity during the night.

On the other hand, Paris (1963) concluded, from his investigations of *Armadillidium vulgare* populations, that greater surface activity occurs when the saturation deficit is low. This correlation between isopod activity and atmospheric moisture was particularly clear during the dry summer and autumn seasons, and led the author to conclude that any intrinsic behaviour pattern geared to the diurnal cycle is overridden by the response to differences in atmospheric moisture. In apparent contradiction to these findings, Den Boer's work with *Porcellio scaber* suggested that activity at the soil surface was greatest when saturation deficit was high, although vertical movement was negatively correlated with saturation deficit.

In attempting a synthesis of these apparently conflicting observations, two general considerations must be borne in mind. First, surface activity may subserve different functions in different species, and this may be reflected in Warburg's (1964) finding that the behavioural responses of different species varied under similar environmental conditions. Second, the response of an animal to a given situation may vary with its physiological state, particularly with its state of hydration; as a corollary to this it may be noted that Warburg also demonstrated that this state can change abruptly as water is lost or gained, and this may be followed by an equally abrupt behavioural change. Edney (1968) resolves the apparent discrepancy between the findings of Den Boer (1961) and Paris (1963), mentioned earlier, by pointing out that surface activity in Paris's *A. vulgare* population was undoubtedly associated with feeding and that the animals involved were probably not overhydrated, whereas surface activity in Den Boer's *P. scaber* was a behavioural device to remove excess water from the body. During the day, *P. scaber* absorbed water from its surroundings, and at night moved out on the surface into drier air where an increased rate of transpiration would allow the water balance to be maintained.

As long as isopods remain on the soil surface in non-saturated air, they will become progressively more dehydrated, and this physiological change brings about changes in behavioural responses. As we noted earlier, Cloudsley-Thompson (1952) suggested that an increasing photonegative response occurring in surface active *Oniscus asellus*, initiated a return to the soil burrows. However, there is strong evidence to indicate that the return to the soil is guided rather by the attraction to the odour of other animals of the same species, for it has been well established (Kuenen and Nooteboom, 1963) that this attraction increases as the body becomes more dehydrated. This explanation is probably more satisfactory than that invoking the photonegative response, for many isopods return to their soil burrows during darkness, long before this response could be elicited.

The detailed studies by Warburg (1964, 1968) revealed that light does not play an important part in influencing the behaviour of many land isopods, although there is some variation from species to species. Woodlice living in damp habitats have a general tendency to be photonegative, except when they are dehydrated or exposed to high temperatures, when the behavioural pattern is reversed. Species living in drier, more exposed sites, for example, *Armadillidium vulgare* and *Hemilepistus reaumuri,* are photopositive, although this response is reversed by exposure to low temperatures in the case of *A. vulgare* and high temperatures in *H. reaumuri.* However, other desert-dwelling species, such as *Venezillo arizonicus* and *Armadillo albomarginatus,* are photonegative; these two species have a nocturnal activity pattern, whereas that of *H. reaumuri* is crepuscular.

Population Size and Structure

Few reliable estimates are available of the sizes of field populations of isopods; there are several possible reasons for this. The mobility of these animals often precludes the use of mark-recapture methods, and direct counts are complicated by seasonal and diurnal vertical migrations of large segments of the population (see above). Furthermore, direct counts suffer from the disadvantage that they may provide estimates of population activity rather than of population size. The nocturnalism of these animals also suggests that the microdistribution pattern may vary during the 24-hour cycle, being strongly aggregated during the day and more dispersed at night when individuals emerge from their shelters to forage for food. By restricting sampling to the wetter months of the year, when most of the population was localized in the upper part of the soil profile, Paris and Pitelka (1962) obtained an estimate of 538 individuals/m² for the grassland population of *Armadillidium vulgare* already referred to. This estimate was regarded as a minimum, for it was based on samples taken just before the beginning of the breeding season. Even so, this appears to be considerably larger than density estimates for other isopod species in forest and woodland (see, for example, van der Drift, 1951; Dunger, 1958).

However, changes in the age structure of populations can be described with confidence because a relationship can be established between body size and the age of the individual. Using this approach, Brereton (1957), Paris and Pitelka (1962), and Paris (1963) have carried out studies on the population biology of terrestrial isopods, and the following account is based largely on their findings.

The natural life span of isopods, such as *Armadillidium vulgare* and *Porcellio scaber,* rarely, if ever, exceeds four years and frequently is shorter than this. Reproduction is restricted to definite times of the year, so that, although several different age classes occur together at any one time, the age class structure of the population at any given time of the year is approximately the same from year to year, at least in the case of *A. vulgare,* in which the population totally replaces itself every four or five years. Obviously, this species provides a good example of continuously overlapping generations (Fig. 6.3); the same is true for *Cylisticus convexus* and *Porcellio scaber* (Hatchett, 1947; Brereton, 1957).

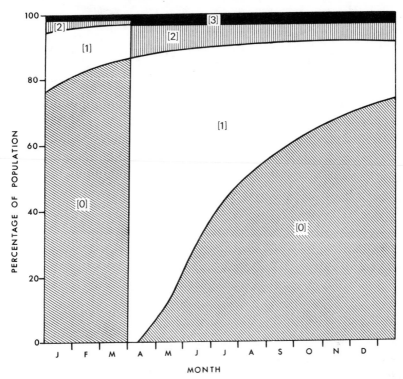

FIGURE 6.3. Generation composition by month of an *Armadillidium vulgare* population in California grassland. Generations (0, 1, 2, 3) arbitrarily advanced one year in age on 1 April (after Paris and Pitelka, 1962).

Information on the seasonal fluctuations in isopod populations is rather scarce. However, Dunger (1958) recorded a May/June peak density in *Armadillidium vulgare,* and this is supported by work carried out in Great Britain and North America. Reproduction occurs from April to September among the species studied, and it has been suggested that, of the various factors operating, day length controls the length of the breeding season in *A. vulgare,* the beginning and end of the period occurring when the photoperiod is about 12 hours (Fig. 6.4). Brood production occurs in two waves during this period, an early peak in April and May representing the breeding activity of individuals of two years old or more, and a late peak in August to which the one-year-old class makes a much greater contribution. This summer recruitment may be expected to produce an increase in population density, although the evidence suggests that

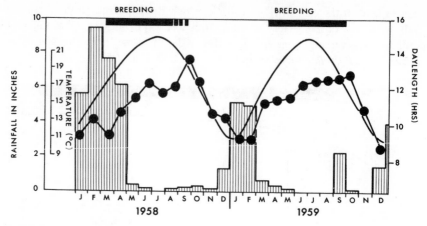

FIGURE 6.4. Breeding periodicity of *Armadillidium vulgare* in relation to monthly rainfall (histograms), monthly mean temperature (solid circles) and day length (smooth curve) (after Paris and Pitelka, 1962).

mortality increases among females after breeding, for the 1:1 sex ratio apparent in the ova and the one-year age group shifts to a high proportion of males in the second year. Furthermore, a high mortality occurs among the young, approximately 80 per cent of which do not survive the breeding season. Under these circumstances, minimum population densities would be expected in the spring, just prior to recruitment.

Feeding Habits

Much needs to be learned about the feeding habits of the Isopoda, although the information presently available suggests that many species are omnivorous and will feed on a variety of dead plant material, faecal pellets, and invertebrate carrion. However, preference may be shown for certain types of food, as, for example, in the case of the *Armadillidium vulgare* population studied by Paris (1963), which selected dead plant material of the tarweed *Picris echioides* in preference to other food items. Decomposing leaf and woody tissue is probably an important component of the diet of many species, although the algae *Pleurococcus* (Brereton, 1957) and fungi may be ingested in considerable amounts, along with mineral soil particles. Wieser (1965) studied food consumption, assimilation, and respiration in *Porcellio scaber* under experimental conditions, with particular reference to the relationship between body weight and these activities, and concluded that the metabolic characteristics are similar to those of the myriapod Diplopoda. This work draws attention to the fact that copper is taken up by isopods, such as *P. scaber,* from natural food materials, and that when the amount of copper in the food was decreased experimentally, the rate of ingestion of food increased. This suggests that the animals can counter deficiencies of essential elements, to some extent, by increasing the intake of food. However, these isopods are incapable of extracting copper directly from food material, and this same author was able to provide strong evidence that copper in the food material is made available to the isopods by the activities of micro-organisms (Wieser, 1968).

Myriapoda

This important Class of soil animals consists of four groups, the Pauropoda, Symphyla, Chilopoda (centipedes), and Diplopoda. Identification keys to families, genera, and species of all of these groups have been given by Verhoeff (1934a).

Pauropoda

This is a small group of progoneate myriapods, rarely exceeding 1 mm in length, easily recognizable by their branched antennae. Little recent ecological information is available about them, although aspects of their biology have been discussed by Verhoeff (1934b), Starling (1944), and Cloudsley-Thompson (1958).

Body shape is variable in the Pauropoda, elongate forms of the genus *Pauropus*, of which the widely distributed *P. huxleyi* illustrated in Fig. 6.5 is

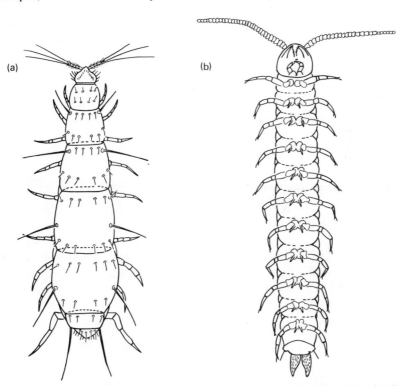

FIGURE 6.5. (a) *Pauropus huxleyi* (Pauropoda); (b) *Scutigerella immaculata* (Symphyla).

representative, contrast with the flattened, almost discoidal members of the genus *Eurypauropus* occurring in Europe and North America. These arthropods live under stones, in damp leaf litter, moss, and fallen trees, often in mountainous regions, where, apparently, they feed on decaying plant material, carrion, and fungi; they may also be predatory on occasion. They occur in such small numbers, as a general rule, that reliable estimates of density cannot be made, although it is probable that such estimates would rarely exceed several hundred individuals per square metre. Under particularly favourable conditions, larger populations sometimes occur, and Starling (1944) estimated pauropod densities over one million per acre under oak and pine stands in eastern North America. The distribution of these animals appears to be governed by their narrow moisture and temperature preferenda, the former varying from 11-20 per cent of oven-dry weight in sandy soil, to 21-30 per cent in clay. The optimum temperature range, 17-23°C, is also that within which soil fungi flourish, and, since these fungi may provide a source of food for the pauropods, it may be this factor, rather than any direct effect of temperature, that is limiting.

Some information is available about the developmental biology of the pauropods. According to Lawrence (1953) and Cloudsley-Thompson (1958), eggs are deposited singly or in clumps in sheltered crevices among damp, decomposing litter. The life history of *Pauropus silvaticus* may be taken as typical of the group as a whole and, in the case of this species, egg development lasts for about two weeks. Hatching produces a quiescent prelarva which develops into a hexapod larva after a period of 3-4 days. As development proceeds, three further larval stages occur, respectively with 5, 6, and 8 pairs of legs. Development to the adult, which has 9 pairs of legs as a general rule, takes 3-4 months. According to Starling (1944), the main period of reproductive activity in the populations studied by him occurred in the early summer months.

Symphyla

Symphylids are delicate, centipedelike myriapods, white in colour, rarely more than 10 mm in length, with 11 or 12 pairs of legs in the adult. They resemble the Pauropoda only in being progoneate, i.e., the genital aperture is located on the ventral side of the third body somite, a characteristic these two groups also share with the Diplopoda. Symphylids are very widely distributed, occurring in Europe, Asia, Africa, North, Central, and South America, the Indo-Malayasian region, and they will probably also be found in many other parts of the world. A very common European and North American species, *Scutigerella immaculata*, is illustrated in Fig. 6.5.

Distribution and Vertical Movements

Although symphylids may be encountered in a variety of soils, ranging from cultivated plots to grassland and forest litter, they are especially abundant in glasshouses, evidently prefering moist, organic soils of the loam type with open texture (Edwards, 1958). Very often, they occur below the soil surface, sometimes at a depth of several centimetres, although seasonal vertical migrations complicate the pattern of depth distribution. Edwards (1958, 1959a, 1961) described the migrations of *Scutigerella immaculata* and *Symphylella vulgaris,* and correlated these with changes in environmental conditions. Surface layers of the soil became desiccated during the summer, when high surface temperatures also occurred, and the combined effect of these two factors evidently provoked a downward migration of litter populations. This trend was reversed during the spring and autumn seasons. On the other hand, this author reported that the phytophagous *S. immaculata* migrated upwards to the surface, even when temperature and moisture conditions were unfavourable, provided that suitable food material was available. This species often reaches pest proportions in glasshouses, where it feeds on the root systems of cultivated plants.

In a comparative ecological study involving the genera *Scutigerella, Symphylella,* and *Symphylellopsis* in cultivated fields in south-western France, Anglade (1967) was able to demonstrate differences between these three genera in their vertical distribution patterns. *Scutigerella* was much more abundant in the top 15 cm of the profile than at greater depths, when counts for the whole year were averaged. A similar pattern was shown by *Symphylella* although, in this case, the diminution in numbers with depth was less sharply marked than in *Scutigerella.* In contrast, the bulk of the *Symphylellopsis* population was generally located lower down the profile at a depth of 15-45 cm (Table 6.3).

TABLE 6.3. Distribution of Symphyla at different sampling levels (averages based on 10 monthly samples from untreated plots) (from Anglade, 1967).

Depth (cm)	*Scutigerella*	*Symphylella*	*Symphylellopsis*
0-15	69%	50%	15%
15-30	22%	33%	44%
30-45	9%	17%	41%

These differences may be explained, in part, by differences in feeding habits; *Scutigerella* sp. is phytophagous, as we have noted, the other two are saprophagous. This author was able to confirm Edwards's findings regarding the seasonal vertical migrations of symphylid populations, the general trend being upwards in spring and autumn, and downwards in summer and winter, although the three genera differed in the timing of their spring activity. Thus, *Scutigerella* reached a spring maximum in the upper part of the profile in May, *Symphylella* in June, and *Symphylellopsis* in July; in the autumn the maximum for all three genera occurred at the beginning of November.

Life History and Population Dynamics
In contrast to most Myriapoda, the Symphyla develop from egg to adult in a relatively short period of time. Egg masses hatch after a development of 1-3

weeks, to produce a larva having 6 or 7 pairs of legs. This larva usually moults six times, adding a pair of legs at each moult, during a period of 12-36 weeks (Edwards, 1955). Development in the field varies with the environmental conditions, and the life span of an individual may extend over several years.

Anglade (1967), in the study already referred to, concluded that oviposition, in the case of *Scutigerella* populations, commenced during the spring and continued through the summer into early autumn. After a mild winter and spring, larval stages began to appear in the population at the beginning of summer and some, at least, of these had completed their development and laid a first batch of eggs by the autumn. The onset of breeding activity in the spring is influenced by the severity of the previous winter, and may be delayed until early summer when the winter has been very cold. Evidently, the main overwintering stage was the adult, for very few juveniles were present in the population at the end of this season.

Symphylid populations in glasshouses have been recorded in densities of 77 millions/acre (Edwards, 1955) and more. Numbers of this order of magnitude probably reflect the particularly favourable conditions occurring in this habitat, for appreciably smaller populations are known to occur under field conditions. Thus, Anglade (1967) estimated autumn densities for populations of *Symphylella, Scutigerella,* and *Symphylellopsis* at 500-1000, 100-600, and 15-150 individuals/m^2, respectively. Drastic fluctuations in numbers are also known to occur and may be related, in part, to changes in the age class composition. For example, population maxima in late summer and autumn may be produced by the appearance of a new generation, whereas the low numbers recorded during winter and summer may, to some extent, be a reflection of a changing vertical distribution pattern characterized by a movement of individuals to deeper levels. The winter decline may also be occasioned by increased mortality among juvenile stages for, as noted above, these form only a small percentage of the population at this time of the year.

The effect on symphylid populations of applications of insecticides to the soil was also studied by Anglade (1967). Treatment with HCH at a dosage of 15 kg/ha immediately reduced the population of *Scutigerella,* and this effect was particularly marked with applications made in summer compared with those made in spring. A similar, although less pronounced, effect also occurred on the *Symphylella* population. The application of aldrin, at a dosage of 4 kg/ha caused an increase in numbers in both of these groups, whereas the deeper-dwelling *Symphylellopsis* population was not affected by either treatment.

In view of their widespread distribution and the large densities in which they sometimes occur, the Symphyla are undoubtedly an important component of the soil fauna, and a good deal more information on their biology is required. They are most successfully extracted from the soil by the flotation process described by Edwards (1955). A general account of the biology of the group is provided by Michelbacher (1949), and identification keys are given by Verhoeff (1934a), and Edwards (1959b).

Chilopoda

The four Orders of centipedes comprising this Class can be divided broadly into two groups depending on whether post-embryonic development is anamorphic or epimorphic. The Lithobiomorpha and Scutigeromorpha are anamorphic, i.e., the larval stage, hatching from the egg, has less than the full complement of adult body somites and legs, but these are added at each successive moult. The Geophilomorpha and Scolopendromorpha are epimorphic, i.e., on hatching, the larva is furnished with the full complement of body somites and legs. Keys to the identification of European and British chilopods are given by Verhoeff (1934a) and Eason (1964), respectively.

Distribution

Centipedes are widely distributed in moist habitats throughout the tropical and temperate regions of the world. The tropical *Scolopendra*, with 21 or 23 pairs of legs, are formidable creatures frequently measuring more than 1 cm across and 15 cm in length. On a smaller scale, the Lithobiomorpha (Fig. 6.6d) are common

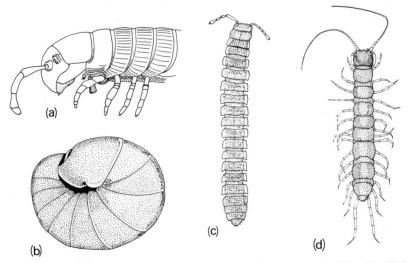

FIGURE 6.6. Common soil myriapod groups. (a) *Iulus* (Diplopoda); (b) *Glomeris* (Diplopoda); (c) *Polydesmus* (Diplopoda); (d) *Lithobius* (Chilopoda).

in many temperate localities, and are often encountered in loose leaf litter of the woodland and forest floor, in crevices under rocks, and under the bark of decaying fallen trees. Some members of this group, such as the common British *Lithobius variegatus*, have become adapted to moorland conditions and acid woodland soils, and their distribution is governed more by moisture conditions than by soil type. The Lithobiomorph cuticle does not possess an efficient waterproofing layer, and consequently these centipedes are confined to damp habitats. However, as Blower (1955) has pointed out, the permeability of the cuticle prevents the colonization of wet sites, for there can be little control of the uptake of water by endosmosis, and such centipedes would suffer distention and distortion of the body as a result. During the wet seasons of the year, lithobiomorphs frequently congregate under the bark of fallen trees or in well-drained situations where they will not be exposed to flooding. These centipedes cannot burrow into the soil, but utilize existing soil spaces. Consequently, we find that the relatively large *Lithobius forficatus* is a surface-dweller, whereas the smaller *L. variegatus, L. crassipes,* and *L. duboscqui* are more truly subterranean (Blower, 1955). Despite the general susceptibility to desiccation among the lithobiids, there is some evidence from distribution patterns that species may vary in their tolerance in this respect, for Lewis (1965) noted that *L. forficatus* was less strongly restricted to damp sites than was *L. variegatus.*

The widely distributed Geophilomorpha, the members of which can often be distinguished by their pale colour and long, narrow, ribbonlike body form, are essentially subterranean, capable of burrowing through the soil by exerting the pressure of the body to enlarge soil spaces. One member of this group, *Strigamia maritima,* is not uncommon in rock crevices of the intertidal region around the shores of the British Isles. The cuticle of the Geophilomorpha evidently has a better developed lipid waterproofing layer than that of the Lithobiomorpha, and while this obviously protects these centipedes from the dangers of endosmotic uptake of water, they can withstand desiccation no better than the lithobiomorphs, a feature which Blower (1955) attributes to the lack of an efficient spiracular closing mechanism in both of these groups. This author records specific habitat preferences among various British geophilomorphs; *Geophilus insculptus* and *G. electricus* are usually associated with good mull soils, whereas *Brachygeophilus truncorum* and *Geophilus carpophagus* are commoner in mor soils. One of the commonest geophilids in Britain, which may be encountered in grasslands and cultivated plots, is *Necrophloeophagus longicornis.*

There are no indigenous British members of the Scutigeromorpha, and the species *Scutigera coleoptrata* recorded from Europe is probably introduced from the tropics and subtropics where the group is widespread. Scutigerids possess extremely long legs, and can move very rapidly; they are active on the surface of the soil and are sometimes found in human dwellings, for example, in the warmer parts of the United States, gaining access through waste pipes. The group is less closely associated with the soil than the remainder of the Chilopoda.

Feeding Habits

Centipedes are generally considered to be wholly carnivorous, the appendages of the first body segment behind the head being modified as a pair of poison claws for the purpose of securing prey animals. Although this may be the preferred habit, some species also feed on decaying plant material. For example, Lewis

(1965) reported that the gut contents of *Lithobius variegatus* and *L. forficatus* consisted of small insects (aphids and flies), Collembola, mites, spiders, other centipedes, nematodes, and molluscs, along with variable quantities of leaf litter. Such plant material may have been ingested accidentally along with the prey animals, but seasonal variations in the composition of the gut contents of *L. variegatus* suggested a change in feeding habit from a carnivorous diet in the spring and summer, to a diet of leaf litter during winter. In contrast, *L. forficatus* ingested leaf litter in appreciable amounts throughout the year. Similarly, vegetable material has been reported to form part of the diet of the tropical Scolopendridae, although Lewis (1966) was not able to confirm this for the Sudanese *Scolopendra amazonica,* which fed mainly on carabid and staphylinid beetles.

Life History

Development from egg to adult is relatively slow in the centipedes, occupying a period of three to four years, so that the total life span of a lithobiomorph, for example, is of the order of five to six years. The Lithobiomorpha and Scutigeromorpha produce eggs singly and carry them in the claspers of the genital segment until they are deposited in sheltered crevices or nests. The eggs are coated with a viscous secretion to which particles of debris adhere, thus providing a protective cover. The Scolopendromorpha show parental care, excavating a nest in soft decaying wood, into which 15-30 eggs are laid. The female then curls around the egg mass, protecting it with her body and legs, and in this position she may remain for several weeks without feeding, until the brood is developed sufficiently to move away from the nest. Geophilomorphs show similar care for their young, but lithobiomorphs do not (Manton, 1965).

In the Lithobiomorpha, the anamorphic character of post-embryonic development is somewhat modified. On hatching, a larva with seven pairs of legs emerges and moults after only a few hours. Anamorphic development then follows with four successive moults, culminating in the appearance of a larva with 12 pairs of legs; the appearance of this larva signals the end of the anamorphic phase. A second, epimorphic phase then occurs with the successive development of four stadia, all possessing 15 pairs of legs, the last stadium giving rise to the sexually mature adult.

The studies by Lewis (1965) on *Lithobius variegatus* and *L. forficatus* have shown that, although egg-laying may occur over a large part of the year, the production of spermatophores by the males, and their uptake by the females, probably takes place over more restricted periods during the spring and autumn, as is the case among the Geophilomorpha. There was a peak of egg-laying during the spring, more marked in *L. forficatus* than in *L. variegatus,* and the author suggests that the more even spread of ovipositional activity in the latter species may be a device to ensure that some, at least, of the eggs survive the dry summer conditions. This may be a reflection of the lower tolerance of *L. variegatus,* compared with *L. forficatus,* already referred to.

Life histories of the Scolopendromorpha are incompletely known, for the most part, although development is epimorphic, and in the case of *Scolopendra amazonica* the adult appears by the end of the third year (Lewis, 1966). This relatively long developmental period which, as noted earlier, is also a feature of the lithobiomorph life histories, results in the occurrence of different age groups, simultaneously, in the same population, producing a pattern of overlapping generations which may be reminiscent of the condition in isopod populations discussed earlier in this chapter.

Diplopoda

The litter-feeding Diplopods may be divided roughly into 'round-back', 'flat-back', and 'pill' millipedes (Fig. 6.6a-c), corresponding approximately to the Orders Iuliformia, Polydesmoidea, and the Pentazonia, respectively, although Blower (1958), in his key to the British species, lists 12 families and a total of 44 species, some of which cannot readily be assigned to one or other of these morphological classes. The group has also been dealt with extensively by Verhoeff (1928, 1932, 1934a).

Distribution

This group is much better represented in calcareous soils than in base deficient profiles, in woodland than in cultivated and grassland soils, and various species show differing preferences for microhabitats within these macro-environmental categories. The pill millipede *Glomeris marginata*, which shows a superficial resemblance to the isopod *Armadillidium vulgare*, sharing with the latter the ability to roll up into a sphere when disturbed, is frequent in chalk grassland, but may also colonize drier, sandy soils for it can tolerate low moisture levels. This species is more successful than most in establishing large populations in soils under ash woodland, where litter decomposition is rapid, but in other deciduous woodlands, such as oak, it is joined by *Polymicrodon polydesmoides, Brachydesmus superus, Polydesmus angustus, P. denticulatus, Cylindroiulus punctatus, Iulus scandinavius,* and *Ophyiulus pilosus*. In acid mor soils, particularly under conifers and beech, the most frequent millipede species are *Schizophyllum sabulosum, Cylindroiulus punctatus,* and *Iulus scandinavius*.

The distinction between flat-backs, such as *Polydesmus* and *Polymicrodon* species, and the cylindrical Iuliformia (Fig. 6.7) has an ecological as well as a taxonomic significance. The Polydesmidae are relatively inactive forms restricted, in the main, to the loose litter layers, through which they progress by squeezing into spaces created by the pressure of the flattened midtrunk region on the substratum. The Iulids may burrow deeper in the soil using the collum of the first trunk segment as an excavator (Manton, 1954). Glomerids are also active burrowers, and are probably very important agents in the mixing of mineral soil and organic material. The distribution of the Polydesmidae is influenced by the amount of soil moisture, for these forms resemble the lithobiomorph centipedes in lacking a well-developed lipid layer in the cuticle, and consequently are less resistant to desiccation than the iulids and glomerids, in which this waterproofing layer is well developed (Blower, 1955). Thus, these flat-backs are unable to survive in sites that are too wet or too dry. The moisture and pH characteristics of a site may influence, or be influenced by, the amount and type of leaf litter or decomposition products present, and different tolerances to these factors may go a long way towards explaining the differences

FIGURE 6.7. The giant West African millipede, *Spirostreptus* (photo by A. Newman-Coburn).

in species composition from site to site. A spectrum of habitat preferences is given in Table 6.4; it must be emphasized that the associations depicted here are by no means exclusive, and few millipede species are narrowly restricted in their choice of habitats. In Britain, *Cylindroiulus londinensis* var. *caeruleocinctus* and *Archeboreoiulus pallidus* are truly calcicole, the former being common on limestone grassland in the Malham Tarn area, but these are exceptional cases of habitat restriction. More often, a given species will be found in a range of somewhat similar habitats. For example, some of the species which regularly inhabit grassland soils also occur in ant nests; examples of these include *Polyxenus lagurus, Proteroiulus fuscus,* and *Blaniulus guttulatus,* and this last-named species also inhabits caves along with *Polymicrodon polydesmoides* and *Brachydesmus superus* (Blower, 1955, 1958). Distribution patterns may also be influenced by human activities as, for example, when suitable soil habitats under woodland are destroyed by deforestation. Under these circumstances, species such as *Cylindroiulus punctatus* may seek refuge under the bark of fallen trees to survive (Blower, 1955).

Despite a relatively efficient spiracular closing mechanism in all millipedes (except the glomerids which, however, can globulate), susceptibility to desiccation is reflected in microdistribution patterns, and moist sites serve as foci for aggregations during the day; in the tropics, this tendency is pronounced during the dry season (Toye, 1967). However, some iulids, which have spiracular closure and a lipid waterproofing layer in the cuticle, such as *Tachypodoiulus niger* and *Schizophyllum sabulosum,* are often observed in Britain during the day, feeding on the aerial parts of brambles.

TABLE 6.4. Distribution of some common British millipedes (from observations supplied by Blower, 1955).

Habitat or site	Species
1. In vegetation or on soil surface	*Tachypodoiulus niger* *Schizophyllum sabulosum*
2. In the soil: (a) Mull profiles	*Glomeris marginata* *Polymicrodon polydesmoides* *Brachydesmus superus* *Polydesmus angustus* *Polydesmus denticulatus* *Ophyiulus pilosus*
(b) Mor profiles	*Cylindroiulus punctatus* *Iulus scandinavius*
3. Under bark and in rotten wood	*Cylindroiulus britannicus* *Cylindroiulus parisiorum* *Isobates varicornis* *Proteroiulus fuscus*

Reproduction and Population Biology

Millipedes belonging to the families Polydesmidae, Iulidae, and Glomeridae have a life span extending over several years. The main period of reproduction is during the spring, summer, and autumn in temperate localities, egg batches being deposited in nestlike cells in the soil. Not only does the onset of the breeding season vary with the species, but the period of time over which the eggs are laid also varies with the age of the adult. According to Verhoeff (1932), egg development takes only a few days in the Iulidae, although the rate probably varies with the species and the environmental temperature conditions. On hatching, a six-legged larva emerges resembling, in many ways, that of an insect. It develops slowly to maturity, progressing through several instars characterized by an increasing number of body somites and legs, i.e., development is anamorphic. In the case of the common *Cylindroiulus punctatus,* there are at least seven developmental instars, and moulting also continues through adult life, which is attained some two years after hatching. Since the adult stage survives the winter, millipede populations are composed of various age classes at any one time during the year, a characteristic these animals share with the isopods and the centipedes.

Density estimates for field populations of *Glomeris marginata* in various forest types have been given by Thiele (1956), who recorded a maximum of 24 individuals/m², and average values within the range: 2·3-7·5 individuals/m². A higher estimate of 80 individuals/m² for a population of *Cylindroiulus silvarum* (= *C. punctatus*) in a beech forest floor was reported by van der Drift (1951). However, these estimates mean very little unless the seasonal fluctuations in population size are taken into account, and these changes are not always easy to interpret. For example, spring and autumn population peaks for Diplopoda have been noted by Dunger (1958), who recorded maxima of 200-300 individuals/m² in moist woodland leaf litter, and Banerjee (1967), who reported that the seasonal growth and decline of populations of *C. punctatus* are complicated by vertical migrations, from mineral soil and humus where overwintering occurs, upwards into surface litter and logs. Mating and reproduction occur under the bark of these logs, and development through to the completion of the third instar takes place before the downward movement into litter, humus, and mineral soil during late summer and autumn. This behaviour pattern results in a single population peak in mineral soil (in winter) and in the logs (in summer), whereas there are two peaks per year in the litter, namely, a spring peak marking the upward migration of the population, and an autumn peak marking the downward movement. These activity peaks must be distinguished clearly from overall density increases; the latter are more difficult to detect and, in view of the relatively long period of development, are probably not well marked.

Feeding Habits

Dead plant material, particularly leaves and decaying wood, is the main source of food for many millipedes, and, although different species may show different food preferences, these choices may be masked by the need for a variety of food (van der Drift, 1965). *Cylindroiulus nitidus* apparently prefers to feed on decaying beech leaves, whereas other members of this genus, such as *C. meinerti* and *C. boleti,* consume the bark and wood of fallen trees. Although some species can feed on fresh litter or even living plant material, for example, the herbivorous *Schizophyllum sabulosum*, most millipedes apparently prefer material that is undergoing microbial decomposition. However, Gere (1956) noted that *Glomeris hexasticha* and *Chromatoiulus projectus,* when fed on slightly decomposed or strongly decomposed oak litter, consumed larger amounts of the latter, but utilized a greater proportion of the former. There is some evidence that certain groups select food materials with a high content of available nitrogen as, for example, do the flat-back Nematophora that show a preference for fungi and carrion (Blower, 1958).

Some attention has been paid to the chemical changes occurring in the ingested food as it passes through the gut of these animals, and a summary of this topic has recently been prepared by Raw (1967). In view of their general distribution, relatively large size and litter-feeding habit, the millipedes may be of considerable importance in the process of organic decomposition, and attempts have been made recently to define precisely the role of these animals in the sequence of events leading up to the production of humus. The early work of Franz and Leitenberger (1948) suggested that appreciable humification occurred during the progress of food material through the gut of millipedes although later work, notably by van der Drift (1951), Gere (1956), Dunger (1958), and Bocock (1963) indicates that the amount of ingested material which is assimilated is, in fact, very small, as is the amount of litter material converted into humus. For example, experiments carried out with *Glomeris marginata*, using oak litter as food, showed that only 6-7 per cent of the ingested food was utilized, and that utilization of nitrogen amounted to 5-7 per cent, that for phosphorus and calcium, 15-20 per cent (van der Drift, 1951). These experiments, which were carried out on starved animals, also demonstrated that maximum consumption of food occurred within a temperature range of 17·5-22·5°C (close to the preferendum for the species) and with material having a 70 per cent moisture content. Dunger's (1958) experiments, designed to determine the amount of humification produced during the passage of food material through the gut of species such as *Cylindroiulus teutonicus, Glomeris connexa*, and *Iulus scandinavius*, showed that an increase in humic acid content occurred only if the food was fresh, nitrogen-rich litter. Bocock (1963) found that most (70 per cent) of the energy assimilated by *Glomeris marginata* feeding on ash leaves was obtained from the digestion of holocellulose, and that the remainder was derived from crude fat (19 per cent) and soluble carbohydrate (10·5 per cent).

None of the investigations discussed above suggest that the Diplopoda make a significant contribution to the chemical degradation of plant litter. It is more likely that these animals resemble other saprophages in that their main effect lies in the mechanical breakdown of plant material, and in providing excrements which are more susceptible to decomposition by the soil microflora than is the uneaten litter.

Tardigrada

The members of this 'degenerate' group of arthropods are microscopic in size; they are sometimes referred to as 'bear animalcules' on account of their rather stout body form. The surface of the body often bears a series of plates, giving the impression of some form of segmentation, and there are four pairs of unsegmented, claw-bearing papillae which resemble legs. The group is essentially an aquatic one, and the soil-dwelling representatives are members of the soilwater fauna. Little is known about the group, although tardigrades have been recorded frequently from moss and wet soils bordering lakes, and from lichens growing in damp sites. Mihelcic (1963) has pointed out that tardigrades may also occur in the upper layers of the soil profile, particularly in the organic strata of woodland soils, and the frequency of occurrence of 12 common soil-inhabiting species in woodland and grassland is given in Table 6.5. Protorendsina and protoranker profiles often harbour a rich tardigrade fauna, whereas this fauna is

TABLE 6.5. A comparison of the frequencies of 12 soil-dwelling tardigrades in woodland and grassland soils (from Mihelcic, 1963).

	Woodland	Grassland	Total
Echiniscus (Bryodelphax) parvulus	15	2	17
Echiniscus (Echiniscus) blumi	22	3	25
Pseudechiniscus suillus	13	5	18
Macrobiotus intermedius	5	3	8
Macrobiotus hufelandi	35	15	50
Hypsibius (Isohypsibius) tuberculatus	12	23	35
Hypsibius (Isohypsibius) franzi	18	13	31
Hypsibius (Hypsibius) dujardini	5	2	7
Hypsibius (Hypsibius) convergens	10	13	23
Hypsibius (Hypsibius) pallidus	8	8	16
Hypsibius (Diphascon) scoticus	5	2	7
Milnesium tardigradum	7	2	9

poorly developed in mull-like moder humus and in cultivated soils with a high mineral content. The tardigrade fauna of soil is quite different from that inhabiting moss and lichens, and differences in species composition between these habitats may reflect different food preferences. Thus, the species associated with, and possibly feeding on, living plant material are rarely encountered in the soil, being replaced by species which feed on organic debris, bacteria, fungi, algae, and the living or dead bodies of small soil animals, such as nematodes and rotifers. Tardigrades share with some other members of the soilwater fauna the ability to encyst in a state of anabiosis during drought conditions.

References

Anglade, P. (1967) 'Étude de populations de Symphyles en sol cultivé et d'influence de traitments du sol' in Graff, O. and Satchell, J. E., eds., Progress in soil biology, 372-81.
Banerjee, B. (1967) 'Seasonal changes in the distribution of the millipede Cylindroiulus punctatus (Leach) in decaying logs and soil', J. Anim. Ecol., 36, 171-7.
Blower, J. G. (1955) 'Millipedes and centipedes as soil animals' in Kevan, D. K. McE., ed., Soil zoology, 138-51.
Blower, J. G. (1958) The Linnean Society of London Synopses of the British Fauna, no.11, 'British Millipedes (Diplopoda)'.
Bocock, K. L. (1963) 'The digestion and assimilation of food by Glomeris' in Doeksen, J. and Drift, J. van der, eds., Soil organisms, 85-91.
Brereton, J. LeGay (1957) 'The distribution of woodland isopods', Oikos, 8, 85-106.
Bursell, E. (1955) 'The transpiration of terrestrial isopods', J. exp. Biol., 32, 238-55.
Cloudsley-Thompson, J. L. (1952) 'Studies in diurnal rhythms. II. Changes in the physiological responses of the woodlouse Oniscus asellus to environmental stimuli', J. exp. Biol., 29, 295-303.
Cloudsley-Thompson, J. L. (1958) Spiders, scorpions, centipedes and mites, Pergamon, London, New York. xiv + 228 pp.
Den Boer, P. J. (1961) 'The ecological significance of activity patterns in the woodlouse, Porcellio scaber Latr. (Isopoda)', Archs. neerl. Zool., 14, 283-409.
Drift, J. van der (1951) 'Analysis of the animal community in a beech forest floor', Tijdschr. Ent., 94, 1-168.

Drift, J. van der (1962) 'The soil animals in an oak-wood with different types of humus formation' in Murphy, P. W., ed., *Progress in soil zoology*, 343-7.

Drift, J. van der (1965) 'The effects of animal activity in the litter layer' in Hallsworth, E. G. and Crawford, D. V., eds., *Experimental pedology*, 227-35.

Dudich, E. (1927) 'Neue Krebstiere in der Fauna Ungarns', *Arch. Balatonicum,* **1,** 343-87.

Dunger, W. (1958) 'Über die Zersetzung der Laubstreu durch die Boden-Makrofauna in Auenwald', *Zool. Jb. (Syst.),* **86,** 139-80.

Eason, E. H. (1964) *Centipedes of the British Isles,* Warne, London. x + 294 pp.

Edney, E. B. (1953) 'The woodlice of Great Britain and Ireland', *Proc. Linn. Soc. Lond.,* **164,** 49-98.

Edney, E. B. (1954a) 'Woodlice and the land habitat', *Biol. Rev.,* **29,** 185-219.

Edney, E. B. (1954b) The Linnean Society of London Synopses of the British Fauna, no.9, 'British Woodlice'.

Edney, E. B. (1967) 'Water balance in desert arthropods', *Science,* **156,** 1059-66.

Edney, E. B. (1968) 'Transition from water to land in isopod crustaceans', *Am. Zool.,* **8,** 309-26.

Edney, E. B. and Spencer, J. (1955) 'Cutaneous respiration in woodlice', *J. exp. Biol.,* **32,** 256-69.

Edwards, C. A. T. (1955) 'Soil sampling for symphylids and a note on populations' in Kevan, D. K. McE., ed., *Soil zoology,* 152-6.

Edwards, C. A. T. (1958) 'The ecology of Symphyla. I. Populations', *Ent. exp. appl.,* **1,** 308-19.

Edwards, C. A. T. (1959a) 'The ecology of Symphyla. II. Seasonal soil migrations, *Ent. exp. appl.,* **2,** 257-67.

Edwards, C. A. T. (1959b) 'Keys to the genera of Symphyla', *J. Linn. Soc. Lond.,* **44,** 164-9.

Edwards, C. A. T. (1961) 'The ecology of Symphyla. III. Factors controlling soil distributions', *Ent. exp. appl.,* **4,** 239-56.

Franz, H. and Leitenberger, L. (1948) 'Biologisch-chemische Untersuchungen über Humusbildung durch Bodentiere', *Osterr. Zool. Z.* **1,** 498-518.

Gere, G. (1956) 'The examination of the feeding biology and humificative function of Diplopoda and Isopoda', *Acta biol. hung.,* **6,** 257-71.

Hatchett, S. P. (1947) 'Biology of the Isopoda of Michigan', *Ecol. Monogr.,* **17,** 47-79.

Hurley, D. E. (1959) 'Notes on the ecology and environmental adaptations of the terrestrial Amphipoda', *Pacif. Sci.,* **13,** 107-29.

Hurley, D. E. (1968) 'Transition from water to land in amphipod crustaceans', *Am. Zool.,* **8,** 327-53.

Kuenen, D. J. and Nooteboom, H. P. (1963) 'Olfactory orientation in some land isopods (Oniscoidea, Crustacea)', *Ent. exp. appl.,* **6,** 133-42.

Kühnelt, W. (1961) *Soil biology with special reference to the animal kingdom* (English edn, trans. Walker, N.), Faber, London. 397 pp.

Lawrence, R. F. (1953) *The biology of the cryptic fauna of forests,* Balkema, Cape Town and Amsterdam. 408 pp.

Lawrence, R. F. (1964) 'The fauna of the forest soil' in Davis, D. H. S., ed., *Ecological studies in southern Africa,* 126-36.

Lewis, J. G. E. (1965) 'The food and reproductive cycles of the centipedes *Lithobius variegatus* and *L. forficatus* in a Yorkshire woodland', *Proc. zool Soc. Lond.,* **144,** 269-83.

Lewis, J. G. E. (1966) 'The taxonomy and biology of the centipede *Scolopendra amazonica* in the Sudan', *J. Zool., Lond.,* **149,** 188-203.

Manton, S. M. (1954) 'The evolution of arthropodan locomotory mechanisms, Part 4. The structure, habits and evolution of the Diplopoda', *J. Linn. Soc. (Zool.),* **42,** 299-368.

Manton, S. M. (1965) 'The evolution of arthropodan locomotory mechanisms. Part 8. Functional requirements and body design in Chilopoda with a comparative account of their skeleto-muscular systems and an Appendix on a comparison between burrowing forces of annelids and chilopods and its bearing upon the evolution of the arthropodan haemocoel.' *J. Linn. Soc. (Zool.)*, **46**, 251-483.

Michelbacher, A. E. (1949) 'The ecology of Symphyla', *Pan-Pacif. Ent.*, **25**, 1-11.

Mihelcic, F. (1963) 'Können Tardigraden im Boden leben?' *Pedobiologia*, **2**, 96-101.

Niering, W. A. (1963) 'Terrestrial ecology of Kapingamarangi atoll, Caroline Islands', *Ecol. Monogr.*, **33**, 131-60.

Palmén, E. (1951) 'A survey of the Oniscoidea (Isopoda Terr.) of Newfoundland', *Ann. Zool. Soc. 'Vanamo'*, **14**, 1-27.

Paris, O. H. (1963) 'The ecology of *Armadillidium vulgare* (Isopoda: Oniscoidea) in California grassland: food, enemies and weather', *Ecol. Monogr.*, **33**, 1-22.

Paris, O. H. and Pitelka, F. A. (1962) 'Population characteristics of the terrestrial isopod *Armadillidium vulgare* in California grassland', *Ecology*, **43**, 229-48.

Raw, F. (1967) 'Arthropoda (except Acari and Collembola)' in Burges, N. A. and Raw, F., eds., *Soil biology*, 323-62.

Reid, D. M. (1947) The Linnean Society of London Synopses of the British Fauna, no. 7, 'Talitridae (Crustacea, Amphipoda)'.

Starling, J. H. (1944) 'Ecological studies on the Pauropoda of the Duke Forest', *Ecol. Monogr.*, **14**, 291-310.

Thiele, H. U. (1956) 'Die Tiergesellschaften der Bodenstreu in den verschiedenen Waldtypen des Niederbergischen Landes', *Z. angew. Ent.*, **39**, 316-67.

Toye, S. A. (1967) 'Observations on the biology of three species of Nigerian millipedes', *J. Zool., Lond.*, **152**, 67-78.

Verhoeff, K. W. (1928) 'Diplopoda I' in Bronn, H. G., ed., *Klassen und Ordnungen des Tierreiches*, **5**, 1-1072.

Verhoeff, K. W. (1932) 'Diplopoda II' in Bronn, H. G., ed., *Klassen und Ordnengen des Tierreiches*, **5**, 1073-2084.

Verhoeff, K. W. (1934a) 'Diplopoda, Symphyla, Pauropoda, Chilopoda' in Brohmer, P., Ehrmann, P., and Ulmer, G., eds., *Tierwelt Mitteleur*, **2**, 1-120.

Verhoeff, K. W. (1934b) 'Symphyla und Pauropoda' in Bronn, H. G., ed., *Klassen und Ordnungen des Tierreiches*, V/II/III/1-2 Leiferung.

Warburg, M. R. (1964) 'The response of isopods towards temperature, humidity and light', *Anim. Behav.*, **12**, 175-86.

Warburg, M. R. (1965) 'Water relations and internal body temperature of isopods from mesic and xeric habitats', *Physiol. Zool.*, **38**, 99-109.

Warburg, M. R. (1968) 'Behavioural adaptations of terrestrial isopods', *Am. Zool.*, **8**, 545-59.

Wieser, W. (1965) 'Untersuchungen über die Ernährung und den Gesamtstoffwechsel von *Porcellio scaber* (Crustacea: Isopoda)', *Pedobiologia*, **5**, 304-31.

Wieser, W. (1968) 'Aspects of nutrition and the metabolism of copper in isopods', *Am. Zool.*, **8**, 495-506.

7. Insecta

This chapter could be written in perhaps a dozen different ways, and it certainly could be expanded to fill the entire book, for many Orders of insects are represented in the soil fauna and a considerable body of information is accumulating about their ecology. However, the majority make only a slight or localized contribution to the soil ecosystem in view of their sporadic distribution and low densities. The Dermaptera (earwigs), Dictyoptera (roaches), Psocoptera (bark-lice), Trichoptera (caddis-flies), Thysanoptera (thrips), Neuroptera (lace-wings), Mecoptera (scorpion flies), Embioptera (web-spinners), and Thysanura (bristle-tails) may be present as adults, immatures, or both, but are rarely regarded as important members of the soil fauna. To a lesser extent, the same is true of the Orthoptera (crickets and burrowing mole-crickets), Hemiptera (true bugs and cicadas), and Lepidoptera (for example the cutworm larvae of the Noctuidae): these groups are sometimes present in abundance, and their influence on the soil may be quite marked, although localized in its extent, for distribution is often limited by the availability of suitable food. An introduction to this insect fauna can be obtained from the comprehensive accounts prepared by Kühnelt (1961) and Kevan (1962). Our present purpose is served better by restricting the following account to the few groups which consistently form an important part of the soil community, notably the soil-dwelling representatives of the Orders Isoptera, Coleoptera, Diptera, Hymenoptera, and Lepidoptera.

Isoptera

Mainly tropical in distribution, the termites constitute one of the two main groups of soil-dwelling social insects, and their moundlike nests are conspicuous features of the landscape in many parts of Africa, Asia, Australia, and South America. Some termites, such as members of the genus *Reticulitermes,* occur in the temperate zone, but none of these are mound-formers. There are no indigenous termites in Great Britain; in Europe, the distribution of the group is limited to the Mediterranean region where it is represented by the genera *Calotermes* and *Reticulitermes.* A key to the identification of African genera has been compiled by Webb (1961).

Population Size and Structure

Termite populations vary in their structural complexity, but in all cases consist of a number of castes which may differ from each other in their morphology, physiology, and behaviour. These castes are of two kinds, reproductive and sterile, both types having approximately equal numbers of both sexes present. Two kinds of reproductive castes may be distinguished, namely, the primary reproductives, which are winged adults primarily concerned with founding new colonies, and secondary reproductives, which only appear if one or other of the primary caste dies. The secondary reproductives are more weakly sclerotized than the primaries, and either have reduced wings or are completely apterous. Unlike the primaries, they do not take part in a nuptial flight; their function is to continue the production of offspring to permit colony development once the primaries have completed their role. Members of the sterile castes are apterous, and the reproductive organs are non-functional. Again, two main castes may be distinguished, namely, soldiers and workers. The soldiers, which are very specialized morphologically, are characterized by the great development of the head, and are either mandibulate (mandibles well developed) or nasute (mandibles reduced, and the head prolonged into a beak). Soldiers may also be classified into major or minor forms according to their size; these two forms may coexist in the same colony. Workers are weakly sclerotized forms which show more resemblance to nymphs than to adults. Members of this caste have well-developed mouth-parts. Their functions in the colony are manifold, and include foraging for food, feeding the queen, cultivating fungus gardens in some species, caring for the young, and constructing the nest. Workers may be dimorphic, major and minor forms frequently occurring together. In the European *Calotermes flavicollis,* which inhabits dry wood, the true worker caste is absent, its place being taken by full-grown larvae called 'pseudergates'. Although the latter is considered as a distinct worker caste in the species in which it occurs, it can moult and undergo further development towards a primary reproductive, a secondary reproductive, or a soldier caste.

The development of a termite colony takes several years to complete. Egg production by the primary queen is low during the first year, but increases in the following years, until thousands of eggs may be produced each year, although the number is lower than this in the more primitive families. Sterile castes are produced first, and generally members of these groups have a life span of two to four years. Winged reproductives do not appear until the colony is several years old, and these live longer than the sterile forms. The king and queen which found the colony may continue to live for a considerable period of time, during which further matings and egg-layings occur. Colonies vary in size and complexity from species to species, the more primitive forms, such as the Calotermitidae, forming aggregations of a few hundred individuals and having only three or four adult castes. Many tropical species, on the other hand, form colonies consisting of many thousands of individuals, and may have as many as seven adult castes (Lüscher, 1961).

Clearly, it is difficult to generalize about population size in such a social group which increases progressively in size as colony development proceeds. In addition, emigration of winged sexual forms may have an appreciable short-term effect on population size and structure, for this produces an imbalance in the relative proportions of the various castes. In *Calotermes*, for example, swarming of the winged adults results in an increase in the relative proportion of soldiers, and the latter are reduced in number by the cannibalistic activities of the pseudergates to redress the balance. Caste differentiation and elimination in termites is delicately controlled by chemical substances, called 'pheromones': for a more detailed review of this topic, the reader is referred to Lüscher (1961).

Feeding Habits

Termites have often been regarded as taking the place of earthworms, in the tropics, as the main agents in the fragmentation of organic material and its mixture with mineral soil. Three nutritional categories in the soil-dwelling members of this group can be defined: first, the wood-feeding species, such as the *Reticulitermes* group; second, the plant- and humus-feeding species of the genera *Hodotermes, Odontotermes*, and *Trinervitermes*; third, the fungus-growers, such as *Macrotermes* spp., which are capable of moulding together organic material and mineral soil into a discrete mass, which evidently forms an ideal substrate for the growth of fungi. The wood-feeders and phytophages can utilize the cellulose in their food through the activities of symbiotic intestinal flagellates which produce the necessary cellulase. This ability suggests that these termites may be important in the chemical decomposition of organic material, although Harris (1955) points out that digestion is so complete in these animals that there appears to be little increase in the soil fertility as a result of their feeding activity. Moreover, the rapidity with which termites remove organic material from the surface of the soil may be detrimental to the formation of humus, particularly in dry localities where herbaceous vegetation may be poorly developed. One of the families commonly occurring in the tropics and well represented in Africa, the Termitidae, does not possess an intestinal protozoan fauna, and its members probably derive more nutriment from a fungal diet than from one containing a high percentage of cellulose.

Coleoptera

The beetles are the most abundant and varied group of soil-dwelling insects in many localities, and we can distinguish three main ecological types, namely, the predatory forms, phytophages, and saprophages. Many representatives of these three groups live on the soil surface or in the uppermost parts of the litter, although some, as we will see, penetrate deeper into the profile.

Composition of the Fauna

Representatives of six families commonly associated with the soil are illustrated in Fig. 7.1. Two of the most widespread of these are the predominantly carnivorous Carabidae, or ground beetles, and the Staphylinidae, which includes both predatory and saprophagous forms. In addition to these, there are several other less numerous, or less conspicuous, predatory beetles living in, or on the surface of, the soil. Tiger beetles of the family Cicindelidae show definite habitat preferences, some species preferring dry, sandy soils, others moist, organic woodland soils. Predatory Histeridae are frequently found in association with decaying woody twigs and branches, habitats which also attract predaceous and

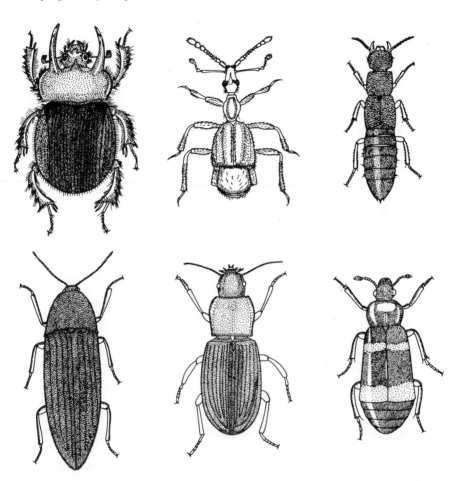

FIGURE 7.1. Representatives of some coleopteran families commonly occurring in the soil. Top row, left to right: Scarabaeidae, Pselaphidae, Staphylinidae; bottom row: Elateridae, Carabidae, Silphidae.

wood-feeding Elateridae (click beetles). Other predatory Coleoptera are to be found among the Pselaphidae, Scydmaenidae, Cantharoidea, Cleroidea, and Cucujoidea (see Raw, 1967). Although many of these groups are surface-dwellers, some of the small-sized forms, such as the Pselaphidae, often penetrate below the surface in search of prey; this is also true of some of the larger beetles, such as species of *Dyschirius, Clivina,* and *Scarites* which burrow actively in the soil.

A number of beetles make an important contribution to the decomposition of organic material by their litter-feeding or carrion-feeding habits. Decaying woody tissue and leaf material support a variety of these forms, including the Passalidae, frequent in the tropics and also North America, larval Lucanidae (stag beetles), larval Elateridae (click beetles), Scarabaeidae (dung beetles), Silphidae (carrion beetles), Nitidulidae (sap-feeding beetles), and the minute Ptiliidae (feather-winged beetles). In desert soils, the Tenebrionidae predominate among the saprophagous and phytophagous insect fauna.

Several species of beetle are represented as geophiles in the soil, the adults living above the ground, often associated with vegetation of various kinds, the larvae and pupae being subterranean. Phytophagous larvae, belonging to the families Elateridae, Scarabaeidae, have already been mentioned, and to these we can add those of the Curculionidae and the carnivorous Cicindelidae, Cantharidae, Meloidae, Cleridae, Staphylinidae, and Lampyridae.

Distribution and Feeding Habits

Among the surface-dwelling insects of predatory habit, the Carabidae have been most thoroughly studied in recent years, notably by Williams (1959) and Greenslade (1964) among others. The predatory species belonging to this group are often more abundant in woodland than in open field, whereas saprophagous and herbivorous forms show the opposite distribution. The carnivorous *Nebria brevicollis*, *Notiophilus substriatus*, and *N. rufipes* are typically woodland species, but unlike *Notiophilus biguttatus* are not restricted to this habitat. *Notiophilus palustris* is more of an exception, being confined to grassland. Williams (1959) noted a difference between the activity patterns of *N. brevicollis* and the common species of *Notiophilus*, the former being nocturnal, the latter diurnal. *Feronia madida*, a scavenger, has an intrinsic nocturnal activity rhythm which it displays in woodland habitats. This pattern is modified in open grassland, where the species also occurs, so that a diurnal activity is shown.

The food of these predators includes a variety of microarthropods and annelids, the diet of *Bembidion lampros*, for example, consisting of fragments of Collembola, small insects, mites, pseudoscorpions, and earthworms (Mitchell, 1963). This beetle is also an important predator of the immature stages of the cabbage root fly *Erioischia brassicae* (see Hughes, 1959; Coaker and Williams, 1963); also important in this respect are the predations of Staphylinidae which are discussed in more detail in chapter 11. For several species belonging to this latter family, notably *Aleochara* sp., *Othius angustus*, *O. punctulatus*, and *Quedius boops*, Collembola and mites may form an important part of the diet, as they do in the diminutive Pselaphidae and Scydmaenidae (Schuster, 1966), although the largest, *O. punctulatus*, also feeds on spiders and other beetles (Delany, 1960). Although a distinction may be made between scavengers which feed on carrion, such as *Feronia madida*, and true carnivores which take living prey, such as *Nebria brevicollis*, gut content analyses often cannot identify the state of the food material at the time of ingestion, and this distinction must be, to some extent, arbitrary.

In fact, beetles are often associated with the early stages of decomposition of carrion, although the species in question, usually members of the Silphidae (burying beetles), are not generally considered as true soil animals.

Many soil-inhabiting species feed on decaying plant material in one form or another, as we have noted in the previous section. The wood-feeders, or xylophages, are of particular interest because of their wide occurrence, although not all are equally proficient at digesting the material they consume (Parkin, 1940, quoted in Raw, 1967). The ability to digest cellulose, possessed by larval Cerambycidae and Scarabaeidae, appears to depend on the presence of gut symbionts, such as flagellates and bacteria. Wood-boring larvae of the Bostrichidae and Scolytidae do not possess this ability, although they are able to utilize cell contents and, in the latter case, hemicellulose of the cell walls.

The wide range of feeding habit which can occur within a single coleopteran superfamily or family is well illustrated by the Scarabaeidae; the feeding biology of this group has been reviewed by Ritcher (1958) and is summarized in Table 7.1. Adult scarabaeids can be divided into two major categories in this respect: first, those that are saprophagous or fungivorous, for example, the soil-dwelling

TABLE 7.1. Food habits of some Scarabaeidae (from Ritcher, 1958). (A = adults, L = larvae).

Subfamily	Carrion	Dung	Humus	Decomposing plant material	Duff	Litter	Wood	Fungi	Seed plants
Coprinae	A + L	A + L		A				A	
Aphodiinae	A + L	A + L	L	A + L				A	L
Geotrupinae	A	A + L	L	L	L	L		A	
Acanthocerinae							L		
Pleocominae									L
Glaphyrinae				L					L
Troginae	A + L								
Melolonthinae			L						A + L
Rutelinae			L				L		A + L
Dynastinae		L	L	L	L	L	L		A + L
Cetoniinae		L	L				L		A

Coprinae, Aphodiinae, and Geotrupinae; second, those that are phytophagous, such as the Melolonthinae, Rutelinae, Dynastinae, and Cetoniinae, which feed on the aerial parts of vegetation or, in some cases, do not feed at all. The soil and dung-dwelling forms are frequently encountered in manure piles and under carrion lying on the surface of the soil where they construct burrow systems. The larvae of phytophagous species are pests of cultivated crops, owing to their habit of feeding on roots, but some of them may also feed on dung, humus, and wood. The root-feeding habit is rare among the larvae of the Coprinae, Aphodiinae, and Geotrupinae, which feed mainly on dung, carrion, and decomposing litter.

The underground nests and burrow systems of the Coprinae, Geotrupinae, and, to a lesser extent, the Dynastinae are provisioned with food transported there by the adults for the developing larvae. Often, this food consists of pieces of dung which have been rolled into spheres by the adult beetle. An egg is deposited into each of these dung balls, and, when the larva hatches, it emerges into a world rich in food material.

A number of scarabaeids are found in association with ants and termites. In Brazil, for example, members of the coprine genus *Canthon* kill queen ants of the genus *Atta*, using the dead body of the prey as food for their larvae; many Cetoniinae live in *Formica* colonies where they apparently feed on vegetable debris; wood-feeding members of the Acanthocerinae in Madagascar and Central and South America are termitophilous (Ritcher, 1958).

Scarabaeids of economic importance in Britain include: *Melolontha melolontha* (common chafer), a pest of potatoes and cereals, but also widespread in grassland and woodland soils; *Phyllopertha horticola* (garden chafer), the commonest British scarabaeid, particularly in grassland soils on chalk or limestone; *Amphimallon solstitialis* (summer chafer); *Cetonia aurata* (rose chafer); and *Serica brunnea* (brown chafer), which is more common in woodland than in grassland soils. In North America, important pests in this group include: *M. melolontha*; *Popillia japonica*, the Japanese beetle; *Pelidnota punctata*, the grapeleaf beetle; *Cotalpa lanigera*, the goldsmith beetle; *Ligyrus gibbosus*, the carrot beetle; and species of *Phyllophaga* which feed on cereals.

Larvae of the Elateridae, known as 'wireworms', are often notable for their root-feeding habits; they are serious agricultural pests in many areas, although some members of this family feed on decaying wood, and others are predatory. The genus *Agriotes* includes three species common in cultivated soils in Britain, namely, *A. lineatus* and *A. sputator* in southern England, *A. obscurus* in northern England and Wales which, together with *Athous haemorrhoidalis* and species of the genus *Corymbites*, infest a variety of crops including potatoes, cereals, lettuce, onions, celery, and tomatoes. Much attention has been devoted to the biology and methods of control of these pests in soils under cultivation (Edwards and Heath, 1964), but less attention to their distribution patterns under more natural conditions. In general, wireworm populations are largest in heavy-textured soils, provided these are not too acid. It is evident, however, that different habitat preferences are shown by different species. For example, Nadvornyj (1968) recorded 41 species of Elateridae from soils in the Smolensk region of Russia, and noted that the greatest diversity occurred in forest (35 species) and bushland (18 species) soils; in arable soil, where members of the genus *Agriotes* predominated, 10 species were present, while the lowest number of species (8) occurred in the heavy soils of meadow and bog, where the genus *Corymbites* was most abundant. Analysing these distribution patterns in more detail, this author concluded that larvae of *Agriotes lineatus*, *A. obscurus*, and *Athous niger* preferred heavy soils, such as loam and clay loam, *Selatosomus aeneus* was restricted to sandy loam, *Limonius aeruginosus* preferred lightly textured soils, whereas *Corymbites sjaelandicus* was restricted to peat.

Life Cycles and Population Biology

Information about life histories and population dynamics varies considerably from one coleopteran group to another, and, in general, more is known about the ecology of economic pests than about their non-injurious relatives.

Elateridae and Scarabaeidae

Many of the life cycles of Elateridae of economic importance are well documented, the duration of development usually being four to five years. It was noted by van der Drift (1951) that first-instar larvae of *Athous subfuscus* occurred during the summer months in a beech forest floor. His observations do not suggest any well-defined population peak, although they point to a life cycle of more than one year's duration, in the course of which there is a considerable decrease in the numbers of individuals of the later instars. In the Elateridae in general, batches of 40-100 eggs are laid in the soil in spring and early summer. The first-stage larva emerges after five to six weeks, and moulting occurs once or twice a year until pupation, which, in Britain, takes place during the month of July (Edwards and Heath, 1964). The pupal period is of approximately one month's duration, after which the adult usually leaves the pupal shell, but remains in the soil to hibernate until the following spring. Occasionally, as in *Athous haemorrhoidalis*, the adult remains within the pupal cell during its first winter.

In the Scarabaeidae, the length of the life cycle varies from one species to another, complete development from egg to adult occurring within a year in *Phyllopertha horticola*, *Serica* spp., *Popillia japonica*, *Ligyrus gibbosus*, *L. relictus*, and many members of the Coprinae, Geotrupinae, and Aphodiinae in temperate latitudes. On the other hand, many Melolonthinae, Rutelinae, and Dynastinae require from one to five years to develop from egg to adult. In *Melolontha melolontha*, for example, eggs are laid in the soil in batches of 12-30, hatching occurs after about a month, and the larval phase occupies three years, with a moult occurring each year, as is also the case in *Pelidnota punctata*, *Cotalpa lanigera*, and *Phyllophaga* spp. The adult stage of many of these species is often active in spring or the early part of summer (April to May), during which time it leaves the soil periodically, but returns to mate and oviposit. Pupation occurs at the end of summer in *M. melolontha*, *Ligyrus relictus*, and species belonging to the genera *Serica*, *Phyllophaga*, and *Anomala*, and the adults may either emerge before winter or remain in the pupal cell until the following spring. Other members of these genera, such as the New World *Anomala nigropicta*, *A. binotata*, *Phyllophaga affabilis*, *P. submucida*, *P. longitarsus*, and *P. lanceolata*, overwinter as fully grown larvae which pupate in the spring, the adults emerging during the summer (Ritcher, 1958; Edwards and Heath, 1964).

The length of the scarabaeid life cycle varies, not only with the species, but also with the food supply. Thus, when food is abundant, *Amphimallon solstitialis* completes its life cycle in a year, but may extend this to three years when food is in short supply. Similarly, species which have a wide distribution in the northern hemisphere, such as *Melolontha melolontha* and *Phyllophaga* spp., have a longer duration of their life cycle in the northern part of their range, compared with populations in warmer, more southerly latitudes. The record for the longest development is apparently held by members of the genus *Pleocoma,* restricted in their distribution to western North America, with a duration of at least eight years (Ritcher, 1958).

It is not known to what extent adult emergence depletes the population of Scarabaeidae immatures living in the soil, although it cannot be very great in those species in which the larval duration extends over a period of years, for here there will be a simultaneous presence of individuals from several generations. Under these circumstances of overlapping generations (Davidson, 1944), regularly recurring population peaks and declines are not usually established as seasonal phenomena. In species which have a short life cycle, population fluctuations may be more readily discernible. For example, in *Ligyrus relictus* there is a post-reproductive decline in adults in June and July, followed by the appearance of a new generation of adults a little later in the summer. The average development time from egg to adult in this species is 72 days (Hayes, 1929), suggesting that the late summer peak is caused by recruitment from eggs laid earlier in the year.

Larval and adult scarabaeids are subject to the attentions of a variety of parasites and parasitoids, among which the hymenopteran Scoliidae and dipteran Tachinidae are prominent. Scoliid and typhiid wasps dig into the soil in search of larval scarabaeids which are then paralysed, and an egg deposited on the surface of the larval cuticle; the larval parasite then feeds externally on the host. Fungal infections, notably by *Metarrhizium anisopliae* and species of the genus *Cordyceps,* also play an important part in controlling larval scarabaeid populations (Ritcher, 1958). Scarabaeids are also preyed upon by a number of insects, especially dipteran Asilidae on *Phyllophaga* and *Anomala* spp., and Tabanidae on *Phyllophaga* spp.; coleopteran Carabidae on *Amphimallon majalis,* Elateridae on *Aphodius* spp., Histeridae on *Aphodius, Cetonia, Anomala,* and *Oryctes* spp.; and the hymenopteran Formicidae, which prey on eggs and early larvae of a number of scarabaeids with which they are associated (see above).

Turning our attention, now, to those Coleoptera that spend the whole of their life cycle in the soil, we may single out for special emphasis three families, namely, the Carabidae, Staphylinidae, and Silphidae. In general, well-defined population peaks and declines can be described for these groups, but these fluctuations are not always indicative of changes in population density. The pitfall trapping method commonly used for sampling adult beetle populations provides information on activity patterns, and, in order to determine the phenology of populations, it is necessary to use this information in conjunction with data on age class structure, to determine whether or not actual peaks are due to recruitment, rather than increased activity, and actual declines to mortality, rather than diapause. A good illustration of this distinction is provided by the observations on the phenology of carabid populations discussed in the next paragraph.

Carabidae

In the large majority of Carabidae, development from egg to adult takes approximately one year to complete. Thereafter, the span of adult life varies from one to three years, although in most cases mortality is high during, or at the end of, the first year of adulthood. Peaks of adult activity usually occur in the spring/early summer and again in the late summer/autumn periods, with intervals of inactivity in winter and in midsummer. Reproduction, mating, and oviposition occur during these active periods, but at different times in different species. For example, within the genus *Carabus, C. nemoralis, C. auratus, C. granulatus, C. cancellatus, C. convexus,* and *C. arvensis* mate and lay eggs during the spring, as do woodland species of *Notiophilus,* while *C. glabratus, C. monilis,* and *C. violaceus* oviposit later in the summer (Kern, 1925; Williams, 1959), and *Abax parallelus* and *Feronia oblongopunctatus* lay eggs in spring and early summer (van der Drift, 1951). The duration of the oviposition period, the number of eggs laid and the rate of development of the egg, the three larval instars, and the pupa depend upon the environmental temperature conditions and the amount of available food, so it is wise, perhaps, not to be too dogmatic about these life histories. For example, the larvae which hatch from the eggs of *Calosoma sycophanta,* laid in March and April by overwintering adults, take one month or so to complete development to the pupal stage, whereas larvae hatching from eggs laid in June develop to this stage in about two weeks (Burgess, 1911). In this species, mating occurs mainly in the early summer (June to early August), according to Balduf (1935), and the eggs are laid singly, as is the case in many Carabids, in a chamber excavated in the soil by the female. Oviposition usually takes place over a period of several weeks, and adult females surviving for more than one year often produce eggs in subsequent years. When mating and oviposition occur in the spring and early summer, development to the adult is usually completed before the onset of winter, and in these cases the adult is the main overwintering stage. The pronounced late summer/autumn activity peak is a reflection of the emergence of these adults. They mature slowly through the winter, and come into the reproductive condition when activity is resumed in the following spring. The peak of activity in the spring and early summer is produced by the reactivation of these adults and not by recruitment.

A number of Carabids, including *C. problematicus, Nebria brevicollis, Abax ater,* and, in some localities, *C. violaceus,* mate in late summer and autumn. The winter population of these species is then composed mainly of developing larvae and pupae along with a few adults which manage to survive. Overwintering adults of *Abax ater* reproduce during the spring and summer, but the main period of reproductive activity in this species occurs during the late summer and autumn, and at this time the major contribution is made by adults that have emerged during the previous spring from overwintering immatures. The early peak of population activity corresponds to this emergence and, hence, is caused by recruitment to the adult population. In *C. problematicus* and *N. brevicollis,* the emerging adults do not mate during the early part of the summer as a rule, probably because the reproductive systems are not fully developed at this time. They enter a diapause condition during the midsummer, and mating and oviposition occur on the resumption of activity during late summer and autumn (van der Drift, 1951; Penney, 1966). The high autumn activity peak (see Fig. 7.2) recorded for these forms is a reflection of this resumption of activity and is not due to any appreciable recruitment.

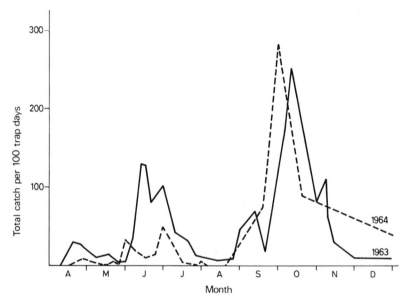

FIGURE 7.2. Activity cycle of the adult *Nebria brevicollis* at Rossdhu estate, Scotland (from Penney, 1966).

Murdoch (1967) has suggested an interesting relationship between the pattern of the life history and the environmental conditions in the case of British Carabidae, for he noted that species living in wet habitats, such as *Agonum* spp., *Bembidion* spp., *Pterostichus minor, P. nigrita,* and *P. trenuus* among others, are spring breeders and overwinter as adults, whereas the majority of species living in drier habitats, breed in autumn and overwinter as larvae. Thus, the species overwintering as adults in wet habitats would have a selective advantage over those represented by eggs and larvae at this time, because these developmental stages would be more liable to succumb to the effects of flooding and restricted food sources, than would the adult stage.

To summarize, the available evidence suggests that Carabids have two activity peaks each year, an early one (spring/early summer) and a late one (late summer/autumn). Species that mate and oviposit in spring and early summer, overwinter as adults. In these cases, the early activity peak is caused by the reactivation of hibernating adults, the late peak by recruitment to the adult population. The decline in activity during midsummer may coincide with the time of pupation. Species that mate and oviposit late in the summer and in the autumn, overwinter as larvae or pupae. For these, the early activity peak is provided by the recruitment of adults, the late peak by reactivation of aestivating adults. The midsummer decline of these populations is caused by the adults going into diapause. However, it is doubtful if particular species populations always adhere to an inflexible life history pattern and phenology. For example, it is possible for the rate of development of eggs laid in the spring by a species such as *Carabus nemoralis,* to be rapid enough to allow the adults which emerge in late summer to mate before the onset of winter (Delkeskamp, 1930).

Staphylinidae

The biology of many of the members of this large and varied family is not completely known. Species of the Aleocharinae (often separated as a distinct family) are found associated with ants and termites, while other representatives of this group are ectoparasitic in the larval stage on the pupae of cyclorrhaphous Diptera. However, the majority of the Staphylinidae are free-living predators for the whole of the life cycle.

The life cycles of the parasitic forms are, perhaps, the best documented, and are often geared to those of the hosts; commonly there is one generation per year. In the case of Swedish populations of *Aleochara curtula* and *A. intricata,* mating and oviposition occur in June and July, the larval and pupal forms appearing in midsummer, developing into the overwintering adult in the autumn (Kemner, 1926). *Aleochara bilineata,* apparently, may have two generations per year in Britain (Wadsworth, 1915), the first instar larvae of brood I overwintering in the pupae of *Erioischia brassicae,* completing their development to adults in the following spring and early summer. These adults produce a summer generation of immatures which become adults in late summer, in time to produce a new generation of overwintering larvae. Other instances have been cited (see, for example, Struble, 1930), in which the pattern of seasonal development varies within the species, the overwintering stage being, on the one hand, the larva, on the other, the adult. Obviously, the phenology of the Staphylinidae is far from uniform and this, coupled with the taxonomic problems presented by many of the larvae, probably accounts for the dearth of detailed information about the group as a whole. Maximum activity peaks for adults of *Staphylinus chalcocephalus* and *Quedius lateralis* have been recorded in summer and autumn, respectively, in a beech forest floor, whereas the smaller forms, such as *Oxypoda annularis, Sipalia circellaris,* and *Atheta fungi,* living mainly below the soil surface, were represented collectively by larvae and adults throughout the year (van der Drift, 1951).

Silphidae

Common species of this family in Europe and North America have a

9

rather uniform seasonal development (Balduf, 1935). The life cycle is usually completed within a year, reproduction occurring mainly in the spring and early summer, and development to the adult being completed in time to allow this stage to overwinter. This is the case in *Phosphuga atrata, Xylodrepa quadripunctata, Ablattaria laevigata,* and several species of the genera *Silpha* and *Necrophorus,* in which adult mortality is high during the post-reproductive midsummer period. Towards the end of summer, recruitment of adults occurs, as the individuals that will overwinter emerge from pupae. Under these circumstances, it is to be expected that some separation of consecutive generations will occur, and that declines and peaks in populations of adults during the summer months will reflect post-reproductive mortality and the emergence of a new generation, respectively. However, there is little direct evidence from field studies that such declines and peaks occur. Taking silphid populations as a whole, the range of fluctuations may be minimized by the fact that different species have their maximum reproductive period at different times of the year. For example, *Necrophorus vespillo, N. vespilloides, N. humator,* and *N. germanicus* enter the reproductive period at the end of spring, whereas *N. investigator* and *N. fossor* do not become sexually mature until August. This late reproduction of these last-named species prevents the life cycle from being completed before winter, and the hibernating stage, in these cases, is the last-instar larva or pupa.

Diptera

The importance of this group of insects rivals that of the Coleoptera in moist soil habitats, although the Diptera are less successful than the beetles in colonizing dry sites.

Composition of the Fauna

Although the adult stages of certain Dipteran families, such as the Mycetophilidae, Tipulidae, and the Phoridae, occur in the organic horizon of the soil profile, it is the larval stages of members of this Order that make the more important contribution to the soil community, and it is with these larvae that we are principally concerned. An impressive number of families are represented by larvae in the soil (Brauns, 1954)—too many to be considered in detail here, although mention must be made of some of the more important and widely distributed groups. The Nematocera are particularly well represented by, for example, the crane flies (Tipulidae), the larvae of which are the well-known leatherjackets; the march flies (Bibionidae); two families of fungus-gnats, the Mycetophilidae and the Sciaridae, the larvae of the latter being commonly known as 'army worms' from their tendency to move in large aggregations; the midges (Chironomidae and Ceratopogonidae); and the moth flies (Psychodidae). Among the Brachycera, larval Tabanidae (horse flies or clegs), Asilidae (robber flies), Empididae (dance flies), Stratiomyidae (soldier flies), Rhagionidae and

Therevidae (stiletto flies) are often present in the soil, while the Cyclorrhapha are represented by larval Phoridae, Syrphidae (hover flies), dung flies belonging to the families Borboridae, Sepsidae, and Scatophagidae, house and stable flies (Muscidae), and carrion flies (Calliphoridae and Sarcophagidae among others).

Distribution and Feeding Habits

Although the factors limiting distribution are not fully understood in many cases, two of the most important are adequate moisture and adequate food. Thus, the various Nematoceran groups are frequent in moist soils, for example, in moorland (Tipulidae), beech woodland (Chironomidae), marshland (Cerato-pogonidae), and compost (Mycetophilidae). These groups are predominantly saprophagous in feeding habit, consuming organic litter material, although some are coprophagous (for example, the dung-inhabiting Scatopsidae), fungivorous, or predaceous (certain Mycetophilidae larvae). The Mycetophilidae, in particular, occur frequently in association with decaying organic material rich in the fungi on which they feed, and thus are to be found commonly in decaying wood, vegetable compost, and mushroom beds, along with larvae of the Sciaridae, Borboridae, Trichoceridae, and Anisopodidae.

The Brachycera are, for the most part, predaceous forms, and their distribution is governed by the distribution of their prey. Since the latter consists of other insect larvae, small molluscs and annelids, and nematodes that inhabit moist, organic soils, the distribution of these predators often coincides with that of the saprophagous species. However, they are often quite abundant in highly organic deposits, such as dung, compost, and decaying wood. The Tabanidae larvae are frequently very common in the wet soil along the margins of lakes and streams, although Kühnelt (1961) has suggested that these larvae show a strong tolerance of dry conditions.

The carrion-feeding and coprophagous Cyclorrhapha are likewise found most commonly in highly organic deposits, such as dungpats and compost heaps. Members of the Calliphoridae and Sarcophagidae appear early in the faunal succession on decaying carcasses, and are important scavengers. Other Cyclor-rhapha, such as the frit fly (*Oscinella frit*) and the carrot fly (*Psila rosae*), are phytophagous, as are the Anthomyiid cabbage root fly (*Erioischia brassicae*) and the wheat bulb fly (*Leptohylemyia coarctata*). These pests are most commonly found in agricultural land associated with their host plants which include grasses, cereals, and various root crops. The larvae feed by burrowing into the root or stem tissue of the plant, thereby causing extensive lesions.

The larvae of certain Diptera, such as the Tachinidae and some Phoridae and Calliphoridae, are parasitic in earthworms, molluscs, and soil-inhabiting arthro-pods, and, although these larvae do not qualify as true soil-dwellers, they may have an indirect effect on the soil community through the mortality they inflict on host populations. This topic is considered in a later chapter, and an account of the biology of these forms is given by Raw (1967), who also provides a general review of the feeding habits of the various soil-inhabiting Diptera.

In a very general way, the feeding activities of the saprophagous insect larvae serve to fragment the larger organic particles in much the same manner as do the annelids, isopods, and millipedes, improving the structure of the soil and creating suitable sites for the development of populations of decomposer micro-organisms. As far as chemical changes in the litter material as it passes through the gut of these larvae are concerned, there is no evidence that appreciable humification occurs from this activity. Karpachevsky *et al.* (1968) found that the feeding activities of larval *Bibio marci* on forest litter had effects comparable with those observed by Bocock (1963) in the case of the millipede *Glomeris.* In both cases, absolute increases in the amounts of lignin and ammonia nitrogen were found in faeces, compared with food, suggesting that some humification may have taken place, even though no large-scale transformation is indicated.

Reproduction and Population Biology

Dipteran larvae can be collected throughout the year in many permanently moist habitats, although peak populations can be defined, in many cases, which correspond to the emergence of first-instar larvae. The timing of these peaks varies with the length of the life cycle and the number of generations per year. As the rate of development is influenced by the temperature conditions, considerable variability occurs from one habitat to another. Thus, the Cyclor-rhaphous pests of cereals and root crops may have two or three generations per year, whereas moorland Tipulidae may have but a single generation in the same time. Larval Anthomyiidae, Dolichopodidae, and Empididae are common during the winter months, and, in the beech forest floor investigated by van der Drift (1951), peak densities occurred during this season. In this same locality, larvae of the Sciarid *Lycoria sociata* occurred in high densities during the spring, summer, and autumn. Larval Tabanids, occurring in damp moss and the waterlogged soil bordering lakes and ponds, are frequent throughout the winter, spring, and early summer in many localities, overwintering as larvae and pupating during the summer. Some of these larval types are illustrated in Fig. 7.3.

As more precise information accumulates on the ecology of insect larvae in the soil, it is evident that general statements about entire families or genera may be misleading, for species within the same genus, occurring in the same locality, may not be synchronized as far as their life cycles are concerned. A good example of this is provided by a study of 10 species of crane fly (*Tipula*) larvae in a fen carr in southern England (Freeman, 1967). Taken as a whole, oviposition of the 10 species extended from April until October, but individual differences in times of oviposition were noted as follows:

T. vittata	April	*T. oleracea*	May, Aug.
T. variicornis	May	*T. maxima*	June-July
T. luna	May	*T. fulvipennis*	Aug.-Sept.
T. pruinosa	May-June	*T. luteipennis*	Sept.
T. unca	June	*T. staegeri*	Oct.

The growth rates of these larvae differed, smaller species, such as *T. vittata* and *T. luna,* growing slowly, but by virtue of their early start were able to attain maximum weight by early winter. The larvae of the larger *T. fulvipennis*

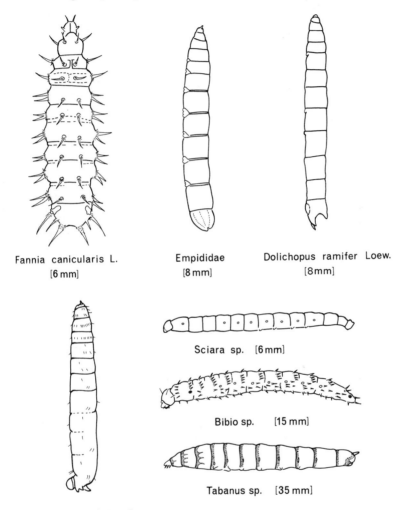

Fannia canicularis L.   Empididae   Dolichopus ramifer Loew.
[6 mm]   [8 mm]   [8mm]

Sciara sp.   [6 mm]

Bibio sp.   [15 mm]

Tabanus sp.   [35 mm]

Tipula sp.   [28 mm]

FIGURE 7.3. Some soil-inhabiting dipteran larvae (redrawn from Peterson, 1951).

appearing for the first time in September, grew at a much faster rate during the autumn than the two smaller species and, although this rate decreased through the winter, there was a steady increase in weight until the following spring. The eggs of *T. luteipennis* and *T. staegeri,* laid in the late summer and autumn, overwintered in a diapause condition. Despite these specific differences, maximum populations of *T. luna* and *T. vittata* larvae were recorded during the summer months, July to September, at a time when the total tipulid larval density was highest. By midsummer, the large majority of the crane flies present in the locality had oviposited and larval hatchings had occurred, hence the population peak at this time. This synchronization is achieved despite the fact

TABLE 7.2. Estimates of population density (per m²) for the larvae of *Tipula* sp. in Matley carr, 1960-61 (from Freeman, 1967).

	T. luna	T. vittata	Total for all *Tipula* species	No. of 0·25 m² samples
Jan.-Mar. 1960	11·0 (IV instar)	4·0 (IV instar)	25·4	50
Mid-Apr. 1960	–	–	10·7	25
July 1960	68·8 (II instar)	72·4 (III instar)	158·0	10
Aug./Sept. 1960	59·6 (III instar)	68·0 (IV instar)	136·6	10
Oct./Nov. 1960	41·4 (IV instar)	25·2 (IV instar)	87·4	20
Feb. 1961	15·6 (IV instar)	12·0 (IV instar)	38·7	10

that larval populations of the various species are at different stages in development: *T. luna* is represented by instars II and III, *T. vittata* by instars III and IV. Populations of both these species, as well as the total larval Tipulid population, suffered a sharp decline during the winter, indicating high mortality in the later instars (Table 7.2).

Hymenoptera

Much has been written about the biology of this group of insects, although little of it relates to the role of these animals in the general life of the soil community. Most of the emphasis, naturally, has been placed on the ants which are widely distributed in soils throughout the world. However, the soil is often invaded by certain bees and wasps in their search for food and nesting sites.

Composition and Distribution of the Fauna

Since the ants are by far the most important group of soil-inhabiting Hymenoptera, much of what follows is concerned with their ecology. Before considering this in more detail, however, a passing reference must be made to the various groups of bees and wasps that are sometimes encountered in the soil.

Bees and wasps

Among the few bees that may be counted as members of the soil fauna, the Andrenidae are noteworthy for their habit of building subterranean nests, while members of the carpenter bee genus *Xylocopa* colonize decaying wood. The wasps are more strongly represented, particularly in sandy and desert soils, by the Mutillidae (velvet ants) and Scoliidae which, in common with other Hymenoptera, such as the Chalcididae, Proctotrupidae, and Tiphiidae, have the habit of parasitizing, as larvae, other soil-dwelling insect larvae. The Scoliidae, in particular, have strongly developed legs which allow them to dig in the soil in search of their victims (Cloudsley-Thompson and Chadwick, 1964).

Sand wasps belonging to the family Sphecidae also burrow in desert soil to produce brood chambers in which are placed paralyzed insects as food for the developing larvae. The activities of these Hymenoptera may serve to aerate the soil, and even enrich it with organic material, although their contribution to the ecosystem is not very great, compared with that of their relatives, the ants.

Ants

Although ants are perhaps most conspicuous in desert habitats where there is little other surface life present, they also occur in woodland and forest litter and in cultivated soil in temperate regions. Furthermore, all ants are social insects and, to some extent, create their own environment. Consequently, it is difficult to generalize about the factors influencing their distribution, although certain habitat preferences are shown, as the following brief survey indicates.

Many ants select the warm, sheltered, moist conditions often found beneath flat stones partially buried in the soil. Others, such as *Camponotus* spp., *Formica rufa* (Formicinae), and *Crematogaster* sp. (Myrmicinae), are generally associated with decaying wood. Members of the more primitive Ponerinae and Myrmicinae often form only small colonies, comprising a few dozen individuals, in highly organic soils under woodland, and examples of these include *Myrmica ruginodis* and *Ponera coarctata*, which occur in European beech and North American oak-hickory woodland, respectively. The Ponerinae are poorly represented in Britain, but this group of ants is the dominant one in Australia, where its members construct subterranean nests, hardly detectable from the surface. The larger and more complex colonies, such as those of the Formicinae, flourish best in sandy soils and, indeed, some of the species belonging to this group, for example, *Lasius brunneus*, apparently avoid or move away from sites in which appreciable amounts of organic matter are accumulating (see Kühnelt, 1961). Species belonging to the genus *Lasius* are often common in pasture soils where their presence is indicated by distinctive mound formations. The mounds of the common European *Lasius flavus* may extend for as much as one metre above the surface of the ground, while those of *Formica rufa* may be even higher.

Mound-building is also common among desert-dwelling ants, which are well represented in various parts of the world by members of the Myrmicinae, such as *Pogonomyrmex, Messor, Pheidole, Holcomyrmex, Pheidologeton,* and *Merano- plus* among others. These are the 'harvester ants', and have a tendency to produce crateriform mounds, with a central depression surrounded by a ridge covered with the matted fragments of vegetation which have been rejected by the ants (Fig. 7.4). Not all desert-dwelling ants are harvesters, of course; many are active predators of other insects, and here may be included certain Ponerines, a few species of *Pheidole,* and members of the genera *Myrmecocystus, Dory- myrmex,* and *Cataglyphis.* Further mention of the feeding habits of these predators is made in the next section.

There is a great diversity in the size and complexity of ant nests, particularly in the extent to which chambers and branching gallery systems are developed. In the 'harvesters' and fungus-growing ants, the underground chambers are used not only for rearing the brood, but also for storing food and cultivating fungus gardens. These interconnecting cavity systems are constructed in an irregular manner and, as a rule, are less complex in the primitive Ponerinae and Dorylinae than in the 'higher' Myrmicinae and Formicinae.

FIGURE 7.4. Mound of California harvester ant, *Pogonomyrmex*. Note the dark-coloured fragments of rejected vegetation (photo by author).

Of the various factors which may influence the distribution of ant species, the availability of food is undoubtedly of great significance, although the physical nature of the substratum in which the nest is constructed may also be important. In deserts, the moisture content of the soil and the amount of exposure to wind also exert limiting influences. According to Wheeler (1910), ants dislike working in soil that is too dry, and many mound-builders construct a higher rim on the windward than on the leeward side of the nest, which presumably affords some protection against the elements.

Feeding Habits
The feeding habits of ants have been reviewed often in entomological texts, and we need to include only a brief survey here. The primitive Ponerinae and Dorylinae, together with many Myrmicinae, are predatory forms, feeding on other ants, insect larvae, spiders, myriapods, and isopods. Driver ants, of the genera *Dorylus, Anomma,* and *Eciton,* are voracious predators occurring in the

tropics, where they move across the surface of the ground in vast armies or columns, attacking and killing not only insects and arachnids, but also large snakes and even mammals where these are confined.

Many of the Myrmicinae, Dolichoderinae, and Formicinae have forsaken the carnivorous habit for a vegetarian diet. Many feed on woody tissue, for example, *Camponotus* spp., others on seeds, and here are included the 'harvester' ants previously mentioned which belong to the Myrmicinae, while liquid food in the form of nectar, sap, and the secretions of certain plant bugs, such as aphids and coccids, provides nutriment for many Formicinae and Dolichoderinae. The leaf-cutter ants of the tribe *Attii*, which are confined in their distribution to tropical and subtropical parts of the Americas, cultivate the fungi on which they subsist in underground chambers where a specially prepared substratum of vegetable material is deposited. Many of these feeding habits are not rigidly fixed, and in many cases the diet consists of what is available. For example, the turf ant, *Tetamorium caespitum*, and the harvester, *Pogonomyrmex badius*, may change their habit from carnivore to seed-feeder as the occasion demands (Kevan, 1962; Golley and Gentry, 1964). This plasticity of feeding habit may have a considerable survival value, for seed stores can be utilized during the winter season when insect food is in short supply.

Population Biology

We are concerned in this section with the ants, for little can be said about the population biology of other soil-dwelling Hymenoptera at this stage. This topic has been reviewed recently by Brian (1965), and only one or two points of a general nature will be considered here.

As we have noted previously, all ants are social insects, the colonies being made up of a number of castes which normally comprise males, queens, and worker females. Colonies reproduce to form new colonies, either by the production of sexual forms which emigrate to new nesting sites, or by the subdivision of the worker and queen population of the parent colony, as in *Formica polyctena.* The large numbers and mobility of these insects make direct counts of population size difficult to obtain, although estimates based on traffic flow and the mark recapture method are available (Holt, 1955; Odum and Pontin, 1961; Golley and Gentry, 1964). Ponerine colonies may often be counted in the tens or hundreds, those of *Formica rufa* in the thousands, whereas species of *Dorylus* and *Eciton* may form colonies comprising a million individuals or more.

The pattern of population growth within a colony is complicated by a number of events. For example, appreciable immigration may occur if smaller daughter colonies fail to become established and are resorbed by the parent colony. External environmental effects, such as shading or human interference, often cause a decline in population numbers. On the other hand, newly established colonies may show a progressive increase in size, at a rate proportional to that of the worker population, over a period of years until maturity, evidenced by the appearance of sexual forms, is achieved. Brian (1957) used geometric recurrence models to estimate that *Myrmica* colonies, commencing with 5 workers, develop for 7 or 8 years before producing males, and 10 years before both males and females are emitted.

The reproductive life of a queen may extend over several years and broods of different ages will occur together, providing overlapping generations which will tend to dampen annual or seasonal fluctuations in population size. Despite this fact, many ants show a periodicity in the occurrence of eggs, larvae, pupae, and adults. In temperate regions, reproduction occurs during the summer, and eggs laid during this period develop to a larval stage by the winter, and to the pupal and adult stages by the following spring and summer. As Brian (1965) has noted, species of the ant genus *Myrmica* show a departure from this pattern; peaks for eggs and pupae are synchronized and occur twice each year, in alternation with a larval peak in summer and one in winter. These peaks do not result from a periodicity in oviposition, although egg production rises quickly to an early maximum and then tails off more slowly. The observed decline in egg numbers is due rather to the consumption of eggs by first-instar larvae. These larvae either metamorphose immediately to form the second pupal peak of the year, or enter diapause along with larvae developing from the second egg peak to produce the winter larval population.

Extreme fluctuations in population size over a short period of time are probably uncommon in the social insects. Indeed, such fluctuations are undesirable for they would serve to disrupt the stable working conditions necessary for the maintenance of the complex behavioural patterns on which these societies are based. The regulation of population size and age structure is important to the success of the colony. This topic cannot, and need not, be pursued in detail here, for it has been treated by Brian (1965), but we may consider briefly the following points. The main factors limiting population size are the availability of nesting and mating sites, and the food supply. The stability of the age class composition may be achieved by internal mechanisms which compensate for any imbalance which may develop. For example, the ratio of workers to larvae tends to be constant in colonies of *Myrmica ruginodis macrogyna,* and this stability is the result of the limited capacity of workers to foster larvae, priority being given to those that are worker-biased (Brian, 1950). The survival of these larvae depends on a number of factors, including adequate food, for which they rely upon nursing workers, freedom from disease, which depends on the amount of cleaning performed by the workers, and protection from cannibalism, again provided by the attentions of the workers. A shortage of larvae, on the other hand, can be compensated by increasing the rate of survival of eggs laid by the queen. This is achieved by the contribution of worker eggs to the egg-mass produced by the queen (Brian, 1962).

Lepidoptera

The larvae and pupae of many butterflies and moths overwinter in the soil, but they are frequently inactive during this period; they are to be regarded more as passive members of the soil community. Many examples of these transients are found in the families Sphingidae, Noctuidae, and Aegeriidae, in which the larvae live phytophagously in the vegetation above the ground until they reach maximum size; they then enter the soil to overwinter as the pupal stage. However, not all Lepidoptera larvae entering the soil become inactive. The cut-worms (Noctuidae), the tuber-worms (Gelechiidae), larval ghost moths (Hepialidae), larval clear-wings (Aegeriidae), and the leaf-cutters (Incurvariidae) feed actively in the soil, often on the root systems of vegetation, but occasionally on leaf litter. According to van der Drift (1951), larvae· of the incurvariid *Adela viridella* are litter feeders; they are active during the summer months and probably pupating during the winter. However, the saprophagous habit is not common among Lepidoptera larvae; most are phytophagous on the green aerial parts of vegetation, where they often become serious pests to the agriculturalist and forester.

References

Balduf, W. V. (1935) *The bionomics of entomophagous Coleoptera*, Swift, St Louis. 220 pp.

Bocock, K. L. (1963) 'The digestion and assimilation of food by *Glomeris*' in Doeksen, J. and Drift, J. van der, eds., *Soil organisms*, 85-91.

Brauns, A. (1954) *Untersuchungen zur angewandten Bodenbiologie;* Bd. I. *Terricole Dipterenlarven*, Musterschmidt, Göttingen.

Brian, M. V. (1950) 'The stable winter population structure in species of *Myrmica*', *J. Anim. Ecol.*, **19**, 119-23.

Brian, M. V. (1957) 'The growth and development of colonies of the ant *Myrmica*', *Insectes sociaux*, **4**, 177-90.

Brian, M. V. (1962) 'Studies of caste differentiation in *Myrmica rubra*. 5. Social conditions affecting early larval differentiation', *Insectes sociaux*, **9**, 295-310.

Brian, M. V. (1965) *Social insect populations*, Academic, London, New York. vii + 127 pp.

Burgess, A. F. (1911) '*Calosoma sycophanta*: its life history, behaviour and successful colonisation in New England', *Bull. Bur. Ent. U.S. Dep. Agric.*, **101**, 1-94.

Cloudsley-Thompson, J. L. and Chadwick, M. J. (1964) *Life in deserts*, Foulis, London, 218 pp.

Coaker, T. H. and Williams, D. A. (1963) 'The importance of some Carabidae and Staphylinidae as predators of the cabbage root fly, *Erioischia brassicae* (Bouché)', *Ent. exp. appl.*, **6**, 156-64.

Davidson, J. (1944) 'On the growth of insect populations with successive generations', *Aust. J. exp. Biol. med. Sci.*, **22**, 95-103.

Delany, M. J. (1960) 'The food and feeding habits of some heath-dwelling invertebrates', *Proc. zool. Soc. Lond.*, **135**, 303-11.

Delkeskamp, K. (1930) 'Biologische Studien über *Carabus nemoralis* Müll', *Z. Morph. Ökol. Tiere*, **19**, 1-58.

Drift, J. van der (1951) 'Analysis of the animal community in a beech forest floor', *Tijdschr. Ent.*, **94**, 1-168.

Edwards, C. A. and Heath, G. W. (1964) *The principles of agricultural entomology*, Chapman Hall, London. xiv + 418 pp.

Freeman, B. E. (1967) 'Studies on the ecology of larval Tipulinae (Diptera, Tipulidae)', *J. Anim. Ecol.*, **36**, 123-46.

Golley, F. B. and Gentry, J. B. (1964) Bioenergetics of the southern harvester ant, *Pogonomyrmex badius', Ecology,* **45,** 217-25.

Greenslade, P. J. M. (1964) 'The distribution, dispersal and size of a population of *Nebria brevicollis* (F.) with comparative studies on three other Carabidae', *J. Anim. Ecol.,* **33,** 311-33.

Harris, W. V. (1955) 'Termites and the soil' in Kevan, D. K. McE., ed., *Soil zoology,* 62-72.

Hayes, W. P. (1929) 'Morphology, taxonomy and biology of larval Scarabaeoidea', *Illinois biol. Monogr.,* **12,** 1-119.

Holt, S. J. (1955) 'On the foraging activity of the wood ant', *J. Anim. Ecol.,* **24,** 1-34.

Hughes, R. D. (1959) 'The natural mortality of *Erioischia brassicae* (Bouché) (Diptera, Anthomyiidae) during the egg stage of the first generation', *J. Anim. Ecol.,* **28,** 343-57.

Karpachevsky, L. O., Perel, T. S. and Bartsevich, V. V. (1968) 'The role of Bibionidae larvae in decomposition of forest litter', *Pedobiologia,* **8,** 146-9.

Kemner, N. A. (1926) 'Zur Kenntnis der Staphyliniden-larven. II. Die Lebensweise und die parasitische Entwicklung der echten Aleochariden', *Ent. Tidskr.,* **47,** 133-70.

Kern, P. (1925) 'Beiträge zur Biologie der Carabiden. II', *Ent. Bl. Biol. Syst. Käfer,* **21,** 114-19.

Kevan, D. K. Mc.E. (1962) *Soil animals,* Philosophical Library, New York. xv + 237 pp.

Kühnelt, W. (1961) *Soil biology with special reference to the animal kingdom* (English edn, trans. Walker, N.), Faber, London. 397 pp.

Lüscher, M. (1961) 'Social control of polymorphism in termites' in Kennedy, J. S., ed., *Insect polymorphism,* 57-67.

Mitchell, B. (1963) 'Ecology of two carabid beetles, *Bembidion lampros* (Herbst.) and *Trechus quadristriatus* (Schrank). I. Life cycles and feeding behaviour', *J. Anim. Ecol.,* **32,** 289-99.

Murdoch, W. W. (1967) 'Life history patterns of some British Carabidae (Coleoptera) and their ecological significance', *Oikos,* **18,** 25-32.

Nadvornyj, V. G. (1968) 'Wireworms (Coleoptera, Elateridae) of the Smolensk region, their distribution and incidence in different soil types', *Pedobiologia,* **8,** 296-305.

Odum, E. P. and Pontin, A. J. (1961) 'Population density of the underground ant, *Lasius flavus,* as determined by tagging with P^{32}', *Ecology,* **42,** 186-8.

Parkin, E. A. (1940) 'The digestive enzymes of some wood-boring beetle larvae', *J. exp. Biol.,* **17,** 364-77.

Penney, M. M. (1966) 'Studies on certain aspects of the ecology of *Nebria brevicollis (F.)* (Coleoptera, Carabidae)', *J. Anim. Ecol.,* **35,** 505-12.

Peterson, A. (1951) *Larvae of insects.* Part II. Lithoprint. Edwards, Ann Arbor. 416 pp.

Raw, F. (1967) 'Arthropoda (except Acari and Collembola)' in Burges, N. A. and Raw, F., eds., *Soil biology,* 323-62.

Ritcher, P. O. (1958) 'Biology of Scarabaeidae', *A. Rev. Ent.,* **3,** 311-34.

Schuster, R. (1966) 'Über den Beutefang des Ameisenkäfers *Cephennium austriacum* Reiter', *Naturwissenschaften,* **53,** 113.

Struble, G. H. (1930) 'The biology of certain Coleoptera associated with certain bark beetles in western yellow pine', *Univ. Calif. Publs. Ent.,* **5/6,** 105-34.

Wadsworth, J. T. (1915) 'On the life history of *Aleochara bilineata* Gyll., a staphylinid parasite of *Chortophila brassicae* Bouché', *J. econ. Biol.,* **10,** 1-27.

Webb, G. C. (1961) *Keys to the genera of the African termites,* Ibadan U. P., Ibadan, 34 pp.

Wheeler, W. M. (1910) *Ants, their structure, development and behaviour,* Columbia U. P. New York. xxv + 663 pp.

Williams, G. (1959) 'Seasonal and diurnal activity of Carabidae, with particular reference to *Nebria, Notiophilus* and *Feronia',* *J. Anim. Ecol.,* **28,** 309-30.

8. Apterygota

We now turn to a group of soil arthropods collectively considered by some authors under the heading of 'primitive insects'. To this group belong the Collembola, numerically one of the most important groups of soil animals, and with which much of this chapter is concerned. Also included here, are several groups of minor importance, such as the Thysanura, Diplura, and Protura.

Thysanura

Of the various mandibulate arthropods, the Thysanura stand closest to the true ancestral insect stock. These animals, commonly known as 'bristle tails', are often encountered in the dry cavities of rock crevices, under tree bark and in loose woodland litter. They are easily recognized by the presence of three long cerciform processes which project posteriorly from the terminal part of the abdomen. Thysanurans are active forms and move rapidly when disturbed; as a consequence, they tend to avoid compact soils. Their distribution pattern reflects a preference for the shelter of rock crevices, in which they often congregate in large numbers, for example, on the seashore. Soil-dwelling species belonging to the family Machilidae rarely occur in high densities, and although they feed mainly on plant debris and fungi, their contribution to the soil-forming process is undoubtedly slight. In an ecological survey of the Apterygota of several contrasting soil habitats in central Europe, Nosek (1963) recorded Thysanura only from one site, a semixerothermic grassland, where two species were identified, a *Machilis* sp. and *Lepismachilis y-signata,* from a total of three individuals. Densities of this order of magnitude are too low to allow any broad conclusions to be drawn regarding the factors limiting distribution, although it is known that thysanurans have a low basic transpiration rate, and can survive desiccating conditions better than most soil animals.

Diplura

The Diplura share with the Protura and the Collembola the 'entotrophic' condition of the mouth-parts, in which these structures are housed in a cavity in the head capsule and are not immediately visible externally. The group is subdivided into the Campodeidae, Japygidae, and Projapygidae, the last-named family being small and restricted in distribution to the tropics and subtropics. The campodeids are delicate creatures, with conspicuous threadlike antennae and a pair of divergent, antenniform cerci projecting from the posterior end of the abdomen; they are predominantly white or yellow in colour, and rarely more than 1 cm in length. The Japygidae are rather more robust, and the tropical representatives of this family may measure several centimetres in length; japygids differ from campodeids in that the abdominal cerci are short, unsegmented, and developed as pincers which are used for capturing prey. The Campodeidae are also predators, and the diet of both of these groups of Diplura consists of small soil arthropods, such as Collembola and dipteran larvae, together with enchytraeids. In these predators, eyes are lacking and the antennae are used for locating their prey. They are strongly thigmotactic and, according to Kühnelt (1961), show a preference for sites with a high and relatively stable moisture regimen; members of the genera *Campodea, Plusiocampa,* and *Japyx* favour deep, porous litter and humus layers and the moist cavities beneath stones and decaying wood. They are rarely encountered with any appreciable frequency, even in woodland and forest litter; in 28 samples taken from a range of sites, Nosek (1963) recorded frequencies of occurrence of 14·3 per cent, 10·7 per cent, and 3·5 per cent for *Campodea fragilis, Catajapyx confusus,* and *Campodea augens,* respectively. Diplura do not appear to be strongly restricted, in their distribution, to woodland and forest soils, for they were encountered as often in grasslands in the study just referred to; Engelmann (1961) recorded japygids from an old field in Michigan. They are also known to inhabit caves.

Protura

The members of this group resemble the Diplura in having an elongate body form and an 11-segmented abdomen, but differ in lacking abdominal cerci and, in some cases, antennae, although the latter are present in some species as small papillae. The taxonomy of the group has been reviewed by Tuxen (1965), and a species collected from beech litter in England is shown in Fig. 8.1.

Proturans are often neglected by the soil zoologist for they are rarely collected in large numbers. However, they may prove to be more abundant than is generally believed when an efficient method of extracting them from the soil has been devised. Raw (1956) encountered the group quite frequently in moist, forest and grassland soils, and Nosek (1963) recorded eight species, mainly from beech and oak forest soils, of which *Eosentomon transitorum, Acerella remyi, Acerentomon gallicum, Acerentulus confinis,* and *Acerentomon carpaticum* occurred in frequencies of 57·2 per cent, 32·1 per cent, 25·0 per cent, 14·3 per cent and 10·7 per cent, respectively. In general, the Protura favour moist, organic soils, provided these are not too acid and, although they are usually restricted to the upper 10 cm of the profile, a distinction can be made between surface-dwelling species, such as *Acerentomon doderoi, Eosentomon spinosum,* and *E. armatum,* which have relatively long legs, and the inhabitants of deeper levels, such as *Acerentulus minimus* and *Protentomon* spp., which have shorter legs (Kühnelt, 1961).

In what is, perhaps, one of the most detailed studies of the reproductive biology, post-embryonic development, and population dynamics of individual proturan species, Tuxen (1949) noted that Danish populations of *Acerentulus danicus* and *Eosentomon armatum* were similar in having five preadult stages in the life cycle: a prelarva, two larval forms, a maturus junior, and a preimago. In many other aspects of their biology, these two species differed considerably. For example, the surface-dwelling *Acerentulus danicus* appears to be markedly univoltine, i.e., having one generation per year. Throughout the summer, when

FIGURE 8.1. A member of the Protura collected from beech litter, Chiltern Hills, England (photo by A. Newman-Coburn).

the population as a whole reaches its maximum size, the maxima for the various juvenile stages succeed each other in a regular sequence from May to September. These juveniles evidently completed their development before winter, for only adult stages were found during this season, and the sex ratio among these adults, which is heavily biased towards the females during the summer, becomes more evenly balanced, suggesting that high post-reproductive mortality may occur among the females. In contrast, the summer population peak for *Eosentomon armatum* is only weakly developed; all stages of the life cycle of this species were encountered throughout the year. Departures from the 1:1 sex ratio among the adults were much less marked than in the case of *Acerentulus danicus,* indicating that mortality may be more evenly spread throughout the year. *E. armatum* was distributed more regularly down the soil profile to a depth of 5 cm than was *A. danicus,* and, although the density of the latter at the surface in summer far exceeded that of the former, the reverse was the case at greater depths during the winter. It is tempting to conclude from these observations that the ability to migrate down the profile in winter to avoid unfavourable conditions at the surface allows *E. armatum* to extend its reproductive activity throughout the year, and obviates the necessity of the juveniles completing development to the adult stage before winter.

Little is known of the feeding habits of the Protura. Their mouth-parts are styliform, which suggests that they are fluid feeders. The enlarged forelegs invite a comparison with the raptorial structures of mantids, but there is no definite evidence that the proturans are predatory in habit, and Sturm (1959) reported that species of *Acerentomon* and *Eosentomon* feed on the contents of fungal hyphae. Clearly, this is a field which deserves further attention.

Collembola

The Collembola, or 'spring tails', represent one of the most abundant and widespread groups of soil arthropods, and often rival only the Acari in these respects. These are small animals, rarely more than a few millimetres in length at the most, and differ from the Diplura and Protura in possessing only six abdominal segments. The common name for the group derives from the ability to jump quite appreciable distances when disturbed; this activity is facilitated by the possession of a springing organ carried on the fourth, and occasionally the fifth, abdominal segment. This organ is a bifid structure, it is folded forwards under the ventral surface of the abdomen and held in place by a retaining retinaculum which is carried on the third abdominal segment when not in use. Not all Collembola possess a springing organ, and not all can jump. This structure is much more strongly developed in surface-dwelling species than in inhabitants of deeper soil layers. The development of the three to six segmented antennae is similarly correlated with the mode of life, these structures being quite short in many groups, but greatly elongated in the surface-dwelling Entomobryidae. Eyes may be present in some groups, represented by clusters of ocelli, or they may be absent, as in the Onychiuridae which possess only pseudocelli. The Collembola are also characterized by the possession of a 'ventral tube' carried on the first abdominal segment. This tube consists of vesicles which can be everted, provided the water content of the body is above a certain minimum level, or retracted, when they are protected by chitinous flaps. Noble-Nesbitt (1963b) has drawn attention to the fact that the eversion of the ventral tube in *Podura aquatica* is stimulated when the claws come into contact with water; he also demonstrated that this tube may be an important site for the exchange of water and sodium ions between the animal and its environment (Noble-Nesbitt, 1963c). In addition, the ventral tube may also be used for attaching the animal firmly to the substratum (see Ruppel, 1953).

The Collembola are divided, systematically, into two major groupings, the Symphypleona and the Arthropleona, easily distinguishable by the form of the body which is short, globular, and indistinctly segmented in the former, and elongate, cylindrical, and visibly segmented in the latter (Fig. 8.2). A further distinction is that the Symphypleona possess tracheae whereas the Arthropleona

FIGURE 8.2. A member of the collembolan Arthropleona, taken from litter under California walnut, Puddingstone Reservoir, San Dimas, California (photo by author).

do not, and this may have important repercussions on the ecology of the two groups; this point will be taken up a little later in this chapter. Some of the Symphypleona, such as members of the family Neelidae and the genus *Arrhopalites,* may penetrate deeply into the soil, but the group is more common in loose, upper litter layers, for example, under beech woodland. They are often found in the aerial parts of vegetation where their phytophagous feeding habits qualify them to be treated as economic pests; a well-known example of this group is the lucerne 'flea', *Sminthurus viridis.*

The Arthropleona are richly represented in the soil, in terms of numbers of individuals and species, with members of the families Onychiuridae, Isotomidae, Poduridae, and Entomobryidae often forming a significant proportion of the fauna. A considerable body of ecological information has been accumulated on the ecology of the group, so the following account cannot cover every aspect in detail. The survey will be concerned mainly with a treatment of distribution patterns and the factors affecting these, feeding habits, life cycles, and population dynamics. The topic of population metabolism is considered in chapter 13, when the contribution of the Collembola to energy flow through the soil community is compared with the contributions made by other groups of the soil fauna.

The taxonomy of the Collembola of the north temperate region is fairly well known: excellent keys for the identification of European and North American species have been compiled by Gisin (1960) and Maynard (1951), respectively.

Horizontal Distribution

Collembola enjoy a worldwide distribution. The habitats colonized by them range from the bleak rock crevices of Antarctica to the equally inhospitable soils of the American Mojave desert; they include such habitats as caves, snowfields, ant and termite mounds, bird nests, free-water surfaces, and the marine littoral, in addition to the soil and the vegetation it supports. They are often as abundant in the soils of grassland and moorland as in forest litter, usually occurring in densities within the range 5000-50 000/m², and occasionally in excess of this (Table 8.1; see also Tables 12.5, 6, and 7). Despite this ubiquity, different

TABLE 8.1. Estimates of population size of Collembola in different habitats (from Hale, 1967).

Habitat type	Density in thousands/m²	Author
Beech mor	0·7	van der Drift (1951)
Douglas fir litter	40·0	Poole (1961)
Vaccinium heath	15·0	Forsslund (1945)
Dactylis grassland	27·0	Glasgow (1939)
Sandy soil	8·5	Weis-Fogh (1948)
Limestone grassland	15·9	Schaller (1949)
Limestone grassland	25·0	Schaller (1949)
Loam grassland	33·0	Dhillon & Gibson (1962)
Limestone grassland	53·0	Hale (1966)
Alluvial grassland	44·0	Hale (1966)
Juncus squarrosus	21·0	Hale (1966)
Phragmites fen	20·0	Strenzke (1949)
Molinia fen	25·0	Macfadyen (1952)
Deschampsia fen	24·0	Macfadyen (1952)
Juncus subnodulosus fen	7·2	Macfadyen (1952)
Calluna moorland	35·0	Hale (1967)
Bracken moorland	17·7	Milne (1962)

Collembola species show different degrees of tolerance to various environmental factors and, consequently, the species composition of the fauna may be a good indicator of microhabitat conditions. Among the various factors which have been considered as important determinants of the species composition, may be included vegetation type, soil structure, soil microflora, and soil moisture content. Each of these factors will now be considered in turn.

In summarizing the relationship between the macroflora and the Collembolan fauna, Christiansen (1964) pointed to the fact that there is generally a moderate amount of correspondence between plant and collembolan associations, but little evidence of restriction of individual Collembola species to one species of plant. A similar conclusion was reached by Bellinger (1954) in his survey of the Collembola fauna of several different vegetation types. This suggests that the influence of vegetation type is an indirect one, being exerted, perhaps, through its effect on soil type, microfloral composition, or soil moisture. The effects of cultivation may operate in a similar way.

The variation in the Collembola fauna from one soil type to another is largely a reflection of differences in pore volume and the diameter of soil spaces which, in turn, are influenced by the size of mineral particles and the organic content of the soil. These influences are most clearly noted when the depth distribution of species is considered, for the larger species, such as members of the genera *Entomobrya, Orchesella,* and *Tomocerus,* together with many Symphypleona, are common in loosely packed surface litter, whereas deeper down in the profile, where the average pore volume is less, the smaller-sized *Onychiurus, Tullbergia,* and *Friesea* species predominate. This topic of vertical distribution is discussed further in a later section.

The importance of the soil microflora is difficult to determine, although three possible effects may be mentioned. First, it is apparent from the work of von Törne (1961, 1967) that certain microflora are present as gut symbionts in Collembola, and may have an important role in the digestion of plant material consumed by the host. However, there is no direct evidence from field populations that distribution is limited by this relationship, although more information on this problem would define more clearly the true nature of the symbiosis. Second, the soil microflora may be important as food for Collembola. The relationship between these arthropods and soil bacteria and fungi is a complex, mutualistic one in all probability, and here again limiting effects are not easily defined. A strong feeding preference for fungal hyphae and spores is shown by some Collembola (see below), and it has been suggested that the distribution of these animals is influenced by the distribution of fungi on which they feed (Knight, 1961). Third, direct competition between Collembola and soil fungi may have a limiting effect on distribution. This is likely to be of the greatest importance when the two groups are competing for the available moisture in the habitat.

The influence of soil moisture can best be observed in localities where a gradient in this factor occurs. Such sites are common in calcareous areas, bogs, fens, and moorland, and the distribution of Collembola species has been documented for these types (see, for example, Schaller, 1949; Murphy, 1955; Hale, 1963). Within these areas, it is often possible to define three main groups of species; first, a hydrophil element occupying the surface of free water, typified by *Podura aquatica, Tetracanthella brachyura, Isotoma antennalis,* and *Sminthurides malmgreni;* second, a mesophil, or cavernicole, group living in the microcaverns of moss plants growing in less wet areas, exemplified by *Folsomia brevicaudata, Friesea mirabilis,* and *Isotoma sensibilis;* third, a xerophil fauna inhabiting exposed sites subject to desiccation during dry weather, of which the species *Tetracanthella wahlgreni* is an example. Although these three groupings may have an objective reality as far as the relationship between species composition and soil moisture is concerned, they must not obscure the fact that, in general, Collembola require an atmospheric relative humidity of not less than 90 per cent in order to survive for any extended period of time. A more detailed analysis of water relations is given in the section on vertical distribution patterns (see below).

The direct influence of the temperature factor on distribution patterns is hard to evaluate, and, indeed, may be meaningless, if it is not considered in conjunction with the effect of moisture. Experiments on the Antarctic collembolan *Isotoma klovstadi* suggested that this species can survive temperatures as low as $-30°C$ under experimental conditions (Pryor, 1962), whereas another denizen of this region, *Gomphiocephalus hodgsoni,* is apparently less tolerant, having an optimum for normal activity at about $11°C$, and succumbing in temperature conditions below $-20°C$ (Janetschek, 1967). However, it would be unwise to make detailed comparisons on the basis of these preliminary observations, for it is not possible to correlate the differences in tolerance with the differences observed in the natural distribution patterns of the two species concerned. Experimental procedures have not yet been standardized, and little attention has been paid to the possibility that cold tolerance may vary within a given species from summer to winter, or that the results obtained may reflect not only responses to given temperature conditions, but also to relative humidity; furthermore, they may vary with the degree of desiccation of the experimental animals.

In concluding this brief survey of the factors which may influence the distribution of collembolan species, it is probably worth noting that the species composition in any given locality may be determined, not by a single limiting factor, but by a complex of factors, both ecological and historical. The degree of similarity in species composition between two sites can then be used as an index of an overall ecological similarity. Habitat comparisons, using vegetation type as a point of reference, are frequently made on this basis.

Vertical Distribution

As a general rule, in most permanent grassland, moorland, and woodland sites, the Collembola fauna is most richly represented, in terms of numbers of individuals and species, in the organic layers, i.e., in the top 10-15 cm (see, for example, van der Drift, 1951; Haarløv, 1955; Poole, 1961; Christiansen, 1964; Wood, 1967). Within this depth range, the largest populations are usually located at the level at which active decomposition of organic material is occurring; in mor type profiles, this level is identified as a 'fermentation' zone, distinct from, and separating, the surface litter and the deeper humus layers. Haarløv (1955) has pointed out that the fermentation layer offers the most suitable conditions for microarthropods, for there is abundant food here, and the cavity system is of smaller diameter, on the average, than that of the upper litter, and consequently is less susceptible to drying out. In confirmation of this, Poole (1963) established that correlations existed between Collembola numbers and the depth and moisture content of the organic layer in a coniferous woodland. In undisturbed grassland soils, where there is no appreciable accumulation of surface litter and no well-defined fermentation zone, Collembola numbers show a progressive decrease with depth. This decrease is related to the decreasing porosity of the soil, as shown by the data of Dhillon and Gibson (1962) presented in Table 8.2. This relationship follows naturally from the fact that

TABLE 8.2. Comparison of soil porosity with vertical distribution of Collembola in a loam grassland soil in Yorkshire, England (after Dhillon and Gibson, 1962).

Depth	% porosity of soil	% of total Collembola
0-38 mm	74·5	92·6
38-76 mm	38·2	5·2
76-115 mm ⎫	36·7	1·4
115-152 mm ⎭		0·9

Collembola are unable to burrow, and so must utilize existing soil spaces. Obviously, then, the amount of available living space decreases with depth, and this has important repercussions on the species composition at various depths. It is usual to find the larger forms (body length 3-4 mm), such as *Tomocerus, Orchesella,* and *Entomobrya,* mainly restricted to the soil surface and loose upper litter layers. The species present in this zone are often strongly pigmented, with well-developed ocelli and large, functional springing organs. In the deeper, more compact litter and fermentation layers, smaller forms predominate, such as members of the genera *Folsomia, Isotoma,* and *Onychiurus,* while the inhabitants of the deeper humus and mineral layers comprise the immatures of some of the larger species, together with such forms as *Tullbergia krausbaueri* and *Friesea mirabilis,* which are often less than 1 mm in length and show a reduction or absence of pigment, ocelli, and springing organs.

The fact that the distribution of a given species may be related to certain of its morphological characteristics has given rise to the definition of 'life forms', and attempts have been made to apply this concept not only to Collembola, but also to soil-dwelling mites and Diptera larvae. As far as the Collembola are concerned, the vertical sequence of species described in the previous paragraph represents a life form series characterized by the progressive reduction, with increasing depth in the profile, in the amount of pigmentation, and in the development of light receptors and mobility, in addition to body size. Earlier, we noted that species could be classified into hydrophilous, mesophilous, and xerophilous groupings, and these, again, can be distinguished morphologically from each other as separate life forms (Christiansen, 1964). The various morphological criteria used are also paralleled by behavioural and physiological characters, particularly respiratory activity and resistance to desiccation. These are now considered in a little more detail.

Respiratory Activity

In a series of experimental studies designed to investigate the respiratory activity of various collembolan species in relation to their ecological characteristics, Zinkler (1966) showed that Symphypleona, such as *Sminthurus viridis*, had a much higher rate of O_2 consumption than Arthropleona of comparable weight, such as *Tomocerus vulgaris*, and that this difference was more marked at 8°C than at 18°C, as shown in Table 8.3. It appears likely that the higher respiratory rate in the Symphypleona is related to their possession of a tracheal system, such a system being lacking in the Arthropleona.

TABLE 8.3. The relationship between body length, O_2 consumption, and temperature for various species of Collembola (after Zinkler, 1966).

Species	Body length (mm)	Mean O_2 consumption (mm^3/g/hr) 18°C	8°C
Arthropleona:			
Neanura muscorum	2·5	195	
Tetrodontophora bielanensis	6·0-8·0	165	65
Onychiurus armatus	2·0	630	241
Isotoma viridis	4·0-4·3	545	
Isotoma viridis (juveniles)	2·0-2·5		146
Orchesella cincta	4·0-5·0	413	
Orchesella flavescens	4·0-5·0		143
Tomocerus vulgaris	3·0-4·0	365	129
Tomocerus longicornis	5·0-6·5	266	91
Symphypleona:			
Sminthurus viridis	2·0-3·0	549	265
Sminthurus fuscus	2·0-3·2	491	
Dicyrtoma minuta	1·5-2·0		147

When comparisons are made between different species within the same major grouping, it is evident that the rate of O_2 consumption increased with a decrease in body weight, as far as members of the Arthropleona were concerned, for Table 8.3 shows that this rate was appreciably higher in the small *Onychiurus armatus* than in the larger *Tetrodontophora bielanensis*. On the basis of these observations, the author was able to demonstrate that the rate of O_2 consumption in small, soil-dwelling Arthropleona was significantly higher than that in the larger, litter-dwelling species. No such relationship could be established for the Symphypleona which, in any event, are primarily litter-dwellers. In addition, he found that the larger, surface-dwelling species, such as *Tomocerus vulgaris* and *Isotoma saltans*, were affected by an increased carbon dioxide content of the air, whereas species inhabiting deeper soil layers, such as *Neanura muscorum* and *Onychiurus fimatus*, behaved quite normally under these conditions. Since the CO_2 content of the soil air is usually higher than that in the air at the soil surface (see Table 1.4, page 20), tolerance of high CO_2 levels is an obvious physiological necessity for soil-dwelling species. Moursi (1962a and b) had previously drawn attention to this topic when he reported that *Onychiurus armatus* and certain mite species were attracted to a source of CO_2 in an experimental vessel, provided the rate of flow of the gas did not exceed 4·2 ml/hr; a similar result was obtained using nitrogen. The author concluded, on the basis of his observations of the behaviour of the experimental animals, that this was not a specific olfactory response, but rather a reaction to changes in composition of the air, particularly with respect to oxygen content. Such a reaction would have adaptive significance for soil animals feeding on organic debris, for it would bring them to the vicinity of the rhizosphere where food would be more plentiful. Such a response would, of course, be of no benefit to phytophagous forms living at the soil surface or to litter-dwelling species which are surrounded by potential food material, and this may provide an explanation for the differences described by Zinkler previously referred to. It is also worth noting that carbon dioxide is lethal to Collembola at levels which vary with the species. For example, Moursi (1962b) gave LD 50 values, i.e., the concentration at which 50 per cent of the experimental animals died in a given period of time, of 1·7 per cent for the soil-inhabiting *Onychiurus granulosus*, 6·7 per cent for *Hypogastrura bengtssoni*, a compost-dweller, and 17 per cent for the manure-inhabiting *Isotomina thermophila*. These differences undoubtedly reflect adaptations to the higher CO_2 concentrations in manure and compost.

It is clear, from the above discussion, that the differences in respiratory activity from one collembolan species to another are adaptive, and are related to differences in natural distribution patterns. In looking for a causal explanation for these physiological variations, attention must be focused on the nature of the respiratory surface. In the case of the non-tracheate Arthropleona, this surface is the general surface of the body and the ventral tube (Ruppel, 1953). Such a respiratory surface must have the necessary permeability to function efficiently for the exchange of gases, but also permits water loss, and, consequently, represents a potential hazard for a terrestrial animal. This leads us into another area of physiological ecology which is considered briefly below.

Resistance to Desiccation
As a general rule, the Arthropleona are very sensitive to desiccation, although the degree of tolerance varies from species to species, and can be related to distribution patterns. Thus, surface-dwellers, such as *Entomobrya muscorum,* can survive for 10 hours in air at 30 per cent RH, whereas other litter inhabitants, such as *Lepidocyrtus lanuginosus* and *Tomocerus vulgaris,* survive for only 1 hour under similar conditions; this lower tolerance is reflected in the movement of these species down to deeper litter layers during periods of drought (Kühnelt, 1961). In contrast, the deeper-dwelling *Onychiurus armatus* can survive for no longer than 15 minutes at 30 per cent RH. The relationship between distribution patterns and tolerance is probably not as simple as these

observations would suggest, however. As Kühnelt (1961) has noted, experimental data are available which suggest that species exhibiting a relatively high resistance to desiccation do not always have low moisture optima, and vice versa. There are several possible reasons for this anomaly. First, resistance to desiccation of any particular individual increases with increasing body size. In addition, the behaviour of an animal in an environmental gradient may vary with its physiological state, in particular with its body water content. We have noted, in chapter 6, that this is the case with terrestrial isopods, and it is also true of certain soil-dwelling mites (see chapter 9). Second, the use of relative humidity gradients may not give an accurate indication of an animal's tolerance, for, as we noted in chapter 1, the drying power of the air is more closely related to saturation deficit than to relative humidity. Unless these variables are taken into account by the experimenter, the results are difficult to interpret and may lead, at the best, to ambiguity and, at the worst, to contradiction.

The high susceptibility of the Arthropleona to desiccation suggests a highly permeable cuticle. On the other hand, this cuticle shows strong hydrofuge properties, i.e., it is not readily wettable, as anyone who has attempted to submerge Collembola in water can testify. Such hydrofuge properties are normally associated with the presence of a surface monolayer of lipid which would confer a high degree of impermeability to the cuticle; this is inconsistent with the low resistance to desiccation already referred to. This apparent contradiction has been resolved by Noble-Nesbitt (1963a and b) in a series of detailed studies into the fine structure and physiology of the cuticle of *Podura aquatica*. This species is not a true soil-dweller, for it lives on the surface of freshwater pools, but comparisons between Noble-Nesbitt's findings and those of Ögel (1958), on the cuticle of the soil-inhabiting *Folsomia candida*, suggest that the cuticular physiology of *P. aquatica* may have certain general characteristics which are applicable to other Arthropleona. Accordingly, the main findings of Noble-Nesbitt's work are summarized briefly below.

Electron micrographs showed that the cuticle of *P. aquatica* has essentially the same layer structure as that of an insect; they also showed that the wax layer overlying the epicuticle is discontinuous. Over much of the body, the cuticle is rough with a microsculpture of minute tubercles, the tips of which have a coating of the hydrofuge agent. The identification of this agent with wax is strongly indicated by the results of experiments in which the cuticular surface was treated with abrasive dusts; after such treatment the rate of transpiration increased on average one-and-a-half to two times the normal values. Treatment with hot chloroform also removed the hydrofuge agent and added confirmation to this interpretation. Similar results were obtained for *Folsomia candida* (Ögel, 1958). In the troughs between the minor tubercles, the wax layer is absent or, at least, interrupted in the bases of the troughs; a high cuticular permeability can be expected at these points. The tips of the hydrofuge tubercles are only about 0.4μ apart, and Noble-Nesbitt (1963b) suggested that such an arrangement would promote a plastronlike effect with water being held away from the surface and air being trapped in the intervening troughs. Such an explanation is perfectly consistent with the hydrofuge nature of the cuticle, and also with its high permeability. The cuticle covering the ventral tube vesicles and the claws is not roughened, however, and it is wettable. This characteristic has important biological implications, for it allows the claws to penetrate the surface of water films to obtain the necessary purchase for efficient locomotion; it also permits the ventral tube to come into contact with free water in the environment enabling this structure to function as an anchoring device, and a site for the exchange of water and ions.

It is not possible to say whether the epicuticular wax is present or absent on these hydrophil areas, for, even if it were present, the absence of tubercles could lower the contact angle to water sufficiently to allow wetting to occur. However, the observations of Ruppel (1953), that about a third of the total respiration occurs through the ventral tube, suggest that this structure may be free of wax. On the other hand, Noble-Nesbitt (1963b) noted that the ventral tube vesicles were withdrawn and closed off by cuticular flaps during the transpiration experiments, and that the stimulus for the eversion of these vesicles was contact between the claws and free water. Water loss across the surface of the ventral tube would be negligible under these circumstances, but this does not discount the possibility that the tube may be used to regulate body water content and respiratory rate, even though it may not be directly responsible for the high rates of transpiration which are characteristic of the Arthropleona. In this respect, it is interesting to note that the estimates of transpiration rate obtained by Noble-Nesbitt (Fig. 8.3) are considerably higher than those for isopods given in Table 6.1.

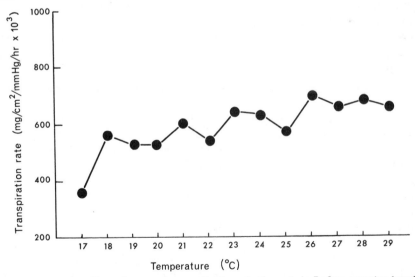

FIGURE 8.3. The effect of temperature on the transpiration rate in *Podura aquatica,* based on mean values corrected for differences in saturation deficits (from Noble-Nesbitt, 1963b).

The ecological implications of these findings may be summarized briefly as follows. Since the Arthropleona possess no special respiratory structures, such as tracheae, the general body surface must assume this function and, as a prerequisite, this surface must be highly permeable. It is obviously of adaptive value for a terrestrial animal to have some degree of resistance to desiccation, and the presence of a discontinuous wax layer undoubtedly confers some benefit in this respect. The hydrofuge nature of the collembolan cuticle also serves to protect these animals from the dangers of flooding and consequent submersion, for not only does the air film which is trapped in the troughs between the tubercles increase bouyancy, but it also allows respiration to continue, even if the animal is submerged for considerable periods of time. Kühnelt (1961) has pointed out that Collembola have strong powers of survival under such conditions. The evolution of a tracheal system in insects relieves the cuticle of its respiratory responsibilities, and the way is therefore open for a more complete waterproofing mechanism to develop in the form of a continuous wax or grease layer. This, in turn, lessens the animal's dependence on the saturated atmosphere of the soil, and allows the colonization of new, and more exposed, habitats.

It would be of considerable interest to have more information of the kind discussed above about true soil-dwelling species, particularly if these are representative of a range of life forms. More information is also needed about the nature of the cuticle of the tracheate, surface-dwelling Symphypleona. Future work in this field can obviously test the adaptive significance of the life form concept, and can also inquire more extensively into the early stages in the evolution of the terrestrial habit among the arthropods.

In concluding this section on distribution patterns and the factors which influence them, attention must be drawn to the fact that the concept of life forms cannot be applied too rigidly, for the distribution of some species extends over a range of habitats, indicating a measure of ecological plasticity. For example, although it has been noted that small-sized species predominate at lower levels in the soil profile, these species are often not restricted to these levels, but may range through the profile, at least in permanently moist localities, occurring commonly within the top two to three centimetres of the organic layer. Such vertical movements, which often occur with the changing seasons, are of great survival value, for they allow the animals to remain in equable temperature and moisture conditions throughout the year. In this way, Collembola can take full advantage of the warm, moist conditions occurring in the upper layers during the spring and autumn, and, by migrating downwards, avoid the drought and temperature extremes at the surface during summer and winter. However, it is sometimes easier to postulate these cause and effect phenomena than to demonstrate them, and Dhillon and Gibson (1962) could find no clear relationship between the observed changes in depth distribution of grassland Collembola and variations in soil temperature, humidity, organic content, and pH. These authors concluded that changes in distribution patterns could most reasonably be interpreted as responses to the cumulative effects of small variations in several factors, rather than a dominant effect of a single factor. Vertical movements of a much shorter period, diurnal in nature, have also been reported (see Christiansen, 1964), but too little attention has so far been paid to these.

Feeding Habits
The mouth-parts of Collembola consist, essentially, of two elements: the mandibles and the maxillae. These structures vary in form and development from group to group in a manner which may be related to variations in the nature of the food ingested. The majority of Collembola chew their food and possess strongly developed mandibles and maxillae, the former bearing a roughened molar plate which is large, for example, in members of the genus *Tomocerus* which feed on hard plant material, or reduced, with less conspicuous ridges, in species feeding on soft material, for example, *Podura aquatica*. In the genus *Friesea*, the mandibles are slender with prominent distal teeth but no molar plate, and the maxillae are strongly toothed; this arrangement may function as a biting device (Dunger, 1964), although it has also been interpreted as a rasping and sucking mechanism (Sharma and Kevan, 1965). Piercing and sucking mouth-parts are also present in certain groups, for example, *Neanura* spp., in which the mandibles are reduced to stylets or are lacking, and the maxillae are styliform. Examples of these various categories are illustrated in Fig. 8.4.

These differences suggest a wide range of feeding habit among the Collembola, and numerous investigations have confirmed this. The broad distinction between chewing and sucking mouth-parts may reflect a dichotomy of habit separating the vegetarians from the carnivores, although there may be obvious

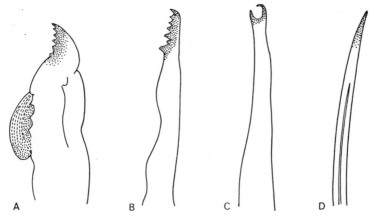

FIGURE 8.4. Variation in the form of the mouth-parts in Collembola: (A) Mandible of the chewing type; (B) Mandible of the biting type; (C) Mandible of the sucking type; (D) Maxilla of sucking type (after Dunger, 1964).

exceptions to this, for styliform mouth-parts can be used to pierce plant tissues. To embark on a detailed survey of individual feeding preferences would be too exhaustive for our purposes and, in any event, would duplicate much of the account given by Christiansen (1964). Accordingly, the following discussion is restricted to a few general points.

Culture experiments indicate that many species can consume a wide variety of organic material including fungal hyphae, spores, bacteria, decaying plant material, unicellular algae, faeces, exuviae, carrion, living prey, and, in the case of surface-dwellers, pollen and living plant material. This unspecialized habit must not obscure the fact that the natural diet of a species is determined by what is available, and, in many cases, fungi and decaying plant material are the most common components. In addition, many species show certain preferences for a particular kind of food material, as indicated in Table 8.4, so that

TABLE 8.4. A summary of the feeding habits of some groups of soil Collembola (mainly after Christiansen, 1964).

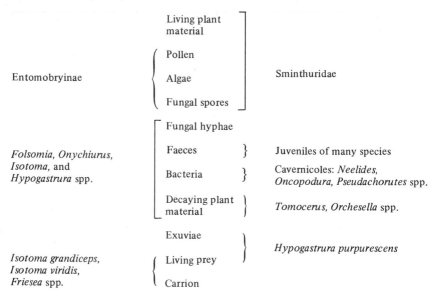

distinctions can be made not only between different species of the same genus, but, in certain cases, also between different individuals of the same species. For example, Poole (1959) found differences within the species *Folsomia quadrioculata,* some individuals preferring fungi, others selecting higher plant material. Sharma and Kevan (1963b) reported that *Folsomia similis* could be bred on a diet consisting of the leaves of sugar maple and elm, and yeasts, but that populations did not reproduce on a diet in which either the yeast or the higher plant material was lacking. In contrast, *Folsomia candida* could be reared successfully in the presence of only one of these two components. However, very specialized feeders are rare among the soil Collembola; phytophagous sminthurids may be included in this category together with certain carnivores, such as *Friesea* spp., which consume rotifers, Protura, and tardigrades. In some cases at least, the carnivorous habit may be facultative, as in *Pseudosinella alba,* which will thrive on decaying plant material and yeasts, but occasionally is cannibalistic on its own eggs (Sharma and Kevan, 1963c).

It is important to distinguish between what is ingested in the way of food and what is actually assimilated. There is strong evidence (Healey, 1965) that fungal feeders, such as *Onychiurus procampatus,* may be highly selective in their digestive processes, utilizing fats and carbohydrates present in the hyphae without interfering with the subsequent germinative powers of the fungus. It has also been suggested (see Christiansen, 1964) that bacteria may form an important source of food, as they do in the Protozoa and Nematoda. On the other hand, it is very probable that some bacteria live symbiotically in the gut of Collembola, and may assist in the digestive process. An example of this is a *Bacillus* sp. which is capable of digesting chitin, a substance which breaks down slowly under normal conditions, and there may be many other associations of this kind which have not yet been described. The fact that yeasts are an important component of the diet of successful breeding cultures indicates that these microflora contribute some essential principle, and emphasizes the selective nature of the digestive processes. The extent to which Collembola, and other soil animals, can utilize free amino-acids which are widely distributed in the soil is not known, but is obviously worth investigating. The absence of any discernible food material in the gut of Collembola which has been noted, for example, by Christiansen (1964), may be a reflection of a bacterial-feeding habit or, alternatively, of a fluid diet rich in these amino-acids. However, it must also be noted that some species of Collembola can survive for a period of 18 months, apparently without feeding, in a state of facultative diapause (Healey, 1965).

Life Cycles and Population Dynamics
In many Collembola, the length of the life cycle varies with the species and with the time of year at which eggs are deposited, but development to the adult stage occurs within the period of a year in most cases, and in some, two or more generations per year may be produced. Seasonal peaks in population density occur quite commonly, and evidence is accumulating to suggest that these peaks coincide with the appearance of a new generation of individuals. Before considering this topic further, we must digress to survey some aspects of the life cycle of these animals.

Life Cycle
(a) Sperm transfer. The transfer of sperm is usually effected without the active participation of the male, although some instances have been recorded (Willem, 1925, also quoted in Hale, 1965a) in the Isotomidae, in which direct transfer of sperm may take place while the genital regions of male and female are in

juxtaposition. Hale (1965a) noted a similar method of transfer in *Onychiurus tricampatus* and *O. furcifer*. More often, at least as far as the species studied to date are concerned, the males deposit sperm on the substratum, either in a stalked spermatophore, or as a free droplet, which is then taken up by the female accidentally or deliberately.

(b) Egg development. Observations on breeding cultures indicate that eggs are laid either singly, as, for example, in *Tomocerus minor, Dicyrtoma fusca,* and *D. minuta,* or more often in batches, for example, in *Hypogastrura denticulata, Onychiurus latus, Tullbergia krausbaueri, Isotoma sensibilis,* and *Lepidocyrtus lanuginosus,* in which the number of eggs per batch may vary from less than 5 to more than 100. Egg production is variable within the life of an individual female, and in species that reproduce before attaining maximum size, such as *Tullbergia krausbaueri,* the size of the egg batch produced by subadult instars is smaller than that of the adult. Recently, von Törne (1967) has shown that the rate of reproduction of laboratory populations may be influenced by the nutritional state which, in turn, is a function of the activity of the intestinal microflora. The importance of the nutritional factor as a population regulatory mechanism is considered in more detail in chapter 11.

The rate of the development of the egg to hatching is dependent on the species and on the temperature conditions. Eggs of *Hypogastrura armata,* cultured at 24°C, hatched in 8 days (Britt, 1951), but this is undoubtedly approaching the minimum period required. Under field conditions, development probably takes considerably longer than this in many species, particularly in northern Europe. Estimates for moorland populations in northern England, for example, range from one month or less in *Isotoma olivacea, I. infuscata,* and *Isotomurus palustris,* through one to two months in *Hypogastrura denticulata, Onychiurus procampatus, O. latus, O. tricampatus,* and *Tullbergia krausbaueri,* to four to six months in the case of winter eggs of *Dicyrtoma fusca* (Hale, 1965a).

(c) Post-embryonic development. The first-instar juvenile that hatches from the egg resembles the adult in general appearance, and has the full complement of six abdominal segments. It is smaller than the adult, and subsequent development occurs through a series of moults during which the body becomes progressively larger and more deeply pigmented. Changes also occur in the pattern of the setae and pseudocelli on the fifth abdominal segment, as one juvenile instar succeeds another. The absence of any marked metamorphosis often makes it difficult to determine the identity of a particular instar, and the distinction between juvenile stages is made on the basis of measurements of some part of the body, usually the length or width of the head. The adult stage is defined as that instar at which maximum size is attained, as a general rule, and this may or may not correspond to the stage in the life cycle at which reproduction first occurs. Information is often conflicting on this point, for Hale (1965b) observed that no eggs were laid before maximum size was achieved in

Onychiurus procampatus, O. latus, O. tricampatus, and *O. furcifer,* whereas Milne (1960) recorded the onset of reproductive activity in the instar immediately preceding that in which maximum size occurred, in this same group of species. Such activity apparently does occur in the last subadult instar in some cases, for example, in *Hypogastrura denticulata* and *Tullbergia krausbaueri,* and, furthermore, the number of instars occurring during development to maximum size varies from species to species. The attainment of maximum size does not signal the end of the moulting process, for the adult continues to moult without increasing in size, and Britt (1951) has recorded what is probably an extreme example of *Hypogastrura armata,* which becomes sexually mature in the third or fourth instar, undergoing 24 moults. Such extended adult moulting probably occurs only in overwintering adults which may live for a year. In those adults that die before winter, Agrell (1941) has suggested a life span of two months, which would allow for a much fewer number of adult moults, judging from the data available relating to the duration of the various instars (Table 8.5). The rate

TABLE 8.5. Average duration in days of instars of various species of Collembola at 15°C (compiled from data provided by Hale, 1965b).

Species	Instars					
	1	2	3	4	5	6
Hypogastrura denticulata	9·0	9·0	8·0	8·0	8·0	8·0
Tullbergia krausbaueri	10·5	10·2	13·2	14·4	13·7	13·9
Onychiurus latus	12·1	13·7	14·2	18·5	20·2	22·0
Onychiurus procampatus	13·7	14·2	16·0	17·7	20·9	18·7
Onychiurus tricampatus	10·5	11·2	12·0	12·7	18·7	
Onychiurus furcifer	10·7	11·5	11·1	11·3	12·8	14·0

of development to maximum size is influenced by the temperature conditions, at least in *Hypogastrura denticulata,* where an increase of 7°C, from 8°C to 15°C, more than halved the development time, according to Hale (1965b). Further, there is a progressive increase in the duration of the instars as development proceeds, the later instars occupying a greater proportion of the total development time than the earlier ones. This phenomenon (Table 8.5) appears to be a very common feature of the post-embryonic development of the Collembola. Once the adult stage is reached, the time interval between successive moults usually becomes rather irregular, although it does not differ too greatly from that of the later subadult instars.

In attempting to relate observations made on laboratory cultures to field populations, it must be remembered that the time of year at which eggs are laid will have an important bearing on their rate of development in the field. Development takes longer when hatching occurs in late summer and autumn than it does when eggs hatch in early summer (Table 8.6). In moorland populations, the minimum time to complete a life cycle under field conditions was 6 weeks—in *Tullbergia krausbaueri;* the maximum time 10 months—in *Onychiurus latus* (Hale, 1965b).

TABLE 8.6. Estimated times, in days, from hatching to development of maximum size in
moorland populations of Collembola (from Hale, 1965b).

Species	Hatching date					
	1 June	1 July	1 Aug.	1 Sept.	1 Oct.	1 Nov.
Hypogastrura denticulata	61	56	61	188	227	222
Tullbergia krausbaueri	50	45	49	67	212	209
Onychiurus procampatus	119	145	286	295	294	277
Onychiurus latus	170	285	304	308	304	291
Onychiurus tricampatus	91	91	224	266	266	254

(d) Breeding season. The considerable amount of information that has been
accumulated on the breeding biology of the Collembola clearly points to the
conclusion that, although there may be seasonal peaks in reproductive activity,
breeding may continue throughout the year in the majority of species. Occasional exceptions to this include members of the genus *Tomocerus* which are
univoltine, producing one generation annually during the spring (Bellinger,
1954). Hale (1965a) reported that egg-laying may occur during spring, summer,
and autumn in Pennine moorland and, although *Onychiurus procampatus, O.
tricampatus,* and *Tullbergia krausbaueri* extend oviposition over much of this
time, many species laid eggs during a restricted period. Under suitable conditions, two, three, and even more generations can be produced each year, even in
northern latitudes where cold winters occur (see, for example, Sharma and
Kevan, 1963a, 1963c).

Population dynamics

It has been well established that collembolan population peaks occur at various
times of the year. The magnitude, frequency, and timing of these peaks vary
with the locality and the length of the seasons. Although it may be meaningless
to generalize, in view of these sources of variation, many authors have reported
two well-defined peaks in European and North American localities, one occurring some time between February and June, the other in the August to
December period (Glasgow, 1939; Bellinger, 1954; Haarløv, 1960; Poole, 1961;
Dhillon and Gibson, 1962; Hale, 1966; Huhta *et al.*, 1967). Such peaks often
coincide with the appearance of the first-instar juvenile of a new generation (see,
for example, Hale, 1966), and since the majority of species in north temperate
localities produce two generations each year, and sometimes more, at least two
population density peaks during this period are to be expected. Local environmental factors obviously have an important influence on the timing of population peaks, and we have already noted that oviposition and the rate of
development of the egg to hatching varies with the temperature conditions. It is
to be expected, then, that populations in different localities will show different
phenological patterns, at least as far as the timing of the peaks is concerned.

In the case of univoltine species, hatching of eggs obviously provides recruitment for only one density peak; in the case of *Isotoma sensibilis* and *Tomocerus flavus*, this peak is in the spring or early summer (Hale, 1966; Bellinger, 1954). On the other hand, species populations producing two or more generations each year usually contribute to the early and late population peaks and may, under particularly favourable conditions, be responsible for subsidiary peaks at other times of the year. For example, Hale (1966) defined two groups of moorland species: those with spring and autumn density peaks, such as *Friesea mirabilis* and *Folsomia* spp., and those that reached peak densities in summer and early winter, as, for example, *Onychiurus* spp., *Tullbergia krausbaueri*, and *Isotomiella minor*. Some, at least, of the Symphypleona can produce summer and winter eggs, for example, *Dicyrtoma* spp. Evidently, the summer eggs develop much more rapidly than those laid in winter, for Dhillon and Gibson (1962) recorded two summer peaks (July and September), in addition to a population peak in March, in total Symphypleona of a Yorkshire grassland soil, and Hale (1966) suggested a summer peak in addition to spring and autumn peaks for this group in Pennine moorland.

The population declines that alternate with the peaks described above are frequently most marked in midwinter (January) and midsummer (July) in Europe and North America. The increased mortality at these times of the year is probably not due to any single factor, although predation by mesostigmatid mites is undoubtedly important. This topic is taken up again in more detail in chapter 11.

References

Agrell, I. (1941) 'Zur Ökologie der Collembolen. Untersuchungen im schwedischen Lappland', *Opusc. ent. suppl.*, **3**, 1-236.

Bellinger, P. F. (1954) 'Studies of soil fauna with special reference to the Collembola', *Bull. Conn. agric. Exp. Stan.*, **583**, 1-67.

Britt, N. W. (1951) 'Observations on the life history of the collembolan *Achorutes armatus*', *Trans. Amer. micr. Soc.*, **70**, 119-32.

Christiansen, K. (1964) 'Bionomics of Collembola', *A. Rev. Ent.*, **9**, 147-78.

Dhillon, B. S. and Gibson, N. H. E. (1962) 'A study of the Acarina and Collembola of agricultural soils. I. Numbers and distribution in undisturbed grassland', *Pedobiologia*, **1**, 189-209.

Drift, J. van der (1951) 'Analysis of the animal community in a beech forest floor', *Tijdschr. Ent.*, **94**, 1-168.

Dunger, W. (1964) *Tiere im Boden*, Ziemsen Verlag, Wittenberg Lutherstadt. 265 pp.

Engelmann, M. D. (1961) 'The role of soil arthropods in the energetics of an old field community', *Ecol. Monogr.*, **31**, 221-38.

Forsslund, K.-H. (1945) 'Sammanfattende översikt över vid markfauna-undersökningar i Västerbotten paträffode djurformer', *Meddn. St. SkogsförsAnst*, **34**, 341-64.

Gisin, H. (1960) *Collembolenfauna europas*, Mus. Hist. Nat., Geneva. 312 pp.

Glasgow, J. P. (1939) 'A population study of subterranean soil Collembola', *J. Anim. Ecol.*, **8**, 323-53.

Haarløv, N. (1955) 'Vertical distribution of mites and Collembola in relation to soil structure' in Kevan, D. K. McE., ed., *Soil zoology*, 167-79.

Haarløv, N. (1960) 'Microarthropods from Danish soils. Ecology, Phenology', *Oikos*, suppl. 3, 1-176.

Hale, W. G. (1963) 'The Collembola of eroding blanket bog' in Doeksen, J. and Drift, J. van der, eds., *Soil organisms*, 406-13.

Hale, W. G. (1965a) 'Observations on the breeding biology of Collembola', *Pedobiologia*, 5, 146-52, 161-77.

Hale, W. G. (1965b) 'Post-embryonic development in some species of Collembola', *Pedobiologia*, 5, 228-43.

Hale, W. G. (1966) 'A population study of moorland Collembola', *Pedobiologia*, 6, 65-99.

Hale, W. G. (1967) 'Collembola' in Burges, N. A. and Raw, F., eds., *Soil biology*, 397-411.

Healey, I. N. (1965) *Studies on the production biology of soil Collembola, with special reference to a species of* Onychiurus. Thesis, University of Wales.

Huhta, V., Karppinen, E., Nurminen, M., and Valpas, A. (1967) 'Effect of silvicultural practices upon arthropod, annelid and nematode populations in coniferous forest soil', *Ann. Zool. Fenn.*, 4, 87-143.

Janetschek, H. (1967) 'Arthropod ecology of South Victoria Land' in Gressitt, J. L., ed., *Entomology of Antarctica*, Antarctic Research Series, Amer. Geophys. U., 205-93.

Knight, C. (1961) 'The Tomocerinae in old field stands of North Carolina', *Ecology*, 42, 140-9.

Kühnelt, W. (1961) *Soil biology with special reference to the animal kingdom* (English edn, trans. Walker, N.), Faber, London. 397 pp.

Macfadyen, A. (1952) 'The small arthropods of a *Molinia* fen at Cothill', *J. Anim. Ecol.*, 21, 87-117.

Maynard, E. A. (1951) *A monograph of the Collembola or springtail insects of New York State*, Comstock, Ithaca. xxii + 339 pp.

Milne, S. (1960) 'Studies on the life histories of various species of Arthropleone Collembola', *Proc. R. ent. Soc. Lond.*, (*A*) 35, 133-40.

Milne, S. (1962) 'Phenology of a natural population of soil Collembola', *Pedobiologia*, 2, 41-52.

Moursi, A. (1962a) 'The attractiveness of CO_2 and N_2 to soil Arthropoda', *Pedobiologia*, 1, 299-302.

Moursi, A. (1962b) 'The lethal doses of CO_2, N_2, NH_3 and H_2S for soil Arthropoda', *Pedobiologia*, 2, 9-14.

Murphy, D. H. (1955) 'Long-term changes in Collembolan populations with special reference to moorland soils' in Kevan, D. K. McE., ed., *Soil zoology*, 157-66.

Noble-Nesbitt, J. (1963a) 'The fully formed intermoult cuticle and associated structures of *Podura aquatica* (Collembola)', *Quart. J. micr. Sci.*, 104, 253-70.

Noble-Nesbitt, J. (1963b) 'Transpiration in *Podura aquatica* L. (Collembola, Isotomidae) and the wetting properties of its cuticle', *J. exp. Biol.*, 40, 681-700.

Noble-Nesbitt, J. (1963c) 'A site of water and ionic exchange with the medium in *Podura aquatica* L. (Collembola, Isotomidae)', *J. exp. Biol.*, 40, 701-11.

Nosek, J. (1963) 'Zur Kenntnis der Apterygoten der kleinarpathischen Wald- und Dauergrünlandböden', *Pedobiologia*, 2, 108-31.

Ögel, S. (1958) *The integument of* Folsomia candida, Willem 1902 *(Collembola, Isotomidae)*. Thesis, University of London.

Poole, T. B. (1959) 'Studies on the food of Collembola in a Douglas fir plantation', *Proc. zool. Soc. Lond.*, 132, 71-82.

Poole, T. B. (1961) 'An ecological study of the Collembola in a coniferous forest soil', *Pedobiologia*, 1, 113-37.

Poole, T. B. (1963) 'The effect of some environmental factors on the pattern of distribution of soil Collembola in a coniferous woodland', *Pedobiologia*, 2, 169-82.

Pryor, M. E. (1962) 'Some environmental features of Hallett Station, Antarctica, with special reference to soil arthropods', *Pacif. Insects*, 4, 681-728.

Raw, F. (1956) 'The abundance and distribution of Protura in grassland', *J. Anim. Ecol.*, 25, 15-21.

Ruppel, H. (1953) 'Untersuchungen über die Bedeutung des Ventraltubus und die Atmung der Collembolan'. *Zool. Jb. (Allg. Zool.)* 64, 429-69.

Schaller, F. (1949) 'Zur Okologie der Collembolen in Kalksteinböden (nebst einigen Bemerkungen über Proturen)', *Zool. Jb. (Syst.)*, 78, 263-93.

Sharma, G. D. and Kevan, D. K. McE. (1963a) 'Observations on *Isotoma notabilis* (Collembola: Isotomidae) in Eastern Canada', *Pedobiologia*, 3, 34-47.

Sharma, G. D. and Kevan, D. K. McE. (1963b) 'Observations on *Folsomia similis* (Collembola: Isotomidae) in Eastern Canada', *Pedobiologia*, 3, 48-61.

Sharma, G. D. and Kevan, D. K. McE. (1963c) 'Observations on *Pseudosinella petterseni* and *Pseudosinella alba* (Collembola: Entomobryidae) in Eastern Canada', *Pedobiologia*, 3, 62-74.

Sharma, G. D. and Kevan, D. K. McE. (1965) 'The mouthparts of Collembola', *Proc. XII Int. Congr. Ent.*, p. 142.

Strenzke, K. (1949) 'Ökologische Studien über die Collembolengesellschaften feuchter Böden Ost-Holsteins', *Arch. Hydrobiol.*, 42, 201-303.

Sturm, H. (1959) 'Die Nahrung der Proturen', *Naturwissenschaften*, 46, 90-1.

Törne, E. von (1961) 'Ökologische Experimente mit *Folsomia candida* (Collembola)', *Pedobiologia*, 1, 146-9.

Törne, E. von (1967) 'Beispiele fur mikrobiogene Einflüsse auf den Massenwechsel von Bodentieren', *Pedobiologia*, 7, 296-305.

Tuxen, S. L. (1949) 'Über den Lebenszyklus und die postembryonale Entwicklung zweier dänischer Proturengattungen', *Biol. Skr.*, 6, 1-50.

Tuxen, S. L. (1965) *The Protura*, Herman, Paris. 360 pp.

Weis-Fogh, T. (1948) 'Ecological investigations on mites and collemboles in the soil', *Natura jutl.*, 1, 135-270.

Willem, V. (1925) 'Notes ethologiques sur divers Collemboles', *Bull. Acad. r. Belg. Cl. Sci.*, 5, 617-36.

Wood, T. G. (1967) 'Acari and Collembola of moorland soils from Yorkshire, England. II. Vertical distribution in four grassland soils', *Oikos*, 18, 137-40.

Zinkler, D. (1966) 'Vergleichende Untersuchungen zur Atmungsphysiologie von Collembolen (Apterygota) und anderen Bodenkleinarthropoden', *Z. vergl. Physiol.*, 52, 99-144.

9. Arachnida

The arachnids are predatory arthropods, for the most part, often occurring in vegetation, on the soil surface, and in loose leaf litter. To this group belong the scorpions (Scorpiones), sunspiders (Solifugae), spiders (Araneida), harvestmen (Opiliones), pseudoscorpions (Chelonethi), mites (Acari), and a few rare groups which need not concern us here. The mites are unusual among the arachnids in that they include saprophagous and phytophagous forms, in addition to predatory species, and the Order Cryptostigmata is composed almost entirely of detritivores and fungivores. These mites are much more intimately associated with the decomposition processes occurring in the soil, than some other arachnids, and much of this chapter is devoted to an account of their ecology. However, we start with some observations on the biology of the surface-dwelling predators.

Scorpiones and Solifugae

There are striking ecological similarities between these two groups, both of which are widely distributed in warm, dry tropical and subtropical habitats. They are nocturnal or crepuscular and live, during the day, under rocks, in crevices, or in burrow systems in the soil which, in the case of the solifugid *Galeodes arabs* and the scorpion *Leiurus quinquestriatus,* may extend for several metres horizontally or in an inclined direction (Cloudsley-Thompson, 1961a and b). They are highly mobile, extremely voracious predators, feeding on a wide variety of surface-dwelling insects and arachnids, as well as small vertebrates, such as lizards, mice, and birds; they also feed, cannibalistically, on members of their own kind. Lawrence (1965) reported that solifugids prey extensively on termites. In both scorpions and solifugids, well-developed chelicerae and pedipalps are used to secure the prey, and the former group possess an additional weapon in the poisonous sting, which can paralyse or kill in a short time. The sting of some scorpions, such as the African *Leiurus quinquestriatus* and *Androctonus australis,* and the North American *Centrurus* spp., is often lethal to humans. The ecology of these arachnid groups has been little studied from the point of view of their effects on the soil community, although they may form important consumer elements in desert ecosystems.

Araneida
Composition of the fauna
There is a considerable volume of literature concerning the biology of spiders

(see, for example, the general accounts by Cloudsley-Thompson, 1958, and Savoury, 1964), although much of it is incidental to our theme, since many species are not true soil-dwelling forms. A close association with the soil community may be established by members of such groups as the Lycosidae, Linyphiidae, Gnaphosidae, Tetragnathidae, Clubionidae, Theridiidae, and Agelenidae, but the extent of their participation and the effects of their predations on soil-dwelling animals have not been critically examined. The taxonomy of the group presents no formidable problems, and identification keys by Locket and Millidge (1951, 1953) and Kaston (1953) are useful for this purpose.

Distribution
Spiders are frequently found in open situations and, in contrast to the scorpions and sunspiders, are cosmopolitan in distribution and well represented in the temperate fauna. Grasslands often support a rich spider fauna, and Duffey (1962) recorded 141 species from a limestone grassland, of which more than half were restricted to the lower parts of the vegetation and the ground surface. About 40 per cent of this total comprised members of the Linyphiidae, a group equally well represented in the litter of oak woodland in south-western England (Gabbutt, 1956). Evidently, this family has a predominantly Arctic and sub-Arctic distribution, and in cold, wet moorland, the representation of Linyphiidae may be as much as 73 per cent of the total spider fauna (Cherrett, 1964b). Under forest conditions, with little or no field layer developed, ground-dwelling forms predominate and are often small in body size. For example, van der Drift (1951) found that the Agelenid *Hahnia helveola*, a species little more than 2 mm in length, was most abundant in a beech forest floor, among a spider fauna which also included representatives of the families Theridiidae, Linyphiidae, Lycosidae, Micryphantidae, Gnaphosidae, and Clubionidae.

There is considerable evidence that the distribution of species populations in small areas is governed by distinct preferences for certain microhabitat conditions, although the exact limiting mechanisms are not always easy to define. For example, Vlijm and Kessler-Geschiere (1967) noted that three species of the lycosid genus *Pardosa* preferred habitats that differed markedly in the amount of moisture present. Thus, *P. pullata* was most abundant in the ground layer of damp sites, *P. nigriceps* in the vegetation of *Salix repens-Carex arenaria* scrub, and *P. monticola* in dry barren sites. In the case of the Linyphiidae, however, habitat specificity may be correlated to the distribution of potential prey, although members of this family show a stratified distribution in vegetation, different species being abundant at different levels. This suggests that the form of the vegetation may also be an important factor in the habitat of these hammock-web spiders (Cherrett, 1964b). The interpretation of the pattern of microdistribution is complicated, in some cases, by the changes in preference that may occur during the course of development. Habitat preference may also differ in the two sexes, and may also be influenced by the reproductive condition of the females. Vlijm and Kessler-Geschiere (1967) noted that in the various sites in which the three *Pardosa* species mentioned above were commonest, the ratio of males to females was lower than in less densely populated sites (Table 9.1), indicating that males may have dispersed to less densely

TABLE 9.1. Comparisons between sex ratios in 'typical' and 'non-typical' areas for three species of the spider genus *Pardosa* (from Vlijm and Kessler-Geschiere, 1967). 'Typical' sites are italicized.

	Numbers		Ratio
	Males	Females	Males:females
Pardosa pullata			
The Pool (marsh)	2347	1042	2·3
Pullata-meadow	339	206	1·6
Nigriceps-dunes	211	45	4·7
P. nigriceps			
The Pool (marsh)	94	18	5·2
Nigriceps-dunes	159	41	3·9
P. monticola			
The Pool (marsh)	309	20	15·5
Monticola-field	542	164	3·3

populated areas after copulation. Females carrying egg sacs also preferred more exposed sites than non-gravid females, at least in the case of *P. pullata* and *P. nigriceps*. A similar pattern of behaviour is also shown by another lycosid, *Pirata piraticus* (Nørgaard, 1951).

Population Dynamics

Maximum population densities of spiders have been noted during the summer and autumn by several workers (Bristowe, 1939; Gabbutt, 1956; Duffey, 1962; Cherrett, 1964a); minimum densities have been reported during winter, although Cherrett (1964a) described a February peak for the Linyphiidae of an English moorland. Summer peaks must be interpreted with caution, for they may reflect the greater activity of the spiders during the warmer weather which would, of course, result in higher captures at this time. On the other hand, summer peaks for Linyphiidae may include a preponderance of immatures (up to 92 per cent in some cases), which suggests that these peaks represent true increases in density resulting from hatching of eggs (Fig. 9.1).

A rather different picture has been described for populations of the lycosids *Pardosa monticola, P. nigriceps,* and *P. pullata* on the dunes of the Friesian island of Schiermonnikoog, studied by Vlijm and Kessler-Geschiere (1967). In these cases, adults appeared in May, and the early summer population peak (in June) coincided with the copulation period. One or two subsequent peaks may occur later in the summer, despite the progressive decrease in the number of adult males during this period. Adult females make a large contribution to these peaks, for juveniles occurred in low densities during the summer. The peaks for juveniles occurred in the autumn and again in the spring, at times when the adult populations were generally low. These observations contrast with those of Gabbutt (1956), Duffey (1962), and Cherrett (1964a), who recorded minimum percentages of adults during July and August. Clearly, there is a good deal of variability in the phenology of different spider populations not only from

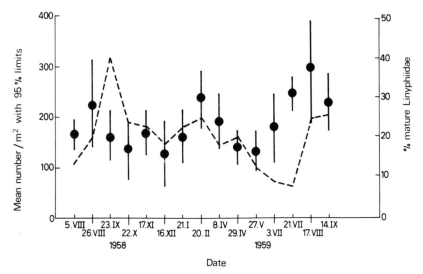

FIGURE 9.1. Seasonal changes in density and maturity of Linyphiidae on *Calluna/ Eriophorum* (percentage matures indicated by broken line) (from Cherrett, 1964a).

species to species, but also from locality to locality. In colder climates, where the winter season is long, the rate of development to maturity is slow and may take up to two years. Cherrett (1964a) has suggested that this may be the cause of the weak density fluctuations and the lack of evidence of seasonal maturity among some English Linyphiidae.

Opiliones

Twenty different species of harvestmen, belonging to the three families Trogulidae, Nemastomatidae, and Phalangiidae, occur in Britain, and may be identified with the key provided by Savoury (1948). According to this author, 14 of these are generally distributed wherever fallen leaves accumulate in moist situations. Members of the family Trogulidae, recognizable by their relatively short legs, are restricted to chalky soils, and may often be encountered in beech litter where they feed on snails.

Ground-dwelling harvestmen, particularly members of the families Trogulidae and Nemastomatidae, are often more abundant in woodland than in open field. Todd (1949) and Sankey (1949) drew attention to the fact that many of these forms undergo a change of habitat during development, leaving the ground and migrating vertically upwards into the vegetation. However, this has been interpreted by Williams (1962) as a spread of the population, rather than a movement away from the ground surface. On the other hand, *Oligolophus agrestis, O. tridens,* and *Odiellus palpinalis* have a closer association with the soil than has, for example, *Leiobunum blackwalli,* and populations of these species may reverse their tendency to migrate, or expand, upwards during the late summer and autumn when the ground vegetation dies back.

The work of Todd (1949), Sankey (1949), and Phillipson (1959) has shown that life histories of British harvestmen can be classified into three types. In the first of these, typified by *Nemastoma lugubre,* the life cycle takes more than a year to complete, and there is an overlap of generations. Williams (1962) noted that this species showed population peaks in July and October which evidently corresponded to two breeding phases (Phillipson, 1959). Species included within the second type, such as *Platybunus triangularis,* overwinter as juveniles. Members of this category probably breed earlier than the majority of harvestmen, which comprise the third category and overwinter as eggs.

All of the species mentioned above are widely distributed in Britain. Other commonly occurring species include *Mitopus morio,* which has two well-defined varieties; an upland form (*M. morio alpinus*), in which the males possess tibial spines; and *M. morio cinerascens,* in which such spines are lacking, *Phalangium opilio,* one of the largest British species, and *Megabunus diadema,* an inhabitant of hilly and moorland areas, and easily identified by the form of the ocular tubercle which bears a series of radiating spikes.

Although harvestmen may be active throughout the 24-hour cycle, peak periods of activity occur at night. For example, *Mitopus morio* feeds mainly at night, according to Phillipson (1960), although it is less restricted to nocturnalism than *Oligolophus tridens.* This difference between these two species is emphasized when their respiration rates during the day and night are compared (see Table 13.1); the more nocturnal, *O. tridens,* shows a much greater difference between day and night rates than does *M. morio.*

Williams (1962) noted that activity patterns, distribution, and the type of life history may be associated together. The species most susceptible to desiccation tend to be more closely associated with the soil throughout the year, are most clearly nocturnal, and often overwinter as an active stage; such is the case with *Nemastoma lugubre.* Species which extend their activity periods into the day, such as *Phalangium opilio,* are more common in the vegetation above the soil, and are less active in winter.

Harvestmen are predacious and undoubtedly find much of their prey among the soil fauna. Phillipson (1960) noted that *Mitopus morio* fed readily on such soil-dwellers as *Campodea* sp., *Sciara* sp., carabid larvae, and small specimens of *Lithobius* sp., but would also feed with equal readiness on a variety of insects living above the ground. It is probable that these arachnids function as tertiary consumers, as far as the soil community is concerned, although the precise effects of their predations on soil populations are largely unknown. On the other hand, some species of harvestmen suffer from the attentions of certain mites which, as adults, live in the soil, and produce larvae which are ectoparasitic. The bright red larval forms of mites belonging to the families Trombidiidae and Erythraeidae may often be found attached to the body, and particularly the legs, of such species as *Mitopus morio, Phalangium opilio,* and *Megabunus diadema;* infestations of these mites in cultures will frequently cause the death of the host. To what extent this association regulates the size of populations of harvestmen under natural conditions is not known.

Chelonethi

Pseudoscorpions are often found in moist, decaying vegetation lying on the soil surface and, although they are not generally abundant, they may be recorded regularly from samples of forest litter and from the crevices under bark or in rocks. Evans and Browning (1954) have provided a key to the identification of the 26 species occurring in Britain and Ireland, of which *Chthonius tetrachelatus, C. ischnocheles, Neobisium muscorum, Cheiridium museorum, Toxochernes panzeri,* and *Lamprochernes nodosus* are widely distributed.

Distribution

The biology of the pseudoscorpions presents a number of interesting aspects, not the least of which is the phoretic behaviour which enables some species to move easily from one site to another attached to flying insects, such as Diptera and Hymenoptera. Such behaviour may account for the distribution of a number of species in a variety of habitats unconnected with the soil, for example, in the nests of birds and mammals and invertebrates, and in human habitations and farm buildings. However, some distinction can be made between the pseudoscorpion fauna of these various habitats. For example, members of the genera *Chthonius* and *Neobisium* are rarely encountered outside the soil, whereas *Chernes cimicoides,* and *Chelifer cancroides* are more often to be found under the bark of trees (Ressl and Beier, 1958). However, the fauna of soil and bark crevices overlaps to some extent, as the data presented in Table 9.2 show.

TABLE 9.2. The distribution of six species of pseudoscorpion in soil and bark crevices (from Ressl and Beier, 1958).

Species	In soil per mille	In bark crevices per mille
Toxochernes panzeri	994·9	5·1
Neobisium muscorum	994·7	5·3
Neobisium sylvaticum	925·4	74·6
Dactylochelifer latreillei	382·7	617·3
Chelifer cancroides	81·0	919·0
Chernes cimicoides	12·3	987·7

Population Biology and Reproductive Activity

Pseudoscorpions reproduce mainly during the spring, summer, and autumn in the north temperate region. According to Ressl and Beier (1958), soil-dwelling forms, such as members of the genera *Chthonius* and *Neobisium,* have a restricted period of reproductive activity, ranging in duration from one to four months, during which time the appearance of nymphal stages may be continuous, as in *Chthonius* spp., or discontinuous, as in most *Neobisium* species. In the case of bark-dwellers, such as *Apocheiridium ferum, Chernes cimicoides,* and *Chelifer cancroides,* nymphal stages may overwinter successfully along with the adults. Overwintering nymphs, mainly deutonymphs and tritonymphs, have also been recorded for soil-dwelling populations of *Chthonius ischnocheles* (Gabbutt and Vachon, 1963; Gabbutt, 1967), *Neobisium muscorum* (Gabbutt and Vachon, 1965), and *Roncus lubricus* (Gabbutt and Vachon, 1967). The phenology of individual species populations is difficult to describe in many cases, owing to the habit of pseudoscorpions of overwintering in silken chambers, during which time the animals are difficult to collect, for they are not susceptible to the usual extraction techniques, and frequently are well camouflaged in their retreats. This fact may explain, in part, the low population densities of all stages recorded during the winter, although the possibility must not be discounted that migrations to more sheltered locations may also be responsible to some extent.

The course of population fluctuations during the remainder of the year apparently varies from species to species and from habitat to habitat. Thus, Ressl and Beier (1958) in Europe and Gasdorf and Goodnight (1963) in North America detected two periods of peak density of total pseudoscorpion numbers, the early one in spring (Europe) or early summer (North America) and the late one in autumn. In the European populations, the larger of the two peaks occurred in autumn (Fig. 9.2), whereas the reverse was true of the North American populations. The fact that nymphal stages were abundant at the times of peak populations suggests that many species had two periods of reproduction per year (Ressl and Beier, 1958), and Godfrey (1910) postulated distinct spring and autumn broods for *Chthonius ischnocheles,* although more recent studies on this species (Gabbutt and Vachon, 1963; Gabbutt, 1967) showed that there was only one population peak per year on sites in southern England— during the summer. Adults reached peak density in July, and these forms belonged to two different generations: first, the generation produced during the previous summer and overwintering either as nymphs or recently mature adults, and second, adults belonging to a previous generation which had already bred the previous year. Protonymphal peaks occurred during August or September, and some representatives of this stage persisted as overwintering stages. However, protonymphs, produced during the early part of the summer, probably completed development to deutonymphs, tritonymphs, and, in a few cases, adults which also overwintered. Since adult pseudoscorpions may live for from two to five years, it is likely that adults of different ages in the same population,

reproducing at different times during the summer season, account for the occurrence of more than one population peak per year described by other workers,
particularly when total numbers of all species, rather than individual populations, are being considered.

On the other hand, local environmental conditions may play an important
part in determining the frequency and timing of peak populations, as is evidently
the case in populations of *Neobisium muscorum*. In south-western England, this

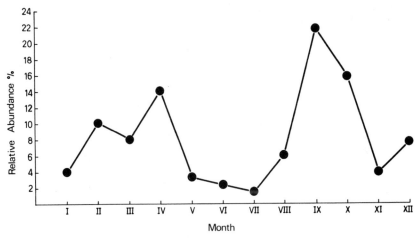

FIGURE 9.2. Fluctuations in pseudoscorpion populations over a yearly period (from Ressl
and Beier, 1958).

species has spring and autumn generations, whereas only the autumn generation
occurred in populations in the northern part of England. Possibly, the duration
of the previous winter may be an important influence on the frequency and
timing of density peaks.

Differing interpretations of the winter decline in pseudoscorpion populations
have been presented by Ressl and Beier (1958) and Gabbutt (1967). The former
workers place particular emphasis on winter mortality resulting from exposure
to conditions of low temperature, whereas the latter author attributes the winter
decline to hibernation and/or migration by nymphal stages, citing, as evidence
for low winter mortality in *Chthonius ischnocheles* populations, the fact that the
difference between nymphal densities in autumn and the following spring is
slight. In addition, Gabbutt estimated that the total prewinter mortality is at
least 85 per cent, and that protonymphal populations have suffered at least 50
per cent mortality before the onset of winter. This suggests that predation or
cannibalism may be important in regulating the growth of the population.

Feeding Habits
The food of pseudoscorpions consists of litter-dwelling arthropods, such as
Collembola, small insects, myriapods, and arachnids, and also enchytraeids. In

cultures, these predators have been observed to attack and consume mesostigmatid mites of the genus *Veigaia* (Wallwork, 1957), large Collembola, such as
Tomocerus longicornis, enchytraeids, and other pseudoscorpions of smaller size.
Although the large chelate pedipalps may be used initially to seize the prey and
narcotize with an injection from the poison gland carried on these organs, the
chelicerae are used to pierce the integument of the prey, and once an entry has
been effected, these mouth-parts move backwards and forwards, thereby

FIGURE 9.3. *Serianus* sp., a pseudoscorpion collected from *Juniperus* litter, Mojave Desert,
California. The dark-coloured contents of the opisthosoma are probably endodermal silk
gland (photo by author).

assisting in the imbibition of the liquid food. During the feeding process, the
pedipalps relinquish their hold on the prey and are held in readiness to ward off
any attackers. Like many arachnids, pseudoscorpions can survive for long
periods in the absence of food, but when prey is secured, feeding may take place
continuously over a period of hours. Although cannibalism appears to be less
common than in the spiders, scorpions, and solifugids, it does occur sometimes,
as, for example, in *Chelifer cancroides* (Ressl and Beier, 1958).

In view of their low numbers and scattered distribution, pseudoscorpions
probably have little effect upon populations of detritus-feeding animals in the
soil. Apparently, they are not preyed upon extensively by other carnivores, and
may be regarded as tertiary consumers occupying the terminal stage of the

detritovore/predator food chain. The ecological importance of this role is probably greatest in ecosystems with a simple community structure such as occur, for example, in desert localities. The species illustrated in Fig. 9.3 is one such desert-dwelling form.

Acari

Mites are the commonest, although not the most conspicuous representatives of the mesofauna in most soils, and are particularly abundant in highly organic woodland and forest sites. This is a very large and diverse group which, in addition to being well represented in the soil, has colonized a variety of terrestrial situations, such as the aerial parts of herbaceous and woody vegetation, rock crevices, the nests of various invertebrates, birds, and mammals, human habitations and decaying refuse. The group also includes many successful endo- and ectoparasites, such as ticks and members of the Mesostigmata, Prostigmata, and Astigmata, and also marine and freshwater forms. A recent estimate of the total number of known mites and ticks exceeds 17 000 (Wharton, 1964), and this probably represents only a small fraction of the total world fauna.

Composition of the Fauna

In the main, soil Acari belong to one of four Orders, namely the Mesostigmata, Prostigmata, Astigmata, and the Cryptostigmata (Fig. 9.4). A general account of the taxonomy of all of these groups has been given by Baker and Wharton (1952), although more recent keys have concentrated on particular groups. For example, Evans (1957) has compiled a key to the families and genera of British Mesostigmata, and Balogh (1961, 1963, 1965) has used the scheme of classification developed by Grandjean (1953) as the basis for identification keys to genera and families of Cryptostigmata. Several hundred families of mites are represented in the soil fauna, and the taxonomy of many of these groups is still incompletely worked out and must remain, for the present, the task of the specialist. General accounts of the biology of the Acari have been prepared by Hughes (1959), Evans *et al.* (1961), Wallwork (1967a); one international journal, *Acarologia,* devotes itself exclusively to this group of arthropods.

The Mesostigmata and Prostigmata include both predatory and detritus-feeding forms; the Cryptostigmata are primarily detritus-feeders. The Astigmata are not generally abundant in soils, although they may occur in local concentrations, particularly in pasture and arable soils (Sheals, 1956), sometimes as resting 'hypopial' stages. The feeding habits of this group are not well known, although it is probable that their diet includes plant detritus, fungi, algae, bacteria, and the liquefied products of decomposition processes.

Horizontal Distribution

Little is known of the factors which influence the distribution of predatory Mesostigmata and Prostigmata, although the distribution of prey animals is obviously important. For example, the mesostigmatid Macrochelidae are most

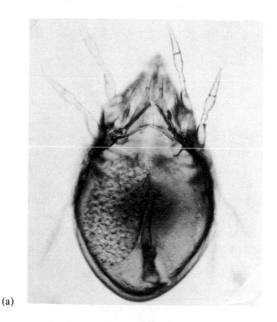

(a)

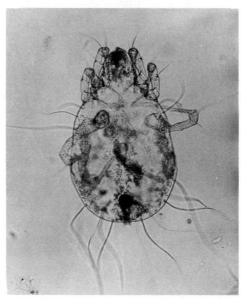

(b)

FIGURE 9.4. Representatives of four common Orders of soil-inhabiting mites: (a) **Cryptostigmata**; (b) Astigmata; (c) Prostigmata; (d) Mesostigmata (photos by author).

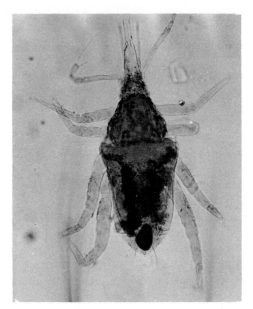

(c)

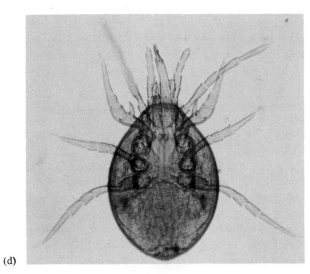

(d)

FIGURE 9.4 contd.

abundant in compost heaps and manure piles which harbour rich populations of nematodes and insect eggs on which these mites feed. Prostigmata are less common in these sites, and evidently are more frequent in true soils, particularly those of a highly organic nature. This group is richly represented by phyto-phagous and predatory forms in the vegetation layer above the ground, where the distribution is clearly influenced by the distribution of host plants and animals. Some of these mites, such as *Bryobia praetiosa*, may find their way into the soil from time to time, although they can never be regarded as more than transients in this environment. Certain of the mesostigmatid predators are phoretic on Diptera and Coleoptera frequenting dung and compost, and a similar habit is shown by the hypopial stages of astigmatid Acarid mites. The latter favour moist, highly organic sites, although they have also been recovered from soils with a high mineral content, such as those under cultivation (Sheals, 1956), and in desert areas. This distribution in a range of soil types may be a reflection of the distribution of the insects and myriapods to which these phoretic forms become attached.

Much of what has been said earlier about the macrodistribution of the Collembola, can also be applied to the Cryptostigmata, for the ecological requirements of these two groups show some striking similarities, particularly with regard to the dependence on saturated relative humidity conditions. Many of these mites may be considered as mesophilous, and flourish in the moist organic soils under woodland and forest. A number of groups, however, have representatives inhabiting more exposed sites above ground, in lichens, moss, and tree bark. This xerophyl element includes members of the genera *Liodes, Eupelops, Platyliodes, Humerobates, Carabodes, Cepheus,* and *Galumna* among others. At the other extreme, are the truly aquatic Hydrozetidae and Limnozetidae.

Species of Cryptostigmata differ in their ability to tolerate different levels of certain environmental factors, such as moisture content, organic content, and, possibly, pH. The extent to which an environmental factor can vary within the tolerance zone of a species is termed the 'ecological valence' of the species; this can be given a numerical value, calculated from the known distribution of the species in a range of habitats (Strenzke, 1952). The higher the ecological valence, the more widespread is the distribution of the species in these habitats, and, clearly, ecological tolerance has an important bearing on the horizontal distribu-tion pattern. An example of this, taken from the study of Karppinen (1955a) on Finnish Camisiidae, is illustrated in Fig. 9.5. It shows that, by considering not one but several factors in conjunction, it is possible to determine which particular factor or combination of factors is limiting for the distribution of the species. Thus, *Heminothrus thori* has the lowest valence in this example, being restricted to wet, highly organic soils with a relatively high pH, such as fenland. *Nothrus silvestris* represents the opposite extreme, with a wide tolerance to variations in soil moisture content, pH, and the amount of organic material present. *Platynothrus peltifer* is able to tolerate a range of pH conditions, but is limited to moist or wet organic soils.

Finally, it is generally true that Cryptostigmata are relatively sparse in cultivated soils, where continual mixing of mineral and topsoil produces an unstable and poorly structured profile. These mites prefer the environment provided by undisturbed organic layers lying on the surface of the mineral soil under woody vegetation. In such situations, Cryptostigmata are relatively more abundant than Collembola in raw humus under conifers, while Collembola increase in relative importance under deciduous forest and grassland.

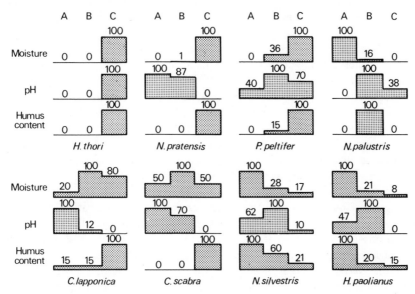

FIGURE 9.5. Ecological valence of some common Camisiidae from Finland, with regard to soil moisture, pH, and humus content. Column A represents dry soil, pH = 4, low humus content; column B moist soil, pH = 4-5, moderate humus content, column C wet soil, pH greater than 5, high humus content. The genera *Heminothrus, Nothrus, Platynothrus* and *Camisia* are represented (after Karppinen, 1955a).

Vertical Distribution

The species composition of the acarine fauna varies with depth in the soil, the larger forms, such as the cryptostigmatid *Steganacarus magnus, Oppia ornata, Damaeus onustus, Adoristes ovatus, Platynothrus peltifer,* and *Achipteria coleoptrata,* and the mesostigmatid *Trachytes* spp. and the predatory *Macrocheles, Parasitus,* and *Pergamasus* sp., being more common in the surface litter than the deeper layers. Medium-sized and smaller forms, such as the cryptostigmatid *Tectocepheus velatus, Scheloribates* spp., *Oppia* spp., *Suctobelba* spp., and *Brachychthonius* spp., which are common in European and North American localities, have a more general distribution in the profile, and penetrate into the humus and even the upper zone of the mineral soil. However, the fauna of the mineral layer is usually an impoverished one and consists, in the main, of small

Oppia and *Suctobelba* species, together with the mesostigmatid *Rhodacarus* sp., small trombidiform Prostigmata, and immature mites, which are usually concentrated in the biologically active zone, the rhizosphere, around plant roots. Clearly, the diameter of the soil spaces is an important limiting factor in the depth distribution of the soil Acari, as it is in the case of Collembola, and, here again, the richest fauna occurs in the top 6 cm of the profile with strong concentrations in the fermentation zone, or the region of intergradation between the litter and humus. Species often common in this zone include the cryptostigmatid *Hypochthonius rufulus, Nanhermannia* spp., *Nothrus silvestris, Oppia ornata, Phthiracarus borealis, Rhysotritia* spp., *Belba* spp., and the mesostigmatid Zerconidae and Digamasellidae (Wallwork, 1967a).

The rather general distribution of many of the medium-sized and smaller species in the soil profile may be a reflection of their ability to undertake vertical migrations. Both long-term (seasonal) and short-term (diurnal) movements occur among the Cryptostigmata (Wallwork, 1959; Tarras-Wahlberg, 1961; Wallwork and Rodriguez, 1961), and these probably occur as a response to changing temperature or moisture conditions in the litter. For example, it has been noted that many of the species present in the litter and fermentation layers during the summer, such as the cryptostigmatid *Nothrus silvestris, N. pratensis, Scheloribates laevigatus,* and *Oppia nova,* decrease in numbers in these layers during the winter, while their numbers increase in the humus at this time. This has been interpreted as a sign of a downward movement from litter into humus at the onset of winter (van der Drift, 1951; Karppinen, 1955b; Wallwork, 1959), although apparently this movement is not universal among the Cryptostigmata (Lebrun, 1964b). Diurnal movements are more difficult to explain, for these take such species as the cryptostigmatid *Scheloribates laevigatus, Galumna* spp. *Eupelops* spp., and *Diapterobates humeralis* out of the litter of pasture soil into the aerial parts of the vegetation. Such movements are of considerable importance to the livestock farmer, since some of these mites can act as intermediate hosts for the anoplocephalid tapeworms of sheep, cattle, and horses (Rajski, 1960).

Humidity and Temperature Reactions

The ability to survive away from the soil requires some waterproofing device. This applies not only to the mites which undertake short-term sorties into the aerial vegetation, but also to those that regularly inhabit the surface litter which may be rather drier than the deeper humus and mineral soil. Although the Cryptostigmata are more generally restricted to the soil than the other groups of mites, a number of species live, more or less permanently, in exposed sites in lichens, moss, and tree bark.

The varying habitat preferences shown by the Cryptostigmata reflect a differing ability to counter the desiccating effect of a non-saturated atmosphere, and represent a gradation of physiological adaptation to a truly terrestrial existence. For instance, Madge (1964a, b, and c) demonstrated that a waterproof cuticular layer of wax was present in *Belba geniculosa* (= *Damaeus onustus*), *Carabodes labyrinthicus*, *Humerobates rostrolamellatus*, *Euzetes globulus*, *Steganacarus magnus*, *Platynothrus peltifer*, and *Fuscozetes fuscipes*; all of these species normally live above the ground or in the upper litter layers. No such waterproofing was present in the deeper-living *Hypochthonius rufulus* and *Nanhermannia nana*. These studies also showed that the critical temperature of the wax layer varied with the species, such that the melting point was higher in *H. rostrolamellatus* and *C. labyrinthicus*, which normally live in habitats subject to large ambient temperature and relative humidity changes, than in litter-dwellers living in more equable conditions. In parallel with the Collembola, species inhabiting exposed situations generally have a better developed tracheal system than the soil-dwellers, and can afford to have a more efficient water-proofing layer in the body cuticle. In the case of species which lack a tracheal system, respiration takes place over the body surface generally; the presence of a wax layer would inhibit this process. The relationship between the development of an efficient tracheal system, the development of a wax layer in the cuticle, and the ability to colonize a variety of habitats outside the soil is well illustrated by Madge's work.

The possession of a waterproofed cuticle does not, of course, confer complete immunity from the vagaries of the environment. Water loss occurs from the tracheae during respiration, through the mouth during feeding, and via the faeces, and, unless this loss is controlled, death due to desiccation may result. In general, this control is achieved by behavioural reactions which cause the mites to seek saturated relative humidity conditions, and the intensity of the reaction is influenced by the water content of the body. For example, Madge (1964b) noted that the arboreal *Humerobates rostrolamellatus*, which has a well-developed wax layer in the cuticle, initially preferred low humidity conditions, when offered a choice, but reversed this to a preference for moist conditions after one-third of the body weight had been lost. *Belba geniculosa* showed an initial preference for moist conditions, and this reaction intensified if members of this species had previously been desiccated to the point at which one-twenty-fifth of the body weight was lost. Compared with *H. rostrolamellatus*, *B. geniculosa* is much less tolerant of water loss, and this difference can again be related to differences in the natural distribution patterns of these two species.

In another series of experiments, too detailed to be described in full, Madge (1965a and b) investigated temperature preferences and survival under extreme temperature conditions of the same species of cryptostigmatid mites that were used in the humidity studies discussed above. Here again, relationships could be established between the behaviour of the mites and their natural distribution patterns. For example, the xerophyl *Humerobates rostrolamellatus* and *Carabodes labyrinthicus* reached thermal death points at $43°$-$44°C$ and $41°$-$42.5°C$, respectively, compared with $28°$-$36.5°C$ and $31°$-$40°C$ for the intolerant *Hypochthonius rufulus* and *Nanhermannia nana*, respectively. Thermal death points for litter-dwelling *Belba geniculosa, Platynothrus peltifer,* and *Euzetes globulus* varied from 39°-41·5°C in 0 per cent RH and 100 per cent RH respectively. Clearly, the species inhabiting more exposed sites are more tolerant of high temperatures than are the inhabitants of moist soil. Madge (1965a) also reported that *H. rostrolamellatus* has the ability, not possessed by the other species studied, to lower its body temperature slightly by evaporative cooling at relative humidities within the range 0-90 per cent. It is, perhaps, significant that this is an arboreal species which might be exposed to rapid temperature increases in its normal habitat, and such a cooling device would be of considerable survival value. The species studied differed not only in their thermal death points, but also in their preferred range of temperature, which was higher in the case of *H. rostrolamellatus* (17°-21°C) than in the litter-dwelling *Belba geniculosa* (11°-15°C) and *Platynothrus peltifer* (10°-14°C). Earlier, Wallwork (1960) had noted that cryptostigmatid species taken from West African grassland soil showed a higher range of temperature preference than species from a hemlock yellow-birch forest floor in Michigan. This work also showed that the temperature preference could be altered by changing the preconditioning temperature, i.e., by acclimatizing the experimental animals, but Madge (1965b) could find no evidence that acclimatization changed the temperature preference of *Belba geniculosa.* Indeed, the narrow preference range shown by this species was not affected by marked variations in other environmental factors, particularly variations in relative humidity. This led him to conclude that the temperature response has an overriding influence on the behavioural characteristics of this species (Madge, 1966), even though the humidity response is normally well developed and, in fact, becomes intensified in desiccated animals. The development of a very sensitive temperature response is obviously of considerable advantage to a litter-dweller, such as *B. geniculosa,* since the temperature gradient in its normal environment is liable to be rather gradual.

Observations of the kind discussed above provide a firm foundation for the interpretation of natural distribution patterns, for they define, in precise terms, the effective microhabitat, and the behavioural and physiological adaptations to the various microenvironmental influences. This is an exciting field of study, in which a great deal more research is possible and necessary.

Life Cycles
The basic pattern of the life cycle of the soil Acari consists of development from the egg through a hexapod larval stage and one, two, or three nymphal stages to the adult. There are variations in this pattern from group to group.

(a) Mesostigmata. We have to rely on scant information for an account of the life histories and population dynamics of this group. Copulation is usually a preliminary to fertilization, the sperm being deposited in the genital tract of the female by the chelicerae of the male. Oviparity is the general rule, although viviparity has been recorded in the Gamasolaelaptidae (Wallwork, 1957). The

typical life cycle consists of larval, protonymphal, deutonymphal, and adult stages, and, if members of the Parasitidae can be considered typical, the duration of development from egg to adult may be relatively short. For example, in the United States, under laboratory conditions at 20°C and 90 per cent RH, *Pergamasus crassipes* and *Amblygamasus septentrionalis* required only three weeks to complete development from egg to adult (Hartenstein, 1962a). On the other hand, Bhattacharyya (1962), working in Britain, noted considerable variability in the duration of development of *P. crassipes* and, although the minimum time for development at 15°C was only about a week longer than that recorded by Hartenstein at 20°C, the average developmental time was 51 days; at 7·3°C this extended to 94 days. Similar variability was noted in the case of *Eugamasus cornutus* which had an average development time of 41 days at 15°C.

(b) Prostigmata. It would be difficult to define a 'typical' life history for this heterogeneous assemblage of families, for the number of nymphal stages varies from one to three. Among species occurring commonly in the soil, such as members of the Bdellidae, Rhagidiidae, Tydeidae, and Cunaxidae, a life cycle involving egg, larva, three nymphal stages, and the adult is probably the most usual. The general appearance of the nymphal stages is similar to that of the adult, the differences being that the immatures are smaller, less strongly pigmented, and have fewer genital setae than the adult.

(c) Astigmata. The soil-dwelling members of this Order belong, in the main, to the Acaridae, in which the life cycle may be one of two kinds. In the first type, the course of development is straightforward, the larval stage being succeeded by two nymphal stages, but in many of the species belonging to the Acaridae and Anoetidae an additional nymphal stage occurs, the hypopus, which is considerably modified as a resting or a phoretic (dispersal) stage. The hypopus may be relatively long-lived, active or inactive, and it becomes dispersed by attaching itself to the bodies of insects, particularly burrowing Hymenoptera, Orthoptera, and Coleoptera. This hypopus has been regarded as a second nymphal stage, for it appears during development between the two normal nymphs.

Another interesting feature of the life cycle of the Acaridae is the presence, in certain genera, of two morphologically distinct kinds of adult males: the 'normal' male and the heteromorphic male, which is distinguished by the strong development of the third pair of legs. Both types of male can mate with the females, and the eggs developing in each case may give rise to either type of male, or to females.

The rates of development in field populations of Acaridae are largely unknown. Under laboratory conditions, the widely distributed *Rhizoglyphus echinopus* may complete development from egg to adult in the relatively short period of one month at 20°C (see Baker and Wharton, 1952).

(d) Cryptostigmata. Many cryptostigmatid mites, including *Nanhermannia nana, Damaeobelba minutissima, Nothrus* spp., *Camisia* spp., and *Oppia nova,* are known to reproduce parthenogenetically, although no evidence is available to suggest whether this method of reproduction is facultative or obligative. On the other hand, many species produce fertilized eggs, and sperm transfer is effected by stalked spermatophores in most cases (Pauly, 1952; Taberly, 1957; Woodring and Cook, 1962), and only occasionally by direct copulation, sometimes preceded by a nuptial dance (Grandjean, 1956; Schuster, 1962). Eggs are deposited through an ovipositor, an extensible tube carrying three articulated valves at its extremity. Often, the eggs are laid in sheltered crevices and cavities, the interior of cast nymphal exuviae being a favoured oviposition site for several species, including *Antarcticola meyeri* (Wallwork, 1967b), *Ceratozetes jeweli* and *Pergalumna omniphagous* (Rockett and Woodring, 1966). The various factors influencing egg production are discussed in detail in chapter 11 and will not be considered at this point.

According to Strenzke (1949), viviparity occurs in some Ameronothridae, a family common in the marine littoral zone, but in most of the other crypto-stigmatids early development of the egg culminates in the formation of an inactive prelarva or deutovum, as in other Acari, which remains completely contained within the egg membrane (Sitnikova, 1960; Grandjean, 1962). In some species, at least, such as *Phthiracarus anonymum, Camisia segnis, C. horridus, Damaeus onustus, Podacarus auberti, Liodes* spp., and *Oribotritia berlesei,* the development of the prelarva occurs before the egg is deposited. On the other hand, prelarvae apparently are not produced in *Ceratozetes cisalpinus, Scheloribates laevigatus,* and *Oppia nova* (Woodring and Cook, 1962).

Without exception, the active immature stages of the Cryptostigmata consist of a hexapod larva and three nymphal stages, the proto-, deuto-, and trito-nymphs, which differ from the larva in having four pairs of legs and a genital aperture. As a general rule, the three nymphal stages may be distinguished from each other by differences in body chaetotaxy and in the number of genital suckers present, the development from protonymph to adult being accompanied by a reduction in the number of hysterosomal setae and an increase from one pair to three pairs of genital suckers—the deutonymph having two pairs, the tritonymph and adult, three. In some groups, for example, in members of the Cepheidae, Metrioppiidae, Crotoniidae, and Liodidae, the immatures differ markedly in appearance, and may occupy a different ecological niche from the adult.

Reliable estimates of the time required to complete development from egg to adult in the field are difficult to obtain. Duration of development varies with the species, and also within the same species under different environmental conditions. The estimates provided in Table 9.3 were obtained under experimental conditions and, in most cases, probably approximate the shortest development time. It is, perhaps, unwise to generalize too far at this stage, but the data provided in the table suggest that there may be a relationship between the

TABLE 9.3. Duration of development time from egg to adult in culture of various Cryptostigmata.

Species	Development time in days	Temperature °C	Authority
Nanhermannia nana	111	25	Sengbusch, 1958
Hypochthonius rufulus	122	25	Sengbusch, 1958
Camisia spinifer	126	25	Sengbusch, 1958
Nothrus silvestris	152	25	Sengbusch, 1958
Platynothrus peltifer	117	20	Hartenstein, 1962d
Damaeus clavipes	64	25	Sengbusch, 1958
Damaeus onustus	130	25	Sengbusch, 1958
Damaeus onustus	150	25	Pauly, 1956
Damaeus boreus	120	25	Sitnikova, 1959
Hermannia scabra	185	20	Jalil, 1965
Oppia nitens	40	25	Michael, 1883
Oppia nova	23	25	Woodring and Cook, 1962
Ceratoppia bipilis	79	25	Michael, 1883
Cepheus palmicinctum	375	25	Michael, 1883
Scheloribates laevigatus	64	25	Woodring and Cook, 1962
Scheloribates parabilis	17	23	Woodring, 1965
Ceratozetes cisalpinus	32	25	Woodring and Cook, 1962
Ceratozetes gracilis	124-149	20	Hartenstein, 1962b
Ceratozetes jeweli	54	25	Rockett and Woodring, 1966
Protoribates lophotrichus	150	25	Hartenstein, 1962c
Minunthozetes semirufus	38	25	Sengbusch, 1958
Rostrozetes flavus	38	23	Woodring, 1965
Galumna nervosa	47	25	Sengbusch, 1954
Galumna longipluma	60	25	Sengbusch, 1954
Galumna confusa	48	23	Woodring, 1965
Galumna parva	37	23	Woodring, 1965
Pergalumna omniphagous	42	25	Rockett and Woodring, 1966
Galumna elimatus ithacensis	87	25	Sengbusch, 1954
Steganacarus diaphanum	150	20	Hartenstein, 1962e

duration of the development period and the body size of the species concerned. Lebrun (1965) pointed out that small-sized species, such as members of the genera *Oppia* and *Suctobelba,* have a life span of about 50 days, whereas larger forms, such as *Euzetes globulus* and *Damaeus onustus,* mature to the adult during a period of 150-200 days, having a total life span of about 400 days. Block (1965) estimated larval duration of 1 month, protonymph at 4-5 months, deutonymph at 2 months, and tritonymph at 1-2 months for *Platynothrus peltifer* and *Damaeus clavipes* under subArctic conditions. On the basis of these observations, it seems reasonable to suggest that the medium-sized and larger species, with a body length in the range 400-1000 μ, require at least 3 months, and probably no more than 12 months, to complete their development under field conditions in the north temperate zone. It is to be expected, therefore, that these species will produce one, two, or three generations per year, but rarely more than this. Lebrun (1964a), in his study of the Cryptostigmata of a Belgian forest floor, attributed one annual generation to *Nothrus silvestris, Chamobates incisus, Rhysotritia ardua, Platynothrus peltifer,* and *Euzetes globulus,* two generations per year for *Suctobelba trigona, Oppia nova, Autogneta willmanni,*

Nanhermannia elegantula, Parachiptera willmanni, Steganacarus magnus, Phthira-carus piger, Minunthozetes semirufus, and *Damaeus onustus,* and three to five generations per year for *Carabodes marginatus, Chamobates cuspidatus, Oriba-tella quadricornuta, Oppia quadricarinata, O. subpectinata, Suctobelba subtri-gona, Tectocepheus velatus,* and *Hypochthonius rufulus.* Further, there appears to be a relationship between the number of generations produced per year and the habitat preference of the individual species, as shown in Table 9.4.

TABLE 9.4. The relationship between the number of generations per year, body size, and preferred habitat of Cryptostigmata (modified from Lebrun, 1964a).

Body size		Large ($\geqslant 0\cdot 8$ mm in length)	Medium ($0\cdot 4$-$0\cdot 7$ mm in length)	Small ($\leqslant 0\cdot 3$ mm in length)
Number of generations per year	Litter-dwellers	1-2	2-3	2-4
	Humus-dwellers	½-1	1-2	2-3

Environmental influences may also have a direct effect, for Haarløv (1960) in Denmark and Murphy and Jalil (1964) in England have recorded two generations per year for *Tectocepheus velatus,* in contrast to Lebrun's findings.

Reproductive activity in the field varies considerably in its time of occurrence and duration from species to species. In England, gravid females of *Rhysotritia duplicata* have been observed throughout the year (Harding, 1967), suggesting that this species has no restricted breeding period. In contrast, *Platynothrus peltifer* in *Festuca-Agrostis* grassland and *Damaeus clavipes* in *Juncus* moorland produced eggs only during the summer months (Block, 1965), the former species breeding in the late summer. The main oviposition period of *Hermannia scabra* in deciduous woodland has been noted by Jalil (1965) to fall in the period September to November. It appears likely that the onset and duration of reproductive activity may be influenced by environmental factors, although more precise information is needed on this point.

Population Dynamics

Seasonal changes in the size of populations of mesostigmatid and astigmatid mites are difficult to detect because the numbers of these mites obtained in soil samples are usually small, and even when sufficient numbers are collected, little fluctuation throughout the seasonal cycle occurs, at least in the cases studied so far (see, for example, Evans *et al.,* 1961). These changes are more marked in the Prostigmata, and most marked in the Cryptostigmata, moreover, since the phenology of this latter group often has a strong influence on the phenological pattern of the Acari as a whole (Fig. 9.6), the following discussion is concentrated around them.

Fluctuations in the total numbers of Cryptostigmata through the seasonal cycle have been described for a variety of different European and North

American localities, including forest (van der Drift, 1951; Evans, 1955; Wall-work, 1959; Lebrun, 1964a, 1965), grassland (Sheals, 1957; Haarløv, 1960; Dhillon and Gibson, 1962), moorland (Block, 1966), and fenland (Macfadyen, 1952). Much of the evidence points to a period of peak density some time during the autumn and winter months, and a marked decline in numbers during midsummer (Fig. 9.6). This pattern is closely correlated with the reproductive

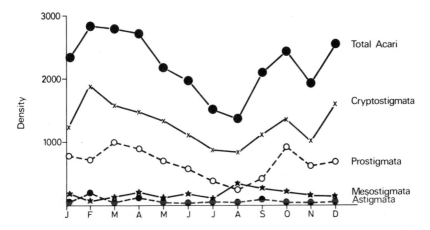

FIGURE 9.6. Seasonal fluctuations in the acarine fauna of litter and soil in a Sitka spruce plantation at Ampthill, Bedfordshire, based on densities expressed as numbers/200 cm² to a depth of 6·5 cm (from Evans *et al.*, 1961).

cycles of these soil animals, for there is a preponderance of early immature forms when the populations are maximal, and a greater percentage of adults in the summer populations. As we have already noted, mating and egg production often occur during the summer, and the eggs laid towards the end of this season hatch in the autumn, producing a marked increase in density of larvae and protonymphs at this time. The long-lived protonymph is probably the main overwintering stage in many cases, and deutonymphs and tritonymphs develop during the late winter and spring. The summer decline in the population probably reflects the fact that only a small percentage of these overwintering immatures survive to reach adulthood. Adults surviving from the previous summer also decline at this time, for the longevity of this stage is rarely more than one year, and often considerably less than this, according to the informa-tion available (Table 9.5). On occasion, it has been possible to demonstrate a subsidiary, but clearly distinct, spring peak in addition to the autumn/winter one. This may occur when a single species population, reproducing in the spring, predominates in the total Cryptostigmata fauna. For example, *Platynothrus peltifer* represented 15 per cent of the total Cryptostigmata of a Belgian oak wood investigated by Lebrun (1965), and the spring peak, in total numbers, could be attributed almost entirely to the fact that this litter-dwelling species produced its single annual generation during the months of April and May. The adult stage apparently lives for at least a year (Table 9.5), and undoubtedly overwinters. Noordam and van der Vaart-Vlieger (1943) suggested that this stage was the main overwintering one in the population studied by them in the Netherlands, but a rather different situation must obtain in England, for Block (1965) found nymphs and adults present during the winter, with protonymphs particularly abundant at this time, indicating that the main period of recruitment was in the late summer and autumn. Clearly, local environmental factors

TABLE 9.5. The longevity of the adult of various species of Cryptostigmata under culture conditions.

Species	Longevity (months)	Temperature	Authority
Platynothrus peltifer	≥12	5°C	Block, 1965
Damaeus clavipes	≥12	5°C	Block, 1965
Oppia nova	1	25°C	Woodring and Cook, 1962
Scheloribates laevigatus	4	25°C	Woodring and Cook, 1962
Ceratozetes cisalpinus	10-12	25°C	Woodring and Cook, 1962
Rostrozetes flavus	3-7	23°C	Woodring, 1965
Galumna parva	2-4	23°C	Woodring, 1965
Galumna confusa	2-6	23°C	Woodring, 1965
Pergalumna omniphagous	>7	25°C	Rockett and Woodring, 1966

can have a profound influence on the pattern of population growth and decline through the year, and on its age class structure at any one time. Little is known about the ability of eggs to survive the winter, either developing slowly or in diapause. The observations already discussed above suggest that eggs belonging to the same generation may develop at different rates, depending upon the time when they are deposited. Thus, eggs laid during the late summer may develop to the protonymphal stage before the environmental conditions become unfavourable during the winter, while eggs laid at the end of the reproductive period in autumn may overwinter as such (Block, 1965). This differential rate of development would result in two distinct peaks for each of the subsequent nymphal and adult stages; this phenomenon has been recorded on several occasions.

Synchronization of Life Cycles
In certain situations, the life cycles of all, or the majority, of the constituent species populations are more or less synchronized, and, in these cases, peaks and declines in Cryptostigmata populations are most clearly marked. This has been observed in the populations of fenland soil (Macfadyen, 1952) and desert soil (Wallwork, unpubl.), where the species composition varied little throughout the year. On the other hand, a fauna comprising a large number of species will undoubtedly contain some which have one, two, or three generations

per year. In this case, the development of individual populations will not be synchronized, and there will be some variation in the species composition throughout the year. Further, the most abundant species may have an over-whelming effect on the total phenological pattern, and each peak in total density may reflect the contribution of different species or groups of species, a point well illustrated if the fauna of litter and humus layers are considered separately. Lebrun (1965) observed that *Platynothrus peltifer* was numerically dominant in a forest litter fauna, and made a significant contribution to a spring peak in total faunal density, whereas, in the humus layer, species belonging to the Ere-maeidae, comprising 49 per cent of the total Cryptostigmata fauna, contributed quite definitely to an autumn peak in total density. Thus, taking the total fauna of the two layers combined, two periods of peak density occurred, with different species predominating in each case. This pattern is somewhat compli-cated, at least as far as the humus populations are concerned, by vertical movements between the soil strata, which have the effect of augmenting the density in humus and depleting that in litter during the autumn, and vice versa in the spring.

Feeding Habits

The predatory Mesostigmata, which include species belonging to the genera *Macrocheles, Veigaia, Parasitus, Pergamasus,* and *Gamasolaelaps,* undoubtedly occupy an important place in the food web of the soil community. Culture experiments have shown that macrochelids and veigaiids can feed on a variety of animals, including Collembola, Protura, and Pauropoda (Hurlbutt, 1964), nematodes and enchytraeids (Rodriguez *et al.,* 1962; Singer and Krantz, 1967), and eggs of the house fly *Musca domestica* (Filipponi, 1955; Axtell, 1961; Rodriguez and Wade, 1961). This range of diet is probably typical of many Mesostigmata, although, in field conditions, the kind of prey most frequently chosen will undoubtedly depend on what is available. For example, macrochelids are often very common in compost and decaying dungpats, where the most plentiful food materials are house fly eggs and nematodes of the *Rhabditis* group, whereas the Vegaiidae, which are commoner in woodland and forest soils, prob-ably feed more extensively on cryptostigmatid mites (Wallwork, 1957) and Collembola. Some of these predators, such as the viviparous *Pergamasus* spp., may be cannibalistic when no other food is available (Wallwork, 1967a). The role of these predators in regulating the populations of prey animals is considered in chapter 11.

Members of the mesostigmatid Uropodina are mainly fungivorous and coprophagous in feeding habit. These forms are much less active than their predatory counterparts, and, although *Fuscuropoda marginata* has been shown to prey on the astigmatid mite *Caloglyphus mycophagus* (Rohde, 1959), the majority of the group may be regarded as scavengers on a variety of decaying plant and animal material. This may also be true of members of the genus *Cilliba,* recognized by their flattened, circular body shape, often recovered from beech litter, and probably phoretic in the deutonymphal stage on beetles, although little direct information is available about the group. Another member of the Uropodina, *Prodinychus* sp., has predatory tendencies (Kühnelt, 1961), although it may also be a carrion-feeder, a habit which may be common among predatory Mesostigmata.

The Prostigmata includes a number of important predators, such as members of the families Bdellidae, Cheyletidae, Rhagidiidae, Erythraeidae, Cunaxidae, and Trombidiidae. Little is known of the food habits of some of the smaller and more abundant prostigmatids, such as the Scutacaridae, Pyemotidae, and Tarsonemidae, which often occur in a parasitic or phoretic association with other soil animals, at least in the developmental stages. The predatory Prostigmata have much the same kind of feeding habit as the predatory Mesostigmata. Bdellid mites will attack Collembola, while erythraeids of the genus *Balaustium* feed on scale insects and thrips (Newell, 1963).

A considerable amount of information has been accumulated about the feeding habits of soil Cryptostigmata, principally from culture experiments and gut content analyses of specimens taken directly from the field (Forsslund, 1938; Schuster, 1956; Riha, 1951; Wallwork, 1958; Woodring and Cook, 1962). It is evident that these mites will feed on a variety of decomposing plant material in culture, although fungal hyphae and spores form a conspicuous part of the natural diet of many species, such as the commonly occurring *Ceratoppia bipilis, Adoristes ovatus, Belba* spp., *Oribatula tibialis, Scheloribates laevigatus, Ceratozetes gracilis*, and *Galumna elimata*. The easily recognized 'box-mites', belonging to the families Phthiracaridae and Euphthiracaridae, usually feed on decaying leaf and woody tissue (Jacot, 1939; Murphy, 1955; Wallwork, 1958) as adults and nymphs, and show individual preferences for various kinds of material. For example, *Steganacarus magnus* selects ash in preference to birch leaves in culture (Murphy, 1955), and the wood of yellow birch in preference to that of hemlock under field conditions in North America (Wallwork, 1967a). This species is also common in beech litter and feeds extensively on decomposing leaves of this species in culture.

Some Cryptostigmata are coprophagous in habit, and faecal-feeding may be of general occurrence among larval stages of phthiracarids that burrow in woody tissue. It is also established that a change of diet occurs during development in many species, for example, in *Cepheus* and *Carabodes* which are often encountered in sheltered cavities beneath bark, where organic particles in an advanced stage of decomposition accumulate. Adults of these species range more widely in the litter, and evidently are more catholic in their feeding habits. A good illustration of this change in diet is provided by the mite *Orthogalumna terebrantis* from Uruguay, in which the nymphal stages burrow actively in the living leaf tissue of the water hyacinth, whereas the adults wander freely over the surface of the leaves and the surrounding water (Wallwork, 1965).

However, fresh, green plant material rarely forms an important part of the diet of true soil-dwelling Cryptostigmata, but although some species can ingest this material in culture, it is doubtful if populations could maintain themselves on this food source alone. It is more likely that higher plant material, particularly that with a low carbon:nitrogen ratio, decomposing under the action of bacteria and fungi, provides the most suitable food. In addition, moist food material is more readily accepted than dry tissues.

Animal food is taken by a number of species of Cryptostigmata, although this is more usually in the form of carrion than of living prey. Members of the genera *Belba, Peloribates,* and *Liochthonius* may be found associated with the later stages in the faunal succession on decaying animal tissues, although there is no evidence that this represents a specialized feeding habit. The same is true of the predatory habit, for, although species such as *Pergalumna omniphagous, Scheloribates laevigatus,* and *Oribella castanea* may feed, for example, on nematodes, it is probable that this activity provides a supplement to the more usual diet of decaying organic material. The Cryptostigmata, in general, are ill-equipped for a predatory role: they are slow moving, and their chelicerae, which are not markedly protrusible, are heavy and armed with blunt teeth more suited to biting and crushing than for piercing and tearing. There are some exceptions to this, however, such as *Eupelops* spp., in which the chelicerae, although chelate, are elongate, and *Suctobelba* spp., in which these structures are fine stylets. Species of the latter genus rarely have any identifiable gut contents, and it is possible that they feed on liquid food or on bacteria. The importance of bacteria in the diet of the Cryptostigmata has not been investigated to any extent, although these microflora may have much the same kind of relationship with the mites as they do with the Collembola.

Although attempts have been made to categorize the feeding habits of Cryptostigmata (Schuster, 1956; Wallwork, 1958) on the basis of gut content analyses and feeding preferences in cultures, it must be emphasized again that a distinction should be made between what is ingested and what is utilized. As in the case of the Collembola, fungal hyphae and spores can pass through the digestive tract of these mites apparently without any structural damage, which suggests that if any digestion occurs it involves mainly fats and carbohydrates. There is no evidence that these digestive processes result in the direct production of humic substances (Schuster, 1956).

References

Axtell, R. C. (1961) 'New records of North American Macrochelidae (Acarina: Mesostigmata) and their predation rates on the house fly', *Ann. ent. Soc. Amer.,* **54,** 748.

Baker, E. W. and Wharton, G. W. (1952) *An introduction to Acarology,* Macmillan, New York, 465 pp.

Balogh, J. (1961) 'Identification keys of world oribatid (Acari) families and genera', *Acta zool. hung.,* 7, 243-344.

Balogh, J. (1963) 'Identification keys of Holarctic oribatid mites (Acari) families and genera', *Acta zool. hung.,* 9, 1-60.

Balogh, J. (1965) 'A synopsis of the world oribatid (Acari) genera', *Acta zool. hung.,* 11, 5-99.

Bhattacharyya, S. K. (1962) 'Laboratory studies on the feeding habits and life cycles of soil-inhabiting mites', *Pedobiologia*, 1, 291-8.

Block, W. (1965) 'The life histories of *Platynothrus peltifer* (Koch 1839) and *Damaeus clavipes* (Hermann 1804) (Acarina: Cryptostigmata) in soils of Pennine moorland', *Acarologia*, 7, 735-43.

Block, W. (1966) 'Seasonal fluctuations and distribution of mite populations in moorland soils, with a note on biomass', *J. Anim. Ecol.*, 35, 487-503.

Bristowe, W. S. (1939) *The comity of spiders* I., Ray Society, London.

Cherrett, J. M. (1964a) 'Notes on the seasonal occurrence of some Linyphiidae (Araneida) on the Moor House National Nature Reserve, Westmorland, with some new county records', *Ent. mon. Mag.*, 99, 152-6.

Cherrett, J. M. (1964b) 'The distribution of spiders on the Moor House National Nature Reserve, Westmorland', *J. Anim. Ecol.*, 33, 27-48.

Cloudsley-Thompson, J. L. (1958) *Spiders, scorpions, centipedes and mites*, Pergamon, London and New York.

Cloudsley-Thompson, J. L. (1961a) 'Observations on the natural history of the "camel-spider" *Galeodes arabs* C. L. Koch (Solifugae: Galeodidae) in the Sudan', *Ent. mon. Mag.*, 97, 145-52.

Cloudsley-Thompson, J. L. (1961b) 'Observations on the biology of the scorpion *Leiurus quinquestriatus* (H. & E.) in the Sudan', *ibid.*, 97, 153-5.

Dhillon, B. S. and Gibson, N. H. E. (1962) 'A study of the Acarina and Collembola of agricultural soils. I. Numbers and distribution in undisturbed grassland', *Pedobiologia*, 1, 189-209.

Drift, J. van der (1951) 'Analysis of the animal community in a beech forest floor', *Tijdschr. Ent.*, 94, 1-168.

Duffey, E. (1962) 'A population study of spiders in limestone grassland', *J. Anim. Ecol.*, 31, 571-99.

Evans, G. O. (1955) 'Identification of terrestrial mites' in Kevan, D. K. McE., ed., *Soil zoology*, 55-61.

Evans, G. O. (1957) 'An introduction to the British Mesostigmata (Acarina) with keys to the families and genera', *J. Linn. Soc. Lond. Zool.*, 43, 203-59.

Evans, G. O. and Browning, E. (1954) The Linnean Society of London Synopses of the British Fauna, no. 10, 'Pseudoscorpiones'.

Evans, G. O., Sheals, J. G., and MacFarlane, D. (1961) *Terrestrial Acari of the British Isles. I. Introduction and biology*, Brit. Mus. Nat. Hist., London, 219 pp.

Filipponi, A. (1955) 'Sulla natura dell associazione tra *Macrocheles muscaedomesticae* e *Musca domestica*', *Riv. Parassit.*, 16, 83-102.

Forsslund, K-H. (1938) 'Bidrag till kännedomen om djurlivets i marken inverkan på markomvandlingen. I. Om några hornkvalsters (Oribatiders) näring', *Meddn. St. Skogs-försAnst.*, 31, 87-107.

Gabbutt, P. D. (1956) 'The spiders of an oak wood in south-east Devon', *Ent. mon. Mag.*, 92, 351-8.

Gabbutt, P. D. (1967) 'Quantitative sampling of the pseudoscorpion *Chthonius ischnocheles* from beech litter', *J. Zool., Lond.*, 151, 469-78.

Gabbutt, P. D. and Vachon, M. (1963) 'The external morphology and life history of the pseudoscorpion *Chthonius ischnocheles*', *Proc. zool. Soc. Lond.*, 140, 75-98.

Gabbutt, P. D. and Vachon, M. (1965) 'The external morphology and life history of the pseudoscorpion *Neobisium muscorum*', *Proc. zool. Soc. Lond.*, 145, 335-58.

Gabbutt, P. D. and Vachon, M. (1967) 'The external morphology and life history of the pseudoscorpion *Roncus lubricus*', *J. Zool., Lond.*, 153, 475-98.

Gasdorf, E. C. and Goodnight, C. J. (1963) 'Studies on the ecology of soil arachnids', *Ecology*, 44, 261-8.

Godfrey, R. (1910) 'The false scorpions of Scotland', *Ann. Scott. nat. Hist.*, 19, 23-33.

Grandjean, F. (1953) 'Essai de classification des oribates', *Bull. Soc. zool. Fr.*, 78, 421-46.

Grandjean, F. (1956) 'Observations sur les Galumnidae (Acariens, Oribates)'. 1er série. *Rev. franç. Ent.*, 23, 137-46.

Grandjean, F. (1962) 'Prélarves d'oribates', *Acarologia*, 4, 423-39.

Haarløv, N. (1960) 'Microarthropods from Danish soils. Ecology, Phenology', *Oikos*, suppl. 3, 176 pp.

Harding, D. J. L. (1967) *Personal communication.*

Hartenstein, R. (1962a) 'Life history studies of *Pergamasus crassipes* and *Amblygamasus septentrionalis* (Acarina: Parasitidae)', *Ann. ent. Soc. Amer.*, 55, 196-202.

Hartenstein, R. (1962b) 'Soil Oribatei. IV. Observations on *Ceratozetes gracilis*', *Ann. ent. Soc. Amer.*, 55, 583-6.

Hartenstein, R. (1962c) 'Soil Oribatei VI. *Protoribates lophotrichus* and its association with micro-organisms', *Ann. ent. Soc. Amer.*, 55, 587-91.

Hartenstein, R. (1962d) 'Soil Oribatei. V. Investigations on *Platynothrus peltifer* (Acarina: Camisiidae)', *Ann. ent. Soc. Amer.*, 55, 709-13.

Hartenstein, R. (1962e) 'Soil Oribatei. VII. Decomposition of conifer needles and deciduous leaf petioles by *Steganacarus diaphanum*', *Ann. ent. Soc. Amer.*, 55, 713-16.

Hughes, T. E. (1959) *Mites or the Acari*, Athlone, London.

Hurlbutt, H. (1964) 'Structure and distribution of *Veigaia* (Mesostigmata) in forest soils', *Acarologia*, 6, (fasc. h. s., C. R. 1er Congrès Int. d'Acarologie, Fort Collins, Col., U.S.A. 1963), 150-2.

Jacot, A. P. (1939) 'Reduction of spruce and fir litter by minute animals', *J. For.*, 37, 858-60.

Jalil, M. (1965) 'The life cycle of *Hermannia scabra* (C. L. Koch, 1879) (Acarina-Oribatei)', *Oikos*, 16, 16-19.

Karppinen, E. (1955a) 'Ecological and transect survey studies on Finnish Camisiids', *Ann. Zool. Soc. 'Vanamo'* 17, 1-80.

Karppinen, E. (1955b) 'Die Oribatiden-Fauna eines *Corylus* avellana=Gebüsches und eines Sumpfmoors in Tvärminne, Südfinnland', *Arch. Soc. 'Vanamo'*, 9 suppl., 131-4.

Kaston, B. J. (1953) *How to know the spiders*, Brown, Dubuque.

Kühnelt, W. (1961) *Soil biology with special reference to the animal kingdom* (English ed., trans. Walker, N.), Faber, London. 397 pp.

Lawrence, R. F. (1965) 'Some new or little known Solifugae from southern Africa', *Proc. zool. Soc. Lond.*, 144, 47-59.

Lebrun, P. (1964a) 'Quelques aspects de la phénologie des populations d'Oribatides (Acari: Oribatei) dans le sol forestier en Moyenne-Belgique', *Bull. Acad. r. Belg. Cl. Sci.*, 5, 370-92.

Lebrun, P. (1964b) 'Note sur les migrations des Oribatides (Acari) de petite taille', *Bull. Soc. R. ent. belg.*, 100, 69-77.

Lebrun, P. (1965) 'Contribution à l'étude écologique des oribates de la litiere dans une forêt de moyenne-Belgique', *Mém. Inst. r. Sc. nat. Belg.*, 153, 1-96.

Locket, G. H. and Millidge, A. F. (1951, 1953) *British Spiders, I, II*, Ray Society, London.

Macfadyen, A. (1952) 'The small arthropods of a *Molinia* fen at Cothill', *J. Anim. Ecol.*, 21, 87-117.

Madge, D. S. (1964a) 'The water relations of *Belba geniculosa* Oudms. and other species of oribatid mites', *Acarologia*, 6, 199-223.

Madge, D. S. (1964b) 'The humidity reactions of oribatid mites', *Acarologia*, 6, 566-91.

Madge, D. S. (1964c) 'The longevity of fasting oribatid mites', *Acarologia*, 6, 718-29.

Madge, D. S. (1965a) 'The effects of lethal temperatures on oribatid mites', *Acarologia*, 7, 121-30.

Madge, D. S. (1965b) 'The behaviour of *Belba geniculosa* Oudms. and certain other species of oribatid mites in controlled temperature gradients'. *Acarologia*, 7, 389-406.

Madge, D. S. (1966) 'The significance of the sensory physiology of oribatid mites in their natural environment', *Acarologia*, 8, 155-60.

Michael, A. D. (1883) *British Oribatidae,* Ray Society, London.

Murphy, P. W. (1955) 'Ecology of the fauna of forest soils' in Kevan, D. K. McE., ed., *Soil zoology,* 99-124.

Murphy, P. W. and Jalil, M. (1964) 'Some observations on the genus *Tectocepheus*', *Acarologia,* 6 (fasc. h. s., C. R. Ier Congrès Int. d'Acarologie, Fort Collins, Col., U.S.A., 1963), 187-97.

Newell, I. M. (1963) 'Feeding habits of the genus *Balaustium* (Acarina: Erythraeidae) with special reference to attacks on Man', *J. Parasit,* 49, 498-502.

Noordam, D. and Vaart-Vlieger, S. H. van der, (1943) 'Een onderzoek naar samenstelling en beteekenis van de fauna van eikenstooisel', *Ned. BoschbTijdschr.,* 16, 470-92.

Nørgaard, E. (1951) 'On the ecology of two lycosid spiders (*Pirata piraticus* and *Lycosa pullata*) from a Danish *Sphagnum* bog', *Oikos,* 3, 1-21.

Pauly, F. (1952) 'Die "Copula" der Oribatiden (Moosmilben)', *Naturwissenschaften,* 24, 572-3.

Pauly, F. (1956) 'Zur Biologie einiger Belbiden und zür Funktion ihrer pseudostigmatischen Organe', *Zool. Jb. (Syst.),* 84, 275-328.

Phillipson, J. (1959) 'The seasonal occurrence, life histories and fecundity of harvest spiders (Phalangida)', *Ent. mon. Mag.,* 95, 134-8.

Phillipson, J. (1960) 'A contribution to the feeding biology of *Mitopus morio* (F.) (Phalangida)', *J. Anim. Ecol.,* 29, 35-43.

Rajski, A. (1960) 'Quantitative occurrence of the chief intermediate hosts of *Moniezia (M.) expansa* (Rud.) in the vicinity of Poznan (In Polish)', *Wiad. Parazyt.,* 7, 39-42.

Ressl, F. and Beier, M. (1958) 'Zur Ökologie, Biologie und Phänologie der heimischen Pseudoskorpione', *Zool. Jb. (Syst.),* 86, 1-26.

Riha, G. (1951) 'Zur Ökologie der Oribatiden in Kalksteinböden', *Zool. Jb. (Syst.),* 80, 407-50.

Rockett, C. L. and Woodring, J. P. (1966) 'Biological investigations on a new species of *Ceratozetes* and of *Pergalumna* (Acarina: Cryptostigmata)', *Acarologia,* 8, 511-20.

Rodriguez, J. G. and Wade, C. F. (1961) 'The nutrition of *Macrocheles muscaedomesticae* (Acarina: Macrochelidae) in relation to its predatory action on the house fly egg', *Ann. ent. Soc. Amer.,* 54, 782-8.

Rodriguez, J. G., Wade, C. F., and Wells, C. N. (1962) 'Nematodes as a natural food for *Macrocheles muscaedomesticae* (Acarina: Macrochelidae), a predator of the house fly egg', *Ann. ent. Soc. Am.,* 55, 507-11.

Rohde, C. J. (1959) 'Studies on the biologies of two mite species, predator and prey, including some effects of gamma radiation on selected developmental stages', *Ecology,* 40, 572-9.

Sankey, J. H. P. (1949) 'British harvest spiders', *Essex Nat.,* 28, 181-91.

Savoury, T. H. (1948) The Linnean Society of London Synopses of the British Fauna, no 1. 'Opiliones (Arachnida) or Harvestmen' (second edn).

Savoury, T. H. (1964) *Arachnida,* Academic, New York. 291 pp.

Schuster, R. (1956) 'Der Anteil der Oribatiden an den Zersetzungsvorgängen im boden', *Z. Morph. Ökol. Tiere,* 45, 1-33.

Schuster, R. (1962) 'Nachweis eines Paarungszeremoniells bei den Hornmilben (Oribatei, Acari)', *Naturwissenschaften,* 21, 502.

Sengbusch, H. G. (1954) 'Studies on the life history of three oribatoid mites with observations on other species', *Ann. ent. Soc. Amer.,* 47, 646-67.

Sengbusch, H. G. (1958) 'Zuchtversuche mit Oribatiden. (Acarina)', *Naturwissenschaften,* 20, 498-9.

Sheals, J. G. (1956) 'Notes on a collection of soil Acari', *Ent. mon. Mag.,* 92, 99-103.

Sheals, J. G. (1957) 'The Collembola and Acarina of uncultivated soil', *J. Anim. Ecol.,* 26, 125-34.

Singer, G. and Krantz, G. W. (1967) 'The use of nematodes and oligochaetes for rearing predatory mites', *Acarologia*, **9**, 485-7.

Sitnikova, L. G. (1959) 'Life cycles of some Oribatei and methods of culture', *Zool. Zh.*, **38**, 1663-73.

Sitnikova, L. G. (1960) 'The prelarvae of oribatids'. (in Russian.) *Parazit. sb.*, **19**, 220-36.

Strenzke, K. (1949) 'Zur Fortflanzung der Moosmilben', *Microkosmos*, **38**, 177-80.

Strenzke, K. (1952) 'Untersuchungen über die Tiergemeinschaften des Bodens: Die Oribatiden und ihre Synusien in den Böden Norddeutschlands', *Zoologica*, **37**, 1-167.

Taberly, G. (1957) 'Observations sur les spermatophores et leur transfert chez les oribates (Acariens)', *Bull. Soc. zool. Fr.*, **82**, 139-45.

Tarras-Wahlberg, N. (1961) 'The Oribatei of a central Swedish bog and their environment', *Oikos*, suppl. 4, 56 pp.

Todd, V. (1949) 'The habits and ecology of the British harvestmen', *J. Anim. Ecol.*, **18**, 209-29.

Vlijm, L. and Kessler-Geschiere, A. M. (1967) 'The phenology and habitat of *Pardosa monticola*, *P. nigriceps* and *P. pullata* (Araneae, Lycosidae)', *J. Anim. Ecol.*, **36**, 31-56.

Wallwork, J. A. (1957) *The Acarina of a hemlock-yellow birch forest floor.* Ph.D. Thesis, University of Michigan.

Wallwork, J. A. (1958) 'Notes on the feeding behaviour of some forest soil mites', *Oikos*, **9**, 260-71.

Wallwork, J. A. (1959) 'The distribution and dynamics of some forest soil mites', *Ecology*, **40**, 557-63.

Wallwork, J. A. (1960) 'Observations on the behaviour of some oribatid mites in experimentally-controlled temperature gradients', *Proc. zool. Soc. Lond.*, **135**, 619-29.

Wallwork, J. A. (1965) 'A leaf-boring galumnoid mite (Acari: Cryptostigmata) from Uruguay', *Acarologia*, **7**, 758-64.

Wallwork, J. A. (1967a) 'Acari' in Burges, N. A. and Raw, F., eds., *Soil biology*, 363-95.

Wallwork, J. A. (1967b) 'Cryptostigmata (Oribatid mites)' in Gressitt, J. L. ed., *Entomology of Antarctica*, Antarctic Research Series, Amer. Geophys. U. 10, 105-22.

Wallwork, J. A. and Rodriguez, J. G. (1961) 'Ecological studies on oribatid mites with particular reference to their role as intermediate hosts of anoplocephalid cestodes', *J. econ. Ent.*, **54**, 701-5.

Wharton, G. W. (1964) Keynote address, First International Congress of Acarology. *Acarologia*, **6**, (fasc. h. s., C. R. Ier Congrès Int. d'Acarologie, Fort Collins, Col., U.S.A., 1963), 37-43.

Williams, G. (1962) 'Seasonal and diurnal activity of harvestmen (Phalangida) and spiders (Araneida) in contrasted habitats', *J. Anim. Ecol.*, **31**, 23-42.

Woodring, J. P. (1965) 'The biology of five new species of oribatids from Louisiana', *Acarologia*, **7**, 564-76.

Woodring, J. P. and Cook, E. F. (1962) 'The biology of *Ceratozetes cisalpinus* Berlese, *Scheloribates laevigatus* Koch, and *Oppia neerlandica* Oudemans (Oribatei), with a description of all stages', *Acarologia*, **4**, 101-37.

10. Vertebrates

The soil fauna is so markedly invertebrate in character that there is perhaps a tendency to overlook the influence of vertebrates on this community. This is partly a reflection of the fact that, although vertebrates of many different kinds seek refuge in the soil for part or all of their lives, the majority find their food above the surface of the ground, and their importance in the food web of the soil community is deemed to be minimal. In these cases, the beneficial effects of vertebrate activity are limited to physical changes brought about in the soil structure by burrowing, and to the enrichment of the soil organic content by the transportation of food and nesting materials underground. However, burrowing not only results in the mineral soil from the deeper strata being deposited at the surface, thus providing the opportunity for its organic component to be increased and enriched, but this activity may seriously impair the stability of the soil. Burrow systems which, in dry weather, serve to aerate the soil, may become watercourses after rain, contributing to soil erosion; extensive burrowing also weakens the soil structurally, and renders it liable to collapse under the trampling of large herbivores. This is often evident where rabbits and rodents are active, their feeding above the ground surface, and their burrows beneath, provide two common ingredients of the conservationist's nightmare.

On the other hand, animal ecologists confine their attentions either to vertebrates or to invertebrates, more often than not, and rarely to the biotic effects that both of these major groupings may combine to produce. The methods used by these two categories of specialists are usually widely different, for the vertebrate ecologist deals mainly with relatively small populations, and his samples are large in comparison with the total population; the animals in question are often more mobile than, for example, soil invertebrates, and greater reliance has to be placed on indirect evidences of activity, such as trails or tracks, frass at feeding sites, and scat. The soil ecologist has not only to solve the problem of separating the animals he wishes to study from their immediate environment, the soil, but also has to recognize the fact that estimates based on samples which are very small in comparison with the total population may include an appreciable sampling error, particularly when the population has an aggregated pattern of distribution.

'Periodic' Vertebrates

It may be argued that studies on the soil fauna need not, indeed, cannot be expanded to include those vertebrates which have but a transient or periodic association with the soil. In this category, are included: birds, such as the puffin, sand martin, and shearwater, which nest in rabbit and rodent burrows; lizards of the families Agamidae, Iguanidae, and Lacertidae, which are active above the ground during the daytime, and may retire to the shelter of soil burrows at night; frogs and toads which lie dormant deep in dry mud during periods of cold or drought, as does the African lung-fish *Protopterus*; and the mammalian rodents, foxes, badgers, and rabbits which excavate refuges in the soil to protect themselves and their offspring from surface predators. This list can be extended by adding the vertebrates that grub in the surface litter layer for their food; a number of common birds, such as the robin, blackbird, thrush, and tit are included here, for these feed extensively on snails, earthworms, and small arthropods, and may have an important influence in regulating the population sizes of these soil invertebrates. It is not only the large-sized soil animals that are subject to such predation, for Betts (1955), reporting on the food of titmice in oak woodland, found appreciable numbers of cryptostigmatid mites in the gut contents of the four bird species investigated. Large herbivores, feeding on surface vegetation, may also serve as accidental carnivores by ingesting soil animals, such as mites, that move up into pasture vegetation during diurnal migration cycles (Wallwork and Rodriguez, 1961). Dung deposits produced by these vertebrates on the surface of the soil provide suitable microhabitats for a wide variety of soil animals, notably earthworms, nematodes, dipteran larvae, and mites, and when these deposits are dispersed and incorporated into the soil, fertility is enhanced. These few examples of the interactions between the soil ecosystem and that above the ground surface illustrate how difficult it is, for practical purposes, to make a rigid definition of the soil fauna.

Although it is recognized that the work and financial budgets of most ecologists do not lend themselves to comprehensive investigations of the precise effects of vertebrate transients on the soil community, there are at least two good reasons why this approach should be encouraged.

First, considerable evidence is available (see Rudd, 1964) that pesticides applied by man to his crops to control populations of insects and other destructive organisms may subsequently accumulate in the soil; DDT, BHC, chlordane, dieldrin, and heptachlor are particularly stable in this respect. These chemical compounds often kill off many animals other than those for which they are intended, but not all animals are equally sensitive to a particular insecticide. For example, slugs, snails, and reptiles can accumulate appreciable quantities of pesticide in their bodies before suffering any toxic effects. Such animals have been termed 'biological concentrators', and theirs is a key role in the transfer of pesticides along food chains, for they act as a link between the soil community and vertebrate predators, particularly birds, living above the soil surface. As these predators consume contaminated prey, they accumulate the pesticide in fat deposits in their bodies. During times of great activity or food shortage, the fat is mobilized, the pesticide is liberated into the circulation, and death follows. Rudd (1964) has coined the term 'delayed expression' to describe the transferral of chemicals along a food chain in such a way that only the top carnivore is killed. He provides strong evidence to show, for example, that the spraying of elms with DDT to control Dutch elm disease has been followed, several months later, by high mortality among robins. The toxic carrier, in this case, was identified as the earthworms living in the sprayed soil: these animals were able to concentrate the pesticide in their bodies to levels 10 times greater than that in the soil. A diet of 100 such earthworms provided a dose of 3 mg of pesticide; a lethal dose as far as the robin is concerned.

Studies such as these emphasize the importance of determining the pathways through which materials and energy leave the soil ecosystem. It is difficult to predict whether the identification of such pathways can make a significant contribution to the solution of the pesticide problem, although we may be optimistic enough to hope so. Certainly, the topic is worthy of more intensive study than has so far been the case, even if, ultimately, the solution may rely more on restricting the use of chemicals to those compounds that decay rapidly after their initial effect has been achieved. As Rudd (1964) remarks:

> The fields, forests, ranges and waters are living systems capable of change. With wise and cautious manipulation these producing environments will continue to supply our needs and pleasures. Prudently directed ecological disturbances for the special satisfactions of man require no justification. When pesticides are skilfully intercalated into living systems with comprehensive knowledge of their target purposes, the effects they produce, and the values they influence, they too require no justification. Unfortunately, most pesticide practices do not measure up to these standards. We have little enough understanding of the dynamics of biological environments. Yet now we are altering them at a rate that precludes our understanding. Moreover, the appearance of new kinds of pesticides and of new and profound effects of those long in use has outpaced the rate at which their effects can be investigated.

Second, it is not only by burrowing in the soil that large vertebrates contribute to erosion. Overgrazing of surface vegetation by herbivorous mammals can expose the soil to the more intensive action of wind and water currents. At the present time, concern is being expressed over such effects produced by elephants overgrazing their pastures in the Kruger National Park. Similar instances could be cited in which rabbits, deer, and cattle are implicated. Wallowing activities of wild pigs, javelina, elephants, and rhinoceros destroy vegetation, converting pasture into mud and dust bowls. The erosion of blanket bog in the English Pennines may be initiated at sites where sheep habitually congregate to shelter against wind and rain, and trampling the vegetation as they do so. The task of the soil conservationist is to identify and correct all possible destructive influences; he must be concerned not only with the events occurring within the soil itself, but also those that impinge on it from outside. Having said this, we must recognize that the task is a formidable one, and at this stage our discussion must be limited to those vertebrates that are considered true soil-dwellers. To this end, we refer briefly to some examples drawn from the Amphibia, Reptilia, and Mammalia.

Amphibia

Apart from certain frogs and toads that burrow in the soil in search of food, such as *Breviceps,* which preys on termites, *Pelobates* (spade-foot toads), and *Microhyla* (narrow-mouthed toads), the main group of amphibian soil-dwellers is the Apoda or Gymnophiona. The Apodans are mainly circum-tropical in distribution, and the 55 known species are classified into about 19 genera, all of which are included in the single family Caecilidae. These animals are well adapted for subterranean life, the body being elongate and vermiform, the skull compact, and the eyes and limbs reduced or absent. They feed on soil insects and other soft-bodied invertebrates. Some Apoda are completely terrestrial as adults and immatures, while the immatures of other species are aquatic. Little is known of the ecology of the group which, for the most part, is regarded more as a zoological curiosity.

Reptilia

Many reptiles use the soil for shelter and concealment, but a few have a closer association with this environment; these include certain tortoises, lizards, and snakes.

The gopher tortoise *Testudo polyphemus* is an inhabitant of desert and sandy soils in North America, and its range extends from Florida to California. It lives in a specially constructed chamber lined with organic debris at the end of a burrow system which may extend to a depth of a metre in the soil. This herbivore feeds at the surface, but undoubtedly transports considerable quantities of vegetable material to the lower layers. The burrow system is almost an ecosystem in miniature, for, in addition to its regular occupant, it provides a home for a variety of non-burrowing animals including cave crickets of the genus *Ceutophilus,* ground beetles, small rodents, and frogs. The enrichment of these underground chambers with organic debris promotes the growth of fungi on which insects, Collembola, and mites feed; these, in turn, serve as food for gopher frogs and skinks.

Special adaptations for living permanently or semipermanently in the soil have been evolved independently in various lizards and snakes. In lizards, streamlining of the body results in the reduction or elimination of the limbs. For example, members of the Scincomorpha (skinks) show various stages in limb regression culminating in limbless forms, such as *Typhlosaurus,* which move in a snakelike manner. Skinks are common in desert regions, and are often referred to as 'sand-swimmers' owing to the ease with which they move through soft sand. In this activity, they are aided by the pointed head which often takes the form of a shovel-shaped rostrum, and protective valves which cover the eyes, nostrils, and mouth against the abrasive effects of the sand. Many of these sand-swimmers burrow as a means of protection against predators and unfavourable conditions at the soil surface, emerging from time to time to feed on insects and other arthropods; the same is true of the 'slow worms' of the family Anguidae which have a widespread distribution from desert to subArctic However, some reptiles are completely subterranean and rarely, if ever, emerge from the soil. Examples of these permanent soil-dwellers are found among the lizards of the family Amphisbaenidae. Slender, for the most part limbless and blind, these lizards travel extensively through the soil in search of their natural diet of worms and insects. Certain snakes, such as members of the genus *Typhlops,* have a similar habit. Little is known of the biology and ecology of these subterranean predators, but it seems reasonable to suggest that their role in the soil community may be quite similar to that of the mole in temperate latitudes.

Mammalia

A close association with the soil is shown by a number of rodents, such as the widely distributed voles (*Microtus*), the gophers (*Geomys* and *Thomomys*) and kangaroo-rats (*Dipodomys*) of North America, the mole-rats (*Spalax*) and spiny-mice (*Acomys*) of the Middle East, various ground squirrels, such as the North American *Citellus leucurus,* and rats (*Neotoma*). These groups, together with the Australian marsupial mice (*Phascogale*), are fossorial in habit, common in deserts, where, with the exception of certain gerbils and ground squirrels, they show a nocturnal activity pattern. The kangaroo-rat *Dipodomys* (Fig. 10.1) of

FIGURE 10.1. The kangaroo-rat *Dipodomys* sp. The powerful hind legs are used for jumping and burrowing.

the American deserts is more closely related to the squirrels than to the rats and mice. It lives in an elaborate burrow system with several entrance and exit holes (Fig. 10.2) leading to a central chamber, often located directly beneath a shrub or bush at a depth of 30 cm to over 2 m below the soil surface. At this depth, the annual range of soil temperature is about 10°C-36°C (Fig. 10.3), and the kangaroo-rat need never be exposed to temperature conditions which would produce undue physiological stress, if it does not emerge from its burrow during

FIGURE 10.2. Burrows made by a kangaroo-rat in the Mojave Desert, near Twentynine Palms, California (photo by author).

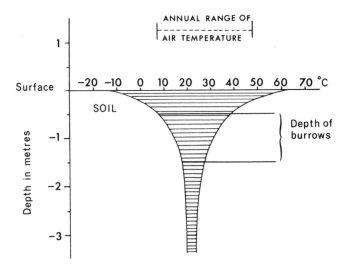

FIGURE 10.3. The relationship between the depth of kangaroo-rat burrows and the annual range of soil temperature in Arizona (after Schmidt-Nielsen, 1964, from Misonne, 1959).

the day (Schmidt-Nielsen, 1964). Kangaroo-rats, along with gerbils, jerboas, and the Australian desert mice *Notomys,* are completely independent of exogenous water: they can live exclusively on dry seeds which are stored in their nests (Schmidt-Nielsen and Schmidt-Nielsen, 1952; Kirmiz, 1962; MacMillen and Lee, 1967), obtaining the water they require mainly from metabolic processes. Such independence requires extremely efficient mechanisms for curtailing water loss through the skin, lungs, and kidney. In these small mammals, the relatively high surface area to volume ratio presents a problem, for if water losses across the skin were not controlled, the water balance of the whole body would be imperilled. The absence of sweat glands may be a method of achieving this control; these animals avoid high temperatures at the soil surface by living underground, so they are not required to expend valuable water reserves in evaporative cooling to resist body temperature increases. During the driest part of the year, many of these small mammals close the mouth of the burrow with a plug of soil, which probably helps to maintain a high humidity in the central nest chamber, particularly when this chamber is situated, as it often is, in the leaf catchment zone (see Cloudsley-Thompson and Chadwick, 1964) directly beneath, or among, the rooting system of a shrub or tree.

Inevitably, some water loss must occur from the lungs during respiration, but even this is restricted to a minimum in the kangaroo-rat, jerboa, and possibly other small mammals of the desert by a nasal cooling device. As dry air is inspired into the nasal chamber, it gathers moisture which evaporates from the nasal mucosa, and the temperature of this mucosa drops due to an evaporative cooling effect. During expiration, the warm, moist air which leaves the lungs is cooled again as it passes over the nasal mucosa, and condensation of water occurs in the nasal chamber. Thus, the air that is eventually released through the nostrils is at a lower temperature than the air in the lungs and, although saturated, contains less moisture than that in the lungs (Schmidt-Nielsen, 1964).

The ureotelic method of excretion occurring among mammals requires that some water be used in the elimination of metabolic waste products. Nevertheless, this process is characterized by a concentration of urea and electrolytes in the kidney. In man, for example, the urine/plasma osmotic ratio is 4·2. Soil-dwelling rodents, living independently of exogenous water, have a much greater capacity for concentrating urine than this: in the kangaroo-rat and gerbil, the urine/plasma ratio is about 14, in the jerboa, it is about 16, and in the Australian *Notomys,* it is higher still, around 18 (Schmidt-Nielsen, 1964; MacMillen and Lee, 1967). Thus, these animals require only about one-quarter to one-fifth of the amount of water to excrete the same amount of urea as does man. This is made possible by the development of a long loop of Henle in the rodent kidney. This loop is the site of an active transport mechanism, producing a considerable concentration difference between ascending and descending parts of the loop.

Although many rodents are associated with the soil to a greater or lesser extent, it is doubtful if any are more completely subterranean than the moles.

The latter are members of the Insectivora, several species of which have become well adapted to life in the soil. The common mole in Europe and western Asia is *Talpa europaea*, an animal which has been the subject of much biological investigation over the years, and to which a recent issue of the *Journal of Zoology* has been almost entirely devoted (see Quilliam, 1966). The genus *Talpa* is also distributed in the Mediterranean region, where it is represented also by the species *T. caeca*, and in eastern Asia, where various subspecies of *T. micrura* occur (Cranbrook, 1966). South African moles belong to a different family, Chrysochloridae, of which *Chrysochloris capensis*, the Cape golden mole, is a well-known example. In North America, the common mole is *Scapanus latimanus*, and in Australia a strong convergence with the true moles is shown by the marsupial *Notoryctes typhlops*. All of these moles excavate burrows in the soil, and, characteristically, show modifications of the pectoral girdle, forelimbs, and associated muscles which allow for such activity. Thus, in *Talpa europaea* and *Scapanus latimanus*, the sternum is elongate, the shoulder joint located far forward in the neck region, the humerus is broad, heavily developed, and capable of being rotated about its long axis, and the manus and claws are strongly developed (Reed, 1951; Yalden, 1966). Similar specializations are present in moles of the *Talpa micrura* group, although these are weaker burrowers than *T. europaea*, probably due to their smaller size (Cranbrook, 1966).

At least in the north temperate zone, moles thrive best in soils of old permanent pasture and deciduous woodland, where organic content is high, and where populations of earthworms, the natural diet of the mole, are flourishing. As a general rule, moles avoid strongly compacted soils under conifer stands where the earthworm fauna is impoverished, although they have been recorded in low numbers in soil under firs, where they produce only surface burrows (Abaturov, 1968). In recent years, the mole has shown an increasing tendency to invade cultivated fields; this may be due to man's destruction of more suitable natural habitats (Armsby *et al.,* 1966).

Talpa europaea excavates burrows of three different types; open trenches, surface burrows, and deep burrows. Open trenches, as their name suggests, are surface channels without any roofing. Surface burrows, located in the topsoil or above ground in litter and moss, are excavated mainly during the summer. They are visible at the surface as ridges formed by the upward compression of the topsoil as the mole digs out the burrow. These burrows are not usually recolonized from year to year, and may be temporary systems produced by young animals soon after they leave the nest. Deep burrows are permanent tunnels, often extending to a depth of 90 cm, and may be used by the moles for several years. They may be extensively developed, forming an anastomosing system (Mellanby, 1966), or short blind alleys (Abaturov, 1968). Deep burrowing occurs chiefly during the autumn and winter in Europe, excavated soil being transported to the surface and heaped into molehills; surface burrowing activity does not usually result in the formation of these mounds. The abundance of molehills is not necessarily indicative of a large population of moles, but rather a reflection of greater searching activity due to scarcity of food (Mellanby, 1966). Thus, in fenland peat soils, where the mole population may be considerably less than in deciduous woodland and where earthworms are scarce, molehills may be produced all the year round.

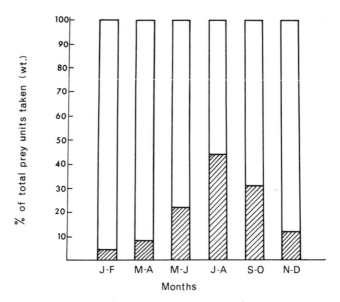

FIGURE 10.4. Seasonal variation in the mole component (shaded areas) of the diet of tawny owls (redrawn after Southern, 1954).

Nests of *T. europaea*, constructed from fragments of vegetation, are located in large surface mounds called 'fortresses'. These mounds are equipped with multiple exit hole systems (Armsby *et al.*, 1966) which may serve not only as escape routes, but also as ventilation shafts. The young are born in early summer, and the population is at a maximum at this time of the year. The dispersal of the young to surface workings during the summer probably encourages predation by tawny owls (Southern, 1954; Morris, 1966), for the mole forms an important part of the diet of these birds at this time of the year (Fig. 10.4). Here is a good example of a simple food chain, organic debris-earthworm-mole-owl, along which materials (including pesticide substances) and energy may be transferred from the soil ecosystem to vertebrates living above the ground.

The mounds of soil deposited at the surface by the deep burrowing activities of the mole have a low organic content, and an impoverished microflora and microfauna. Such molehills are usually colonized by ants, and their organic content increases with time. According to Voronov (1968), such sites are recolonized by xerophytic plants. His investigations at Kazan, USSR, showed that early colonizers included *Brachythecium salebrosum, Marchantia polymorpha, Urtica dioica,* and *Stellaria holostea,* and were followed later by the grasses *Festuca rubra, Agrostis syreistschnikovi, Poa angustifolia,* and *P. pratensis.* He concluded that when molehills are formed in deciduous woodland, the colonization of these by grass species may prevent the regeneration of tree species. This work also included an investigation of the invasion of mole burrows by other animals; a list was compiled of Oligochaetes (8 species), spiders (20 species), beetles (50 species), insect larvae (20 families), Amphibia (5 species), in addition to mice, shrews, and voles. As with the gopher tortoise, the burrow of the mole is a microcosm of animal life, a community system which could well reward further study.

It has long been recognized that earthworms form the main item of the diet of the European mole, and that *Lumbricus terrestris* is particularly favoured in this respect. The prey is not always consumed immediately on capture, for stores of living earthworms, partly immobilized by having the first three or four segments of the body bitten off or mutilated, may be found in or near mole fortresses. However, the mole is not exclusively a predator of earthworms. Analyses of stomach contents have shown that insects and their larvae, myriapods and molluscs are also eaten (Godfrey and Crowcroft, 1960; Raw, 1966), although the proportions of the last two groups are lower than would be expected if random feeding occurred; this suggests that they are less palatable to the moles than are insects and earthworms. The main kinds of insects consumed by *T. europaea* in England are Elateridae, Coleoptera, Bibionidae, Tipulidae, and Lepidopteran larvae. It is unwise, however, to generalize about the diet of the mole under natural conditions, for this may vary with the locality and with the time of year. For example, Oppermann (1968) studied the stomach contents of 293 moles collected throughout the year in the vicinity of Berlin, from various localities including grassland, deciduous forest, and pine forest, and noted that the proportion of Lumbricidae in the stomach contents varied from 10 per cent by volume in pine forest sites in October, to over 90 per cent in deciduous forest in August. The proportions of the various kinds of insect larvae also varied with their availability in the sites investigated. The stomach contents of moles working in soil under pine forest had a larger proportion of insect adults, myriapods, spiders, mites, molluscs, and vertebrates (15 per cent) than was the case in populations living under deciduous woodland and grassland, where these groups constituted 5 per cent, at the most, of the stomach contents. In addition, fragments of *Ascomycetes* were identified in about 30 per cent of the stomachs of moles inhabiting pine forest soil.

It has been estimated (Raw, 1966) that the European mole may consume between 18 and 36 kg of earthworms and insects each year over an area of 0·1 acre. To what extent this predation may regulate the populations of these invertebrates is not known; clearly, this is a question that deserves further study. At present, we know that the activities of moles can have beneficial effects by, for example, increasing aeration and drainage of the soil, promoting the mixing of mineral and organic material, providing suitable habitats for a variety of other animals, and, from man's point of view, possibly controlling populations of potential pests, such as wireworms and Tipulid larvae. The detrimental aspects of the mole's activities include the disturbance of the soil profile, increasing the danger of erosion, preventing natural regeneration of vegetation or, rather, altering the course of ecological succession, and causing mortality in populations of beneficial soil organisms, such as earthworms and myriapods. On balance, is the mole a beneficial or a destructive influence? It is hard to say, but it is certain that these are fascinating creatures.

References

Abaturov, B. D. (1968) 'Vlijanie rojuščej dejatel'nosti krota (*Talpa europaea* L.) na počvennyj pokrov i rastitel'nost' v širokolistvenno-elovom lesu', (English summary.) *Pedobiologia*, **8**, 239-64.

Armsby, A., Quilliam, T. A., and Soehnle, H. (1966) 'Some observations on the ecology of the mole', *J. Zool., Lond.*, **149**, 110-12.

Betts, M. (1955) 'The food of titmice in oak woodland', *J. Anim. Ecol.*, **24**, 282-323.

Cloudsley-Thompson, J. L. and Chadwick, M. J. (1964) *Life in deserts*, Foulis, London, 218 pp.

Cranbrook, Earl of (1966) 'Notes on the relationship between the burrowing capacity, size and shoulder anatomy of some eastern Asiatic moles', *J. Zool., Lond.*, **149**, 65-70.

Godfrey, G. and Crowcroft, P. (1960) *The life of the mole*, Museum, London.

Kirmiz, J. P. (1962) *Adaptation de la gerboise au milieu désertique. Étude comparée de la thermorégulation chez la gerboise* (Dipus aegyptius) *et chez le rat blanc.* Soc. Publ. Égyptiennes, Alexandria. 154 pp.

MacMillen, R. E. and Lee, A. K. (1967) 'Australian desert mice: Independence of exogenous water', *Science*, **158**, 383-5.

Mellanby, K. (1966) 'Mole activity in woodlands, fens and other habitats', *J. Zool., Lond.*, **149**, 35-41.

Missone, X. (1959) 'Analyse zoogeographique des Mammiferes de l'Iran', *Mem. Inst. r.* Sci. Nat. Belg. 2me. ser., **59**, 157 pp.

Morris, P. (1966) 'The mole as a surface dweller', *J. Zool., Lond.*, **149**, 46-9.

Oppermann, J. (1968) 'Die Nahrung des Maulwurfs (*Talpa europaea* L.) in unterschiedlichen Lebensraumen', *Pedobiologia*, **8**, 59-74.

Quilliam, T. A. ed. (1966) 'The mole: its adaptation to an underground environment', *Proc. Ciba Found. J. Zool., Lond.*, **149**, 31-114.

Raw, F. (1966) 'The soil fauna as a food source for moles', *J. Zool., Lond.*, **149**, 50-4.

Reed, C. A. (1951) 'Locomotion and appendicular anatomy in three soricoid insectivores', *Am. Midl. Nat.*, **45**, 513-671.

Rudd, R. L. (1964) *Pesticides and the living landscape*, Faber, London. xiv + 320 pp.

Schmidt-Nielsen, K. (1964) *Desert animals*, Oxford, New York and Oxford. 277 pp.

Schmidt-Nielsen, K. and Schmidt-Nielsen, B. (1952) 'Water metabolism of desert mammals', *Physiol. Rev.*, **32**, 135-66.

Southern, H. N. (1954) 'Tawny owls and their prey', *Ibis*, **96**, 384-410.

Voronov, N. P. (1968) 'Über die Wuhltätigkeit des Maulwurfes (*Talpa europaea* L.)', *Pedobiologia*, **8**, 97-122.

Wallwork, J. A. and Rodriguez, J. G. (1961) 'Ecological studies on oribatid mites with particular reference to their role as intermediate hosta of anoplocephalid cestodes', *J. econ. Ent.*, **54**, 701-5.

Yalden, D. W. (1966) 'The anatomy of mole locomotion', *J. Zool., Lond.*, **149**, 55-64.

11. The regulation of population size

It must be clear, from the accounts given in the previous pages, that there are considerable fluctuations in the size of populations of many soil animals over a period of time. In this chapter, these fluctuations, and the factors that influence them, are considered in some detail.

Theory and Practice

The changes in size taking place in many natural populations often coincide with changes in structure, i.e., changes in the age class composition of the population. Change in size is a function of the difference between the number of individuals added—by birth or immigration, and the number of individuals leaving—by death or emigration. The effects of immigration and emigration on population size and composition are most clearly demonstrated among transient species using the soil as a refuge, and among temporary species that spend only a part of their life cycle in the soil (see chapter 3). The ecological distinction between these two geophilous categories is that the presence of the former group in the soil is due to an avoidance of unfavourable conditions above ground, whereas the presence of temporary species in the soil coincides with the development of a particular stage or stages in the life history. The difference between the geophiles and the true soil-dwellers, the geobionts, is that in the former, one or more age classes (often the adult, at least) are absent from the soil, whereas all stages of the geobionts are represented at some points in the seasonal cycle.

The subject of population dynamics is an extremely broad one, for the description of population changes leads to a more detailed theoretical and practical examination of the factors which regulate the size of animal populations. A knowledge of the effects of these factors enables the ecologist to construct mathematical equations, or models, which describe and predict trends in the growth of populations in the laboratory and the field. Mathematical ecology is a well-established approach to population biology, particularly among experimental ecologists and entomologists whose desire to be able to predict the growth of populations of potential pest species has produced many important contributions (see, for example, Andrewartha and Birch, 1954; Morris, 1959; Slobodkin, 1961; Watt, 1961; Clark *et al.*, 1967). Basic to the method, is the accumulation of life table data, notably concerning natality and the differential mortality of various stages in the life cycle (Southwood, 1966).

Natality

The production of new individuals in many groups of soil animals occurs through the production of eggs, although this method of reproduction may be supplemented occasionally by asexual fragmentation, as in some Enchytraeidae. The total number of eggs produced provides an estimate of fecundity of the adult female, and fertility is measured by the number of viable eggs laid.

Fecundity

Eggs are sometimes deposited singly or, very often, in batches, either naked or in specially constructed cells or chambers. For example, the eggs of Scarabaeid beetles and Diplopods are encased in dung or soil pellets, each containing one or more eggs. In the Annelida, eggs are contained in cocoons, and in the Collembola and Acari, they are deposited in sheltered crevices without a protective covering. Some Acari are viviparous; isopods and pseudoscorpions retain the eggs in a special brood pouch until hatching occurs.

To determine the total number of eggs produced by an adult female it is necessary to know: (a) the size of individual egg batches and (b) the frequency of deposition of egg batches during (c) the reproductive life of the female. These functions are considerably influenced by environmental factors, particularly temperature and moisture conditions and the amount and quality of available food. For example, it has been shown by Rockett and Woodring (1966), that the size of the egg batch produced by the mites *Pergalumna omniphagous* and *Ceratozetes jeweli* varies seasonally; in the former case, eggs are laid singly during the winter, in clumps of four during the spring. This immediately raises the question of what factor, or factors, control egg production, and several possibilities may be considered. Temperature changes, acting directly on the metabolic rate, may influence ovarian activity; this relationship has been demonstrated in the Lumbricidae. The nutritional state of the animal is important, for egg production in *Ceratozetes cisalpinus* in cultures can be reduced to one-tenth of the maximum by varying the diet (Woodring and Cook, 1962). The nutritional factor can be analysed further: into the effects of temperature and moisture, and the amount of suitable food on feeding activity. This activity varies seasonally in the Cryptostigmata, the Lumbricidae, and possibly other groups. Cocoon production, an index of egg production, in the Lumbricidae is reduced when drought inhibits feeding activity, nutrition and fecundity being closely related in this case (Satchell, 1967). On the other hand, too much moisture may also lower cocoon production. Age may also be an important factor, as it is in the Isopoda, where the size of the brood carried by females is strongly correlated with age (as reflected by body size) in *Armadillidium vulgare, Cylisticus convexus,* and *Porcellio scaber* (Hatchett, 1947; Brereton, 1956; Paris and Pitelka, 1962).

There is undoubtedly a relationship between age and the nutritional state in many soil animals, and this is clearly illustrated by feeding experiments with the millipede *Glomeris marginata,* which showed that the ratio between food consumption and body weight decreased with increasing body size (van der Drift, 1951). Feeding activity ceases, or becomes sporadic, in older adults of the cryptostigmatid *Scheloribates laevigatus* and *Ceratozetes cisalpinus* during the post-reproductive period; this may be a sign of senescence, a feature also noted among some Lumbricidae (Satchell, 1967). All these rather isolated pieces of evidence point towards the nutritional state as the most important ultimate factor in determining fecundity; age and environmental effects exert their strongest influence on the reproductive process through their influence on feeding activity.

TABLE 11.1. Size of egg batches deposited in culture by various species of Cryptostigmata.

Species	No. of eggs in batch	Authority
Platynothrus peltifer	3-4	Grandjean, 1950
Belba spp.	1	Pauly, 1956
Ceratozetes cisalpinus	10-16	Woodring and Cook, 1962
Scheloribates laevigatus	3-8	Woodring and Cook, 1962
Oppia nova	1-3	Woodring and Cook, 1962
Pergalumna omniphagous	1-6	Rockett and Woodring, 1966
Ceratozetes jeweli	1-4	Rockett and Woodring, 1966
Galumna confusa	2-9	Woodring, 1965
Rostrozetes flavus	1	Woodring, 1965
Galumna parva	6-8	Woodring, 1965
Scheloribates parabilis	2-3	Woodring, 1965

A word of caution may be interposed here. The use of egg batch size as an index of egg production may not always be valid, although apparently it is in the cryptostigmatids *Pergalumna omniphagous, Ceratozetes jeweli,* and *C. cisalpinus* (Woodring and Cook, 1962). In the last-named species, 10 to 16 eggs may mature simultaneously and be deposited in a single batch (Table 11.1). In contrast, females of *Scheloribates parabilis* can mature 8 to 10 eggs at a time in culture, and deposit these in batches of 2 or 3 over a period of days. The difference in egg production between these two species is obviously not as great as the discrepancy in egg batch size would suggest.

For some of the larger soil animals, such as the Lumbricidae and Diplopoda, and also for nematodes belonging to the genus *Heterodera,* the number of cocoons, egg chambers, or cysts represents the number of egg batches produced, and this can be estimated by direct counts from soil samples or by examination of flotation extracts (Cooper, 1955; Williams and Winslow, 1955). As already noted, the number of cocoons produced in the Lumbricidae is influenced by environmental factors. In the case of the Isopoda, brood production occurs once or twice during each breeding season, as estimated from collections of gravid females. It is much more difficult to determine the number of egg batches produced during the reproductive period by the microarthropod Collembola and Acari, for these masses are small and cannot readily be separated intact from the soil. Culture observations indicate that there is considerable variability in the frequency with which egg batches are produced not only from species to species, but also within the same species as the environmental conditions vary. In small-sized species of Cryptostigmata, such as the brachychthoniid shown in Fig. 11.1 and the common *Oppia nova,* only one egg may mature at a time, and

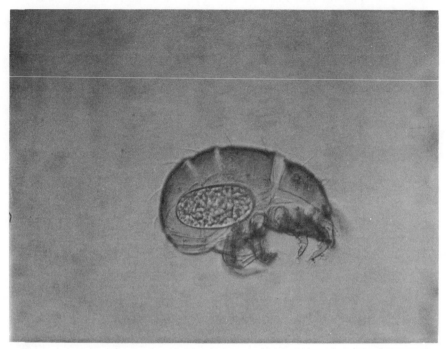

FIGURE 11.1. An adult female cryptostigmatid mite of the family Brachychthoniidae carrying a single egg (photo by author).

oviposition occurs continuously throughout the reproductive life of the female, eggs being laid singly or in small batches with no more than a few hours or a few days between successive ovipositions. In larger species, as noted earlier, several eggs may mature at one time, and successive maturations, if they occur, may be separated by no more than a few weeks. However, in *Galumna parva* only one batch, consisting of six to eight eggs, has been recorded. In *Ceratozetes cisalpinus,* temperature conditions can determine whether or not more than one batch of eggs is laid, for the deposition of a second batch is triggered by exposure to low temperatures for an extended period of time (Woodring and Cook, 1962).

When successive egg batches are produced, it is necessary to determine not only the frequency of deposition, but also the reproductive life of the female, if fecundity is to be estimated. The ease with which this can be done varies from group to group and, in general, is less difficult when the breeding season is clearly defined, as in the case of the Isopoda. In the Californian populations of *Armadillidium vulgare* studied by Paris and Pitelka (1962), many of the one-year-old females produced only one brood, late in the season, whereas two-year-old individuals more often produced two broods. This variability reflects the fact that many one-year-old individuals have not reached sexual maturity by the beginning of their first breeding season. The reproductive life of soil animals is often considerably shorter than the total life span, for example, lumbricids may live for several years and breed only over a period of a few months. The adult of the mite *Oppia nova,* cultured at 25°C, lives for about one month, the reproductive activity of the female being restricted to a period of one week during this time. Other members of this group, *Ceratozetes cisalpinus* and *Scheloribates laevigatus,* commence oviposition two or three weeks after emerging as adults; in the former, as already noted, the reproductive life may be short and confined to the deposition of one egg batch, or longer, producing at least two batches, if low environmental temperatures are sustained. In the absence of low temperatures, the adult female of *C. cisalpinus* will live for about a year without producing any more eggs (Woodring and Cook, 1962).

Fertility

An estimate of the number of viable eggs produced by a population of reproducing females can often be obtained from counts of newly hatched immatures. A measure of egg survival is then given by expressing the counts as a percentage of the total number of eggs produced. This is conveniently done in the Isopoda by examination of gravid females, for a distinction can be made between ova which will develop and those which will not on the basis of opacity and colour (Paris and Pitelka, 1962), in addition to which, newly hatched larvae are retained in the brood pouch along with these eggs. Brereton (1956) calculated that egg survival in *Porcellio scaber* was 82 per cent; in the Californian grassland populations of *Armadillidium vulgare,* survival was higher, around 92-93 per cent (Paris and Pitelka, 1962). Egg survival values of a similar order of magnitude have been recorded for Enchytraeidae, such as *Lumbricillus lineatus,* in which 76 per cent of the eggs were fertile and 74 per cent of these hatched, and *Enchytraeus albidus,* in which the corresponding values were 83 per cent and 97 per cent (Reynoldson, 1939, 1943). Evidently, survival values for the eggs of Lumbricidae are lower than these, for although several eggs are deposited within a cocoon, it is usual for only one to hatch (Gerard, 1967). We know little about egg survival in the microarthropods apart from a few observations on laboratory cultures. For example, Woodring and Cook (1962) showed that diet influenced hatching success, and the subsequent development through the immature instars to the adult, in *Ceratozetes cisalpinus,* 90 per cent survival being obtained with artificial diets and with mushroom and lichen given separately or in combination, compared with a 10 per cent completion of the life cycle on a diet of fungal hyphae alone. However, estimates of this kind, obtained from controlled cultures, may bear little relation

14

to survival rates in natural populations exposed to the effects of a variety of mortality factors.

Mortality

As a general rule, not all of the individuals entering a particular stage in the life cycle survive to enter the succeeding one, and the numerical difference provides an estimate of the mortality in that stage. Mortality rate usually varies from stage to stage, as does the susceptibility to the influence of various environmental factors.

The Efficiency of the Estimate

The efficiency with which mortality can be estimated depends on the efficiency with which successive population estimates can be made. Some of the collecting methods used to obtain population estimates of soil animals either do not extract dead individuals (for example, funnel extractors) or, if they do, fail to separate those living from those dead at the time of sampling (for example, flotation extractors). In the former event, a satisfactory estimate of mortality may be obtained from successive estimates of population size, assuming that the effects of immigration and emigration balance each other, but the absence of dead individuals prevents any examination to determine the causes of death. Counts from flotation extracts may tend to give overestimates of population size and underestimates of mortality.

Mortality Factors

Methods for identifying the causes of natural mortality have been reviewed recently by Southwood (1966), and we are concerned here only with those applied to the soil fauna. Within this context, the small amount of biological material usually available to the investigator precludes the use of some of the more sophisticated methods, such as precipitin testing and isotope labelling, for the detection of predator/prey relationships for example, except in the case of larger arthropods, such as ground beetles (see later). Information obtained from laboratory experiments designed to test the influences of predators, parasites, and climatic factors can have only a limited applicability to natural populations, for it is often difficult to recreate normal environmental conditions and behaviour patterns. For example, it may be demonstrated that the eggs of many cryptostigmatid mites living in temperate regions are killed by exposure to freezing conditions in the laboratory. In the field, there is considerable evidence that many of these species move down the soil profile far enough below the surface to deposit eggs outside the range of freezing temperatures. Thus, the normal behaviour can counter potential mortality factors, and evidence from cultures may be quite misleading in these cases. On the other hand, the determination of tolerance limits in temperature and relative humidity gradients may be useful in interpreting field mortality in poorly developed and exposed soils.

A direct approach to the determination of causes of death may be possible for the larger arthropods, such as the ground beetles, myriapods, spiders, pseudoscorpions, and the Lumbricidae, by the identification of dead or dying individuals in soil samples. Sometimes the cause of death is apparent or, at least, suggested by the physical appearance. As noted earlier, the aborted eggs of isopods can be detected by this means, as can desiccated lumbricids and clumps of pseudoscorpions frozen beneath stones or in bark crevices.

A second method involves the identification of fragments of prey animals in the gut contents of predators. This method may be usefully applied to the larger beetles and centipedes which actually consume the prey, in contrast to those that merely suck the juices.

Finally, causes of death are often inferred from comparisons between population fluctuations and changes in various environmental conditions. For example, summer drought may coincide with a period of population decline in Enchytraeidae or *Tipula* larvae, and, although this coincidence does not establish a cause and effect relationship, this can be tested by determining the tolerance limits of the animals concerned.

We now turn to a more detailed consideration of the specific effects of various mortality factors on populations of soil animals, dealing in particular with such obvious causes as drought, temperature extremes, predation, parasitism, and competition for food.

(a) Drought. Few soil animals can survive for long periods in dry conditions, and when drought occurs it undoubtedly causes considerable mortality among many groups. Enchytraeidae living in sandy permanent pasture in Denmark suffered a population decline during dry summer months, the heavy mortality being directly attributed to the effects of drought (Nielsen, 1955a and b). Declines in the population of *Tipula* larvae inhabiting moorland sites in the English Pennines similarly may have been caused by drying out of the soil during summer drought (Cragg, 1961). On the other hand, animals frequently avoid the effects of drought by moving deeper into the soil. Examples of such movement have been recorded for the slugs *Agriolimax reticulatus, Arion hortensis,* and *Milax budapestensis* in arable soil (Hunter, 1966), and the isopod *Armadillidium vulgare* in Californian coastal grassland (Paris, 1963). This isopod is normally distributed through the top 4 cm of the soil profile, but will descend through cracks and rodent burrows to a depth of 45 cm in some cases, although the majority occurred at a depth between 15 and 25 cm. A similar vertical movement may also be made during the summer months by the lumbricids *Allolobophora caliginosa* and *A. chlorotica* (Gerard, 1967). It may also be recalled that the isopod *Oniscus asellus* has an activity pattern designed to prevent the animal from being entrapped in dry conditions (see chapter 6). When such conditions occur, the normal photonegative response of the animal is

reversed, and it will leave its shelter to search for more moist conditions. The photonegative response is again assumed with the return to damp surroundings (Cloudsley-Thompson, 1952).

Although avoiding reactions are common among soil animals faced with exposure to drying conditions, other members of the fauna are adapted in one way or another to tolerate such conditions. This tolerance may be achieved through anabiosis, as in the nematode *Tylenchus polyhypnus* and the snail *Helix desertorum,* or through a resistant inactive stage which may be produced either

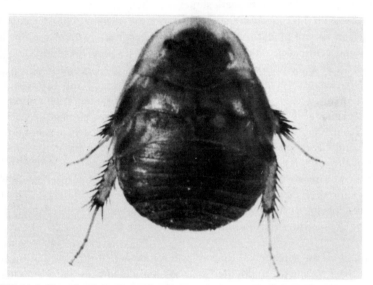

FIGURE 11.2. Nymph of the desert-dwelling roach *Arenivaga.* Note the flattened, discoidal shape of the body and the spiny legs adapted for burrowing in soft sand. Specimen collected in Baja California, Mexico (photo by G. Ott).

rapidly and directly as a response to an environmental change, as among nematodes and protozoans, or as a phenological mechanism which ensures that a drought-resistant stage in the life cycle coincides with drought conditions; the appearance of the pupal stage in soil-dwelling holometabolous insects is a good example of this. Remarkable morphological and physiological adaptations to arid conditions are shown by desert insects which have in common a characteristically low basic transpiration rate, and some of these animals, such as the sand roach *Arenivaga* (Fig. 11.2), are able to take up water from an unsaturated atmosphere against a potential difference of several hundred atmospheres (Edney, 1967).

(b) Temperature extremes. The actual role of temperature conditions in the regulation of size in soil animal populations has been the subject of much speculation, but there is no conclusive evidence that high or low temperatures

have any controlling influence on population size. Except in the most exposed and poorly developed soils, the surface organic layer acts as a buffer against violent fluctuations in temperature (see chapter 1), and even when the surface layer becomes heated or frozen, as occurs in some hot and cold desert soils, many animals can move down the profile to more favourable conditions. A good example of this is provided by the isopod *Hemilepistus reaumuri*, an inhabitant of North African and Middle Eastern deserts, which constructs a burrow system into which it can retreat during the heat of the day. Harvester ants are active on the surface of desert soil in southern California and northern Mexico during the early part of the day, but retreat into their mounds as the surface temperature rises above 30°C.

However, not all soil animals can withdraw easily into the deeper layers of the profile. In temperate regions, non-burrowing forms, such as *Lumbricus castaneus* and *L. rubellus,* and polydesmid millipedes and pseudoscorpions, are sometimes liable to suffer from extremes of temperature; if they cannot find adequate shelter and protection under rocks, in fallen logs, or in clumps of surface vegetation, such as moss, they may succumb. Entire colonies of pseudoscorpions beneath tree bark have been frozen to death during winter, according to Ressl and Beier (1958); death due to frost was considered to be the most important mortality factor among immatures of the slugs *Agriolimax reticulatus* and *Arion hortensis* by Hunter (1966). However, although a particular environmental factor may cause mortality, it does not necessarily follow that this factor exerts a regulating effect on population size. Thus, temperature extremes may cause death among various groups of soil animals, but, as we have already noted, it has not been widely established that this mortality directly determines population size. It is more likely that any regulating effect that the temperature factor has is exerted, directly or indirectly, by limiting fecundity.

(c) Predation. The varied assemblage of predatory forms, to which almost every major group contributes representatives, indicates that this activity is widespread in the soil community, although it is difficult to establish the scale on which it operates as a mortality factor. For example, terrestrial isopods are preyed upon by Carabidae, soil-dwelling urodeles, and lizards, but Paris (1963) could find no evidence that heavy mortality resulted from such predation. Observations on laboratory cultures have shown that pseudoscorpions will attack and devour enchytraeids; a sharp jab from the styletlike mouthparts of bdellid mites will kill Collembola instantly; the mesostigmatid mite *Veigaia mitis* will kill adult Cryptostigmata, and even the latter group, which is predominantly detritivorous in feeding habit, includes at least one species, *Pergalumna omniphagous,* which feeds preferentially in nymphal and adult stages on the nematode plant parasite *Tylenchorhynchus martini* in culture (Rockett and Woodring, 1966). However, it is one thing to demonstrate these relationships in the laboratory, but quite another to confirm that population sizes of prey animals are effectively regulated by this mechanism.

The real difficulty, here, stems from the essential nature of predation in the soil. Much of the information from laboratory cultures suggests that the predator/prey relationship is usually not a simple one, in that the predator is rarely restricted to one kind of prey. For example, veigaiid mites will attack a variety of soft-bodied microarthropods, such as proturans, collembolans, and pauropods (Hurlbutt, 1964), while another mesostigmatid mite *Macrocheles muscaedomesticae* will feed on house fly eggs (Wallwork and Rodriguez, 1963), the nematode *Rhabditella leptura* (Rodriguez et al., 1962), and acarid mites (Axtell, 1963).

Nevertheless, some idea of the effect of predators under natural or semi-natural conditions can be obtained by excluding these animals and noting the subsequent change in prey density. Axtell (1963) reported appreciable decreases (43-96 per cent) in the production of house flies in manure piles with macrochelid mites present, compared with production in fresh manure to which these mites had not been added. However, this effect is undoubtedly over-estimated, for other mortality factors, such as fungal infections, could not be taken into account. A similar reservation has been applied to the estimated predatory effect of carabid and staphylinid beetles on the cabbage root fly *Erioischia brassicae* (Raw, 1967), in which 90 per cent of the mortality occurring in the egg stage was attributed to predation, principally by *Bembidion lampros* (Hughes and Salter, 1959). Carabids and staphylinids have been tested with anti-cabbage root fly serum to identify tissues of this prey in the gut contents (Coaker and Williams, 1963, also quoted in Raw, 1967). This method was used, together with estimates of natural populations of predators, and the survival of the prey in the presence and absence of the predator, to determine that predation accounted for about 60 per cent of the mortality of the immature instars of the prey (Table 11.2). A rather different approach used, for example, by Sheals (1955) excludes the predatory effect by the application to the soil of the insecticide DDT. Predatory mesostigmatid mites are susceptible to this compound, whereas Collembola are not, and Sheals was able to show that Collembola densities increased markedly following the suppression of the mite predators.

A simple system is provided by the soil fungi which prey upon nematodes (Fig. 11.3). Inoculation of soil with *Hyphomycetes* spores, a fungus noted for its development of adhesive discs and ring traps, has provided protection against the

TABLE 11.2. Comparative predation by carabids and staphylinids on immature stages of *Erioischia brassicae* attacking summer cabbages, April, May 1961 (from Raw, 1967).

	Estimated nos.	Mean % reacting with anti-serum	Estimated no. of meals taken	Estimated % mortality on *E. brassicae*
Carabids	11 729	12·3	7209	24
Staphylinids	26 235	7·7	11 351	34

root knot eelworm which parasitizes begonias, and against the sheep nematode *Strongyloides papillosus* (Roubaud and Deschiens, 1941; Deschiens *et al.*, 1943, both quoted in Duddington, 1955), and thus clearly establishes the fungi as an important contributor to the mortality of these nematodes.

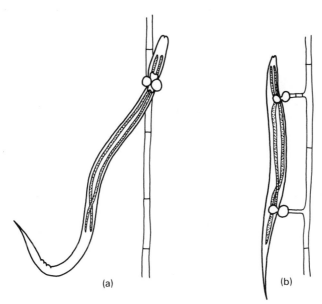

(a)   (b)

FIGURE 11.3. Nematode traps of the predaceous *Hyphomycetes.* (a) Constricting ring of *Dactylella bembicodes,* lateral view; (b) adhesive knobs of *Dactylella ellipsospora* (from Duddington, 1963).

These preliminary observations indicate strongly that predation must be considered an important mortality factor in soil populations. An additional effect may be provided by cannibalism which is known to occur in several groups, including the isopod *Porcellio scaber* (Brereton, 1956), larval lepidopteran cutworms (Singh, 1955), centipedes (Eason, 1964), pseudoscorpions (Ressl and Beier, 1958), and mesostigmatid mites (Axtell, 1963; Wallwork, 1967). However, the picture of predator/prey relationships in the soil is far from complete, for the dynamics of predator populations are not well documented. Populations of predatory mesostigmatid mites often show little or no seasonal fluctuation in size, which suggests that the intensity of predation may be static and unrelated to population changes in the prey organisms. In such cases, regulation of predator populations may be controlled very largely by physical factors in the environment or, as may occur in some pseudoscorpions, by emigration.

(d) Parasitism. The presence of various kinds of parasites has been recorded from a number of groups of soil animals, but their effect as a population regulating

mechanism is not clear. For example, the infestation of cocoons of earthworms, particularly those of *Allolobophora chlorotica,* by the anoetid mite *Histiosoma murchiei,* may produce a high fatality among the eggs of these worms, but, despite the fact that infestation rates of 40-45 per cent have been recorded, fluctuations in the size of the worm population under natural conditions have not been related to this factor (Oliver, 1962). The amount of infestation apparently varies little from year to year, suggesting that parasite and host populations are finely balanced. The occurrence of dipteran tachinid larvae in isopods has been recorded by several workers, but no heavy infestations have been reported. Paris (1963) noted that parasite frequencies of 1·3 per cent and 9·1 per cent in *Porcellio scaber* had been obtained by earlier workers, but could find no evidence of parasitization of populations of *Armadillidium vulgare.*

The effects of parasitism and predation are sometimes difficult to separate, as, for example, in the case of many 'parasitoid' insect larvae. These larvae are parasites during their early development, living in the tissues of the host, but must eat their way out of the host to complete their development. During this process, the host is killed and a major portion of its tissues consumed. Examples of parasitoid larvae are found in the dipteran Sciomyzidae which feed on slugs (Knutson *et al.,* 1965), the hymenopteran Ichneumonidae which infect the wireworm *Agriotes,* and the Staphylinid *Aleochara bilineata* which occurs in dipteran pupae. The mortality resulting from these infestations is difficult to evaluate and distinguish from the effects of predation among soil populations, although it is well worth further study.

(e) Food supply. Restriction to one particular source of food is rare among soil animals. Predators can usually select from a variety of prey animals, as we have seen, and detritivores and fungivores are able to change their diet, depending, in many cases, on the kind of food available to them. This has been demonstrated in the Cryptostigmata (Wallwork, 1958), lithobiomorph centipedes (Lewis, 1965), nematodes (Banage, 1963), and the isopod *Armadillidium vulgare* (Paris, 1963) among others.

In view of this unspecialized feeding activity, it is hard to imagine that death through starvation could contribute significantly to mortality and population regulation in soils having a well developed organic layer, and there is no evidence that it does. However, more information is needed before this effect can be evaluated completely. The feeding habits of immature forms, for example, of the cryptostigmatid mites, are not always easy to define, and there is some evidence to indicate that these stages may be more selective than the adults. For example, culture experiments showed that the larvae of *Ceratozetes cisalpinus* would not survive if they were prevented from feeding on fungal hyphae soon after hatching (Woodring and Cook, 1962). If such a food source were lacking under natural conditions, larval mortality could be appreciable. Further, it must be borne in mind that it is not the amount of food present, but the availability of this food to competing individuals which may act as a population regulating mechanism; Satchell (1967) provides evidence that this competition is an important determinant in earthworm populations. However, this regulation is achieved through the influence of available food on fecundity, rather than on mortality, a point which is taken up in more detail in the next section.

Population Regulation

The identification of mechanisms that regulate the size of natural populations is a difficult and, at best, a speculative exercise, for we have to draw largely on information obtained from observations in the laboratory. The size of these populations is a function of two opposing tendencies, the tendency to increase, through natality or immigration, and the tendency to decrease, through mortality or emigration. The interaction of these two tendencies often causes regular and rather violent fluctuations in numbers about an equilibrium level in stabilized populations. However, it is perhaps important to make the distinction between the factors that produce these fluctuations and those that determine the stability of the population, i.e., those that are truly regulative.

To judge from the information available, no one regulating mechanism can be applied to populations of all groups of soil animals. To a certain extent, this reflects a lack of information about the factors that influence population processes, but it also seems likely that a particular influence, for example, predation, exerts its influence more strongly on some populations than on others. In developing this point further, we can select, in addition to predation, two effects worthy of consideration, namely, climate and food supply.

Predation clearly emerges as a primary population determinant in the case of Collembola, nematodes, and also, possibly, some dipteran larvae. The results of predator exclusion experiments, described earlier in this chapter, point to this and confirm, at least in part, the suggestion by Hairston et al. (1960) that predation is the main regulating influence on primary consumers. However, exceptions to this general statement are not hard to find. For example, the limiting influence of temperature conditions on the length of the reproductive season has been suggested as the principal controlling influence in moorland populations of Cryptostigmata (Block, 1966), in populations of Enchytraeidae inhabiting permanently moist sites (O'Connor, 1967), and in the slug populations of arable soil (Hunter, 1966). This interpretation follows the general principle, proposed by Andrewartha and Birch (1954), that the interaction of favourable and unfavourable environmental factors governs population size in a density-independent manner. As a corollary to this, it must be inferred that no mechanism exists in this system to stabilize population size, for such a mechanism would need to be density-related, i.e., it would have to intensify with increasing population density (Nicholson, 1954). Climatic factors are not, in themselves, density-related, although, in certain cases, their effects on a population may be (Chitty, 1960). Paris (1963) has countered this objection by suggesting that climatic factors (drought in summer, flooding in winter) regulate populations of Armadillidium vulgare, but do so by interacting with population numbers and the amount of available living space, in a density-dependent manner.

The relationship between fecundity and the nutritional state provides another possible mechanism for population regulation, and apparently this is a controlling influence in earthworm populations (Satchell, 1967). These animals feed selectively on material having a high nitrogen content, and this frequently leads to competition. In these cases, the availability of food to competing populations regulates, in a density-dependent fashion, the population size through its effect on fecundity. This particular mechanism may be more widespread among soil populations than is realized at present, for we know little of the relationship between reproductive performance and diet in the case of many soil animals. Very little information is available, for example, about the regulation in predator populations in which competition for available prey may be an important stabilizing factor. In addition, we need to know more of the results of complexes of factors in which density-related effects may act in conjunction with climatic influences to regulate population size. It seems reasonable, from the evidence reviewed in this chapter, to suggest that regulation may be achieved by such a combination of effects in many cases. Many soil animals breed during the spring and early summer, and if a long and adverse winter precedes the breeding season this season will be delayed, and may also be shortened, with the result that the capacity for increase of the population will be lowered. This density-independent, climatic component probably acts in conjunction with predation to control the size of populations of primary consumers in the soil. This interpretation of population regulation conforms with Milne's (1962) suggestion that density-independent (climatic) and imperfectly density-dependent (interspecific competition) factors are primary regulators, and that it is only when these fail that the true density-dependent influence of intraspecific competition for food comes into play.

Little can be said about the possible regulating influence of immigration and emigration, as far as the populations of true soil-dwelling animals are concerned, for there is no evidence that such populations undertake mass movements of the type shown by certain phytophagous insects, for example. Seasonal shifts in the centre of population density are well marked in many soil animals, but these shifts are reversible, as, for instance, in the case of diurnal and seasonal vertical movements, and may have little controlling effect on population size. Exceptions to this may be found among the ants and termites, in which periodic mass emigrations may seriously deplete the parent colonies. These movements may be the outcome of intraspecific competition for nesting and mating sites and food supply, as noted in chapter 7, in which case true density-dependent regulation may be of primary importance in the social insects. Many geophilous insects immigrate to the soil as eggs or larvae, and emigrate as emerging adults, but, although these movements may cause considerable fluctuations in the numbers present in the soil, they are cyclical phenomena and have little to do with regulation.

References

Andrewartha, H. G. and Birch, L. C. (1954) *The distribution and abundance of animals*, Univ. of Chicago, Chicago.

Axtell, R. C. (1963) 'Manure-inhabiting Macrochelidae (Acarina: Mesostigmata) predaceous on the house fly' in Naegele, J. A., ed., *Advances in Acarology, I*, 55-9.

Banage, W. B. (1963) 'The ecological importance of free-living soil nematodes with special reference to those of moorland soil', *J. Anim. Ecol., 32*, 133-40.

Block, W. (1966) 'Seasonal fluctuations and distribution of mite populations in moorland soils, with a note on biomass', *J. Anim. Ecol., 35*, 487-503.

Brereton, J. LeG. (1956) *A study of some factors controlling the population of some terrestrial isopods*. Ph.D. Thesis, Oxford University.

Chitty, D. (1960) 'Population processes in the vole and their relevance to general theory', *Canad. J. Zool., 38*, 99-113.

Clark, L. R., Geier, P. W., Hughes, R. D. and Morris, R. F. (1967) *The ecology of insect populations in theory and practice*, Methuen, London. xiii + 232 pp.

Cloudsley-Thompson, J. L. (1952) 'Studies in diurnal rhythms. II. Changes in the physiological responses of the woodlouse *Oniscus asellus* to environmental stimuli', *J. exp. Biol., 29*, 295-303.

Coaker, T. H. and Williams, D. A. (1963) 'The importance of some Carabidae and Staphylinidae as predators of the cabbage root fly, *Erioischia brassicae* (Bouché)', *Ent. exp. appl., 6*, 156-64.

Cooper, B. A. (1955) 'A mechanical device for concentrating *Heterodera* cysts (Nematoda)', in Kevan, D. K. McE., ed., *Soil zoology*, 385-9.

Cragg, J. B. (1961) 'Some aspects of the ecology of moorland animals', *J. Anim. Ecol., 30*, 205-34.

Deschiens, R., Lamy, L., and Vautrin, E. (1943) 'Essais practiques de prophylaxie de l'anguillulose des végétaux par l'emploi d'Hyphomycètes prédateurs', *C. R. Acad. Sci., Paris, 216*, 539-41.

Drift, J. van der (1951) 'Analysis of the animal community in a beech forest floor', *Tijdschr. Ent., 94*, 1-168.

Duddington, C. L. (1955) 'Inter-relations between soil micro-flora and soil nematodes' in Kevan, D. K. McE., ed., *Soil zoology*, 284-301.

Duddington, C. L. (1963) 'Predacious fungi and soil nematodes' in Doeksen, J. and Drift, J. van der, eds., *Soil organisms*, 298-304.

Eason, E. H. (1964) *Centipedes of the British Isles*, Warne, London. x + 294 pp.

Edney, E. B. (1967) 'Water balance in desert arthropods', *Science, 156*, 1059-66.

Gerard B. M. (1967) 'Factors affecting earthworms in pastures', *J. Anim. Ecol., 36*, 235-52.

Grandjean F. (1950) 'Observations éthologiques sur *Camisia segnis* (Herm.) et *Platynothrus peltifer* (Koch)', *Bull. Mus. Hist. nat.* Paris, *22*, 224-31.

Hairston, N. G., Smith, F. E., and Slobodkin, L. B. (1960) 'Community structure, population control and competition', *Amer. Nat., 94*, 421-25.

Hatchett, S. P. (1947) 'Biology of the Isopoda of Michigan', *Ecol. Monogr., 17*, 47-79.

Hughes, R. D. and Salter, D. D. (1959) 'Natural mortality of *Erioischia brassicae* (Bouché) (Diptera, Anthomyiidae) during the immature stages of the first generation', *J. Anim. Ecol., 28*, 231-41.

Hunter, P. J. (1966) 'The distribution and abundance of slugs on an arable plot in Northumberland', *J. Anim. Ecol., 35*, 543-57.

Hurlbutt, H. (1964) 'Structure and distribution of *Veigaia* (Mesostigmata) in forest soils', *Acarologia, 6*, (fasc. h.s., C.R. Ier Congrès Int. d'Acarologie, Fort Collins, Col., U.S.A., 1963), 150-2.

Knutson, L. V., Stephenson, J. W., and Berg, C. O. (1965) 'Biology of a slug-killing fly, *Tetanocera elata* (Diptera: Sciomyzidae)', *Proc. malac. Soc. Lond.,* **36,** 213-20.

Lewis, J. G. E. (1965) 'The food and reproductive cycles of the centipedes *Lithobius variegatus* and *L. forficatus* in a Yorkshire woodland', *Proc. zool. Soc. Lond.,* **144,** 269-83.

Milne, A. (1962) 'On a theory of natural control of insect population', *J. theor. Biol.,* **3,** 19-50.

Morris, R. F. (1959) 'Single factor analysis in population dynamics', *Ecology,* **40,** 580-8.

Nicholson, A. J. (1954) 'An outline of the dynamics of animal populations', *Aust. J. Zool.* **2,** 9-65.

Nielsen, C. O. (1955a) 'Survey of a year's results obtained by a recent method for the extraction of soil-inhabiting enchytraeid worms' in Kevan, D. K. McE., ed., *Soil zoology,* **202-14.**

Nielsen, C. O. (1955b) 'Studies on the Enchytraeidae. 2. Field studies', *Natura jutl.,* **4,** 1-58.

O'Connor, F. B. (1967) 'The Enchytraeidae' in Burges, N. A. and Raw, F., eds., *Soil biology,* 213-57.

Oliver, J. H. (1962) 'A mite parasitic in the cocoons of earthworms', *J. Parasit.,* **48,** 120-3.

Paris, O. H. (1963) 'The ecology of *Armadillidium vulgare* (Isopoda: Oniscoidea) in California grassland: food, enemies and weather', *Ecol. Monogr.,* **33,** 1-22.

Paris, O. H. and Pitelka, F. A. (1962) 'Population characteristics of the terrestrial isopod *Armadillidium vulgare* in California grassland', *Ecology,* **43,** 229-48.

Pauly, F. (1956) 'Zur Biologie einiger Belbiden und zür Funktion ihrer pseudostigmatischen Organe', *Zool. Jb. (Syst.),* **84,** 275-328.

Raw, F. (1967) 'Arthropoda (except Acari and Collembola)' in Burges, N. A. and Raw, F., eds., *Soil biology,* 323-62.

Ressl, F. and Beier, M. (1958) 'Zur Okologie, Biologie und Phanologie der heimischen Pseudoskorpione', *Zool. Jb. (Syst.),* **80,** 407-50.

Reynoldson, T. B. (1939) 'On the life history and ecology of *Lumbricillus lineatus* Müll. (Oligochaeta)', *Ann. appl. Biol.,* **26,** 782-98.

Reynoldson, T. B. (1943) 'A comparative account of the life cycles of *Lumbricillus lineatus* Müll. and *Enchytraeus albidus* Henle in relation to temperature', *Ann. appl. Biol.,* **30,** 60-6.

Rockett, C. L. and Woodring, J. P. (1966) 'Biological investigations on a new species of *Ceratozetes* and of *Pergalumna* (Acarina: Cryptostigmata)', *Acarologia,* **8,** 511-20.

Rodriguez, J. G., Wade, C. F., and Wells, C. N. (1962) 'Nematodes as a natural food for *Macrocheles muscaedomesticae* (Acarina: Macrochelidae), a predator of the house fly egg', *Ann. ent. Soc. Am.,* **55,** 507-11.

Roubaud, E. and Deschiens, R. (1941) 'Essais relatifs à la prophylaxie de l'anguillulose du mouton par l'usage des Hyphomycètes prédateurs du sol', *C. R. Soc. Biol., Paris,* **135,** 687-90.

Satchell, J. E. (1967) 'Lumbricidae' in Burges, N. A. and Raw, F., eds., *Soil biology,* 259-322.

Sheals, J. G. (1955) 'The effects of DDT and BHC on soil Collembola and Acarina' in Kevan, D. K. McE., ed., *Soil zoology,* 241-52.

Singh, M. P. (1955) 'A note on cutworms and their rearing' in Kevan, D. K. McE., ed., *Soil zoology,* 281-3.

Slobodkin, L. B. (1961) *Growth and regulation of animal populations,* Holt, Rinehart, and Winston, New York.

Southwood, T. R. E. (1966) *Ecological methods,* Methuen, London. xviii + 391 pp.

Wallwork, J. A. (1958) 'Notes on the feeding behaviour of some forest soil mites', *Oikos,* **9,** 260-71.

Wallwork, J. A. (1967) 'Acari' in Burges, N. A. and Raw, F., eds., *Soil biology,* 363-95.

Wallwork, J. H. and Rodriguez, J. G. (1963) 'The effect of ammonia on the predation rate of *Macrocheles muscaedomesticae* (Acarina: Macrochelidae) on house fly eggs' in Naegele, J. A., ed., *Advances in Acarology, I* 60-9.

Watt, K. E. F. (1961) 'Mathematical models for use in insect pest control', *Canad. Ent.,* **93,** suppl., 1-62.

Williams, T. D. and Winslow, R. D. (1955) 'A synopsis of some laboratory techniques used in the quantitative recovery of cyst-forming and other nematodes from soil', in Kevan, D. K. McE., ed., *Soil zoology,* 375-84.

Woodring, J. P. (1965) 'The biology of five new species of oribatids from Louisiana', *Acarologia,* **7,** 564-76.

Woodring, J. P. and Cook, E. F. (1962) 'The biology of *Ceratozetes cisalpinus* Berlese, *Scheloribates laevigatus* Koch, and *Oppia neerlandica* Oudemans (Oribatei), with a description of all stages', *Acarologia,* **4,** 101-37.

12. The character of the soil community

The various groups of organisms that live in the soil form an integrated system, sometimes referred to as the 'soil community' or, when the definition includes the effective environment, the 'soil ecosystem'. In this chapter, we consider some of the methods used to define this community, and also the variations in its character from place to place; in the next chapter, the community is considered as a functional system. This system is intimately connected with the decomposition of organic material in the soil, and the subsequent release of inorganic nutrients which then become available to the higher plants growing in the soil.

Throughout this chapter and the next, the soil community is treated as a unit, isolated from other terrestrial and aquatic communities. This is purely a matter of convenience and is not intended to imply that the boundaries of this community are rigidly defined. As Ghilarov (1968) has pointed out, there is considerable overlap between species populations inhabiting the soil and those living above the surface of the ground. Horizontal variations in the distribution of soil animals are often described in terms of not one, but a series of communities, although it would be more correct, perhaps, to consider these as a continuum, a mosaic of species populations with overlapping ranges. However, it is unnecessary for us to be concerned with these problems of definition, for they have been adequately dealt with by Macfadyen (1963a). Since a functional system implies an association of species populations, it is with the definition of such associations that we are initially concerned.

Natural Associations of Species

One of the first tasks to be undertaken in studying the soil community is to determine its composition. This can be achieved by taking samples, as soil cores, in a random manner from the locality in question. Animals can be extracted from these cores (see chapter 14) and identified and counted. The information obtained by this procedure can be used, not only to compile a check list of the fauna present, but also to gain some idea of the distribution patterns of various species populations and their numerical importance in relation to the total fauna. This relationship can be expressed in a number of ways, the most common of which make use of the concepts of 'frequency' and 'abundance'.

Frequency

The microdistribution pattern of many populations of soil animals is such that any given species may be encountered in some of the samples but not in others, and hence has a frequency of occurrence which can be expressed as a percentage:

Frequency per cent

$$= \frac{\text{Number of sampling units with species A present}}{\text{Total number of sampling units taken}} \times 100$$

Abundance

The density or abundance of a particular species is a relationship between the numbers present and a unit measure of the environment. Often, this is expressed as a mean, or average, number of individuals per unit area or volume, and is based on a sample consisting of a certain number of sampling units (soil cores). Counting every soil animal can be a tedious process, particularly when the sampling unit size is large; however, it is sometimes sufficient, for comparative purposes, to use one of the several schemes of abundance rankings that have been proposed. Thus, a species can be considered 'rare' if its average density is, say, less than five, 'occasional' if its average density lies between 5 and 14 individuals per unit area, 'frequent' if this density is between 15 and 29, 'abundant' between 30 and 99, and 'very abundant' if more than 100. Obviously, these rankings are, to a large extent, subjective; their definition will depend on the order of magnitude of the population under consideration, and will vary from group to group.

Quite often, for example, when it is desired to compare the horizontal patterns of several species, use is made of the relationship between the number of individuals of any one species in a sampling unit and the total number of individuals of all species occurring in this unit. This provides a measure of the relative abundance of a given species, such that:

Relative abundance per cent

$$= \frac{\text{Number of individuals of species A/unit}}{\text{Number of individuals of all species/unit}} \times 100$$

Relationship between Frequency and Relative Abundance

In soil faunal studies, at least, it is often the case that frequency and relative abundance, although not necessarily related, go hand in hand, i.e., the higher the frequency the higher the relative abundance and vice versa. This is very convenient from the point of view of the ecologist whose main concerns may be to describe a community in terms of its faunal composition, and to compare two or more communities on this basis. Frequency determinations are much easier to make and much less laborious than the detailed counts required for estimates of relative abundance, and if they can be substituted for the latter, much dull routine work may be avoided. The two-way classification scheme presented in Table 12.1 emphasizes this fact, for it may be noted that species with a high relative abundance are also the most frequent, and that the majority of the species showing a low relative abundance also have a low frequency.

TABLE 12.1. Two-way classification of cryptostigmatid species from two pasture soils in Kentucky, USA. Species are listed in order of relative abundance (data from Ibarra *et. al.,* 1965).

		SHEEP PASTURE		CATTLE PASTURE	
		CATEGORIES OF RELATIVE ABUNDANCE			
		Prominent 10%	Subordinate 1-10%	Prominent 10%	Subordinate 1-10%
CATEGORIES OF FREQUENCY	Constant F >50%	*Scheloribates laevigatus* *Parapelops* sp. *Eupelops* sp.	*Anachipteria* sp. *Oribatula* sp. *Pergalumna* sp.	*Eupelops* sp. *Galumna curvum*	
	Accessory F <50%		*Oppia nova* *Galumna curvum* *Tectocepheus velatus*		*Oribatula* sp. *Zygoribatula rostrata* *Tectocepheus velatus* *Galumna virginiensis* *Lamellobates* sp. *Platynothrus peltifer* *Oppia nova* *Pergalumna* sp.

Delimitation of Natural Associations of Species

The concepts of frequency and, to a lesser extent, relative abundance form the bases for faunal comparisons which may provide a way of defining a recurrent group of species, identifiable with a particular locality or habitat. The problems involved in this approach have been discussed by Fager (1957), Balogh (1958), and Mountford (1962) among others, and a detailed account of these cannot be included here. However, mention may be made of a few simple methods of analysis commonly used in faunal comparisons, of which Sørensen's (1948) Quotient of Similarity (Q/S) is a good example.

The index Q/S is calculated from comparisons of the fauna taken in two samples or series of samples, using the expression:

$$Q/S = \frac{2j}{(a+b)} \times 100$$

Where j is the number of species common to both samples, a is the number of species recorded from sample A, and b the number of species recorded from sample B. Sørensen's quotient increases as the value of j increases, and expresses 100 per cent similarity when all species are common to both samples. An illustration of the application of this method is provided in Table 12.2 in which

TABLE 12.2. Coincidence table showing Sørensen's Quotient (Q/S) calculated for four habitats on Hermitage Plain, Denmark (from Haarløv, 1960).[1, 2]

	Hawthorn thicket	Level pasture	Ant mound N. side	Ant mound S. side
Hawthorn thicket	70	39	35	28
Level pasture	39	49	50	42
Ant mound, N. side	35	50	59	52
Ant mound, S. side	28	42	52	66

[1] Q/S values pooled from 5 x 5 sample comparisons for each pair of habitats.
[2] 'Internal Q/S', calculated from 5 samples taken within each habitat, is underlined.

the microarthropod fauna of four habitats is compared. Faunal similarities between sampling units taken from the same habitat can be calculated ('internal Q/S'), in addition to quotients of similarity determined from comparisons of samples taken from pairs of habitats. These latter comparisons are only valid if the similarity between samples taken from the same habitat or site (i.e., the internal Q/S) is greater than that obtained when this habitat is compared with another. Referring to the table, it may be noted that a distinction can be made between the fauna of the habitats *hawthorn thicket, ant mound south side,* and *ant mound north side,* for these three habitats have internal Q/S values which are higher than those obtained by comparing them individually with other habitats. The internal Q/S value for *level pasture* is lower than that for the comparison: *level pasture* x *ant mound north side,* indicating that the species composition and distribution pattern in the level pasture site is too variable to allow comparison with the fauna of the ant mound, north side.

The Sørensen quotient measures the amount of diversity (or, more correctly, the lack of it) of the fauna of a particular site or sites, and it can be used to obtain an approximate idea of the limits of the horizontal distribution of a particular group of species. From it, we learn that the species composition of the soil community varies with soil type, vegetation, and climate, as do certain biological processes occurring in soil, for example, the type and rate of decomposition of organic material, the extent and development of organo-mineral complexes, and the rate of release of plant nutrients. From the functional point of view, we are interested in determining how variations in the species composition of the soil fauna influence these various processes. It must be borne in mind, however, that the character of the soil community may vary not only qualitatively but also quantitatively. To take a hypothetical example, it is conceivable that a comparison of two samples, one taken from chalk grassland and the other from a neighbouring beech woodland, would provide a high quotient of similarity, using Sørensen's method, i.e., the two sites would have many species in common. Despite this qualitative similarity, it is equally possible that a particular species common to both is rare in one site and very abundant in the other. Such quantitative differences may be reflected in the way the soil community functions in the two sites. Thus, in grassland, where lumbricids are relatively more abundant, the formation of organo-mineral complexes will be more extensive than in the woodland. The Sørensen approach is based on frequency rather than relative abundance, and will be insensitive in analysing the functional limits of the community where these two parameters are not related in a linear manner. Several methods of comparison have been proposed based on differences in abundance of a given species in two sites, and as an illustration of this approach we may consider two of these, namely, Bellinger's Coefficient and Renkonen's Number.

The Bellinger Coefficient seeks to detect significant discontinuities in the horizontal distribution of individual species populations; it has been applied to Collembola (Bellinger, 1954) and cryptostigmatid mites (Wallwork and Rodriguez, 1961). The abundance of a given species in two sites or samples is compared, and the coefficient calculated from the expression:

$$\frac{(p - q)^2}{p + q}$$

Where p is the number of occasions on which the species occurs in greater numbers in site (or sample) I than in site II, and q the number of occasions when the reverse is the case. This method can be used to test for significant differences between population sizes of a given species in two samples taken from the same or different habitats, for the coefficient will increase as the difference between population sizes increases. If the calculated coefficient exceeds 3·84, it is significant at the 5 per cent level.

Renkonen's (1938) method differs from the above in being based on a comparison of the total faunal content of two or more sites, and in using the criterion of relative abundance rather than abundance. The Renkonen Number is calculated for any pair of sites (or samples) by determining the lower relative abundance value for each of the species present in both sites (species present in only one of the two sites are ignored), and then summing these values. For example, if species A and B are present in two sites, such that the relative abundance of A in site I is 60 per cent and in site II is 10 per cent, and the relative abundance of B in the two sites is 40 per cent and 90 per cent, respectively, the Renkonen Number, expressing the faunal similarity between sites I and II, is given by:

$$10 + 40 = 50\%$$

The reliability of the index increases with the number of species involved in the comparison. Furthermore, if several sites are compared in pairs in this way, they can be arranged in a hierarchical relationship to indicate the extent of the similarities of their fauna. For example, if we consider the data provided in Table 12.3, each of the five sites can be compared with all of the others, and Renkonen's Number calculated for the comparisons: I/II, I/III, I/IV, I/V, II/III, II/IV, etc., and the results expressed in the tabular form shown in Table 12.4.

TABLE 12.3. Relative abundance values for 20 species of soil mite in 5 different woodland sites (hypothetical data).

Species	Sampling sites				
	I	II	III	IV	V
A	20·6	11·3	15·1	17·5	28·2
B	5·2	–	–	6·0	2·6
C	17·1	3·6	5·6	–	–
D	–	4·4	–	5·1	1·8
E	–	1·0	–	10·8	5·7
F	3·2	–	10·8	3·4	–
G	5·7	–	7·4	–	8·6
H	13·8	10·9	1·8	–	5·5
I	12·2	21·5	15·6	–	–
J	–	7·7	–	7·1	10·4
K	1·6	15·0	7·1	9·9	2·3
L	–	2·1	9·6	10·4	–
M	3·4	–	2·4	–	5·6
N	2·1	–	5·6	–	1·8
O	–	6·5	3·0	5·3	–
P	–	10·0	–	1·6	–
Q	–	4·6	8·5	8·9	–
R	8·6	2·1	–	4·0	7·5
S	4·0	–	1·5	–	13·6
T	2·5	–	6·0	10·0	6·4

TABLE 12.4. Coincidence table showing Renkonen numbers calculated for pairs of sites from the data presented in Table 12.3.

I	II	III	IV	V	
100	41·7	53·7	34·0	55·2	I
	100	49·1	49·4	31·7	II
		100	52·7	38·3	III
			100	47·4	IV
				100	V

These results can then be arranged in the hierarchical form shown in Fig. 12.1, which is based on a scheme of classification proposed by Mountford (1962), and developed in the following way. The coincidence table is examined, and the pair

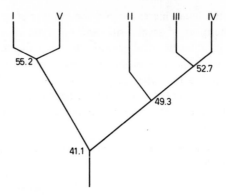

FIGURE 12.1. Classification of the faunal similarities between five sites (for explanation, see text).

of sites having the highest similarity index (in this case, I and V with 55·2 per cent) are grouped together, and the indices of similarity between this group (I, V) and each of the remaining sites are determined from the following equations:

$$\text{Index (I, V: II)} = \frac{(\text{I} \times \text{II}) + (\text{V} \times \text{II})}{2} = 36·7 \tag{1}$$

$$\text{Index (I, V: III)} = \frac{(\text{I} \times \text{III}) + (\text{V} \times \text{III})}{2} = 46·0 \tag{2}$$

and so on, until the following reduced table is obtained:

	(I, V)	II	III	IV
(I, V)		36·7	46·0	40·7
II			49·1	49·4
III				52·7

The highest index in this table is between sites III and IV, and indices are now calculated between this group and (I, V) and II, respectively. The equations involved are:

$$\text{(III, IV: I, V)} = \frac{(\text{III} \times \text{I}) + (\text{III} \times \text{V}) + (\text{IV} \times \text{I}) + (\text{IV} \times \text{V})}{4} \tag{3}$$

$$= \frac{53·7 + 38·3 + 34·0 + 47·4}{4} = 43·3$$

$$\text{(III, IV: II)} = \frac{(\text{III} \times \text{II}) + (\text{IV} \times \text{II})}{2} = 49·3 \tag{4}$$

Thus, the table reduces to:

	(I, V)	(III, IV)	II
(I, V)		43·3	36·7
(III, IV)			49·3

from which it is evident that site II has a greater similarity to the group (III, IV) than to (I, V). By this analysis, the five sites have been classified into two groups, for which an index of similarity can be calculated using the following equation:

Index (I, V: II, III, IV)

$$= \frac{(I \times II) + (I \times III) + (I \times IV) + (V \times II) + (V \times III) + (V \times IV)}{6} \tag{5}$$

$$= 41 \cdot 1$$

Thus, the relationship between the two groups of sites is:

	(II, III, IV)
(I, V)	41·1

Mountford (1962) used this method in conjunction with an Index of Similarity based on frequencies, for which the expression:

$$\frac{2j}{2ab - (a + b)j}$$

is an approximation; the quantities a, b and j being defined as in Sørensen's method.

These are but a few of the many methods that can be used to describe the variations in the horizontal distribution pattern of populations of soil animals, and these variations are usually analysed with respect to variations in some environmental factor, such as vegetation type, soil type, or soil moisture content. We now consider some of the results obtained by these analyses, using differences in vegetation type as a general point of reference.

The Fauna of Grassland Soils

Natural grassland, variously termed 'prairie', 'pampas', 'savannah', and 'steppe', occurs in the interior of many of the great land masses where the annual rainfall is inadequate for forest development. Such 'climatic' grasslands contrast with those in western Europe which are maintained by the activities of grazing animals and by burning. The broad category 'grassland' comprises various subdivisions, the best documented of which, from the point of view of the soil fauna, are lowland permanent pasture and sandy heath, and upland moorland and heath, of temperate regions.

Lowland grasslands support a very varied fauna, as a general rule, particularly where mull humus formation occurs. In base-rich grasslands, earthworms of the family Lumbricidae occur in densities of up to, and occasionally in excess of, 500/m² (Reynoldson, 1955; Svendsen, 1957; Satchell, 1967); at these higher densities, their biomass may exceed 100 g/m², and their contribution to the overall effect of the soil community overshadows that of the rest of the fauna. However, the arthropod component of the fauna in these soils is far from impoverished, as Table 12.5 shows, and Salt *et al.* (1948) recorded no less than

TABLE 12.5. Densities, expressed as thousands/m², and numbers of species (in parentheses) of Acari and Collembola in various lowland grassland soils (after Wood, 1966).

Acari	Collembola	Total	Habitat and authority
232 (?)	66 (25)	298 (?)	Old pasture (Salt *et al.,* 1948)
172 (52)	32 (21)	204 (73)	*Molinia* fen (Macfadyen, 1952)
221 (87)	14 (20)	235 (107)	Old meadow (Hairston and Byers, 1954)
179 (161)	109 (32)	288 (193)	Old pasture (Haarløv, 1960)
24 (83)	8 (16)	32 (99)	Old pasture (Weis-Fogh, 1948)
34 (36)	23 (18)	57 (54)	Old grassland (Sheals, 1957)
32 (19)	26 (16)	58 (35)	Old pasture (Dhillon and Gibson, 1962)
18 (51)	18 (21)	36 (72)	Old pasture (Davis, 1963)

19 arthropod Orders from a Cambridgeshire pasture soil, of which the Coleoptera, Diptera, Thysanoptera, Hemiptera, Thysanura, Collembola, and Acari were represented, in most cases in densities of several thousand per square metre. Lower, but still appreciable, populations of Diplopoda, Chilopoda, Symphyla, and Protura were also present. The microdistribution pattern of this fauna is far from uniform and is influenced by a number of factors. Variations in faunal composition occur vertically, and also horizontally, within a particular grassland area. We have already noted in chapter 5 that certain earthworm species, such as *Allolobophora chlorotica, A. caliginosa,* and *A. rosea,* are restricted to the upper layers of the soil profile, whereas *Octolasium cyaneum* and *Lumbricus terrestris* are often found deeper in the profile. In the case of soil microarthropods, many of which do not burrow actively but make use of existing pore spaces in the soil, small-sized species tend to predominate in the lower regions of the A horizon,

and here there is a preponderance of cryptostigmatid mites, belonging to the genus *Oppia,* collembolans, such as *Onychiurus, Tullbergia,* and *Friesea* species, symphylids, pauropods, and proturans. In the surface layers, are located the larger and more active Collembola, such as *Entomobrya* and the Symphypleona, macrochelid, prostigmatid and cryptostigmatid mites, and insects such as the Coleoptera, Orthoptera, Hemiptera, and Thysanura. Microdistribution patterns also appear to be influenced by soil moisture content. For example, a detailed investigation of the horizontal distribution of mites and Collembola in a Danish pasture (Weis-Fogh, 1948) showed that Collembola and prostigmatid mites were relatively more abundant on dry sites than on wet ones, whereas the reverse was the case with the mites belonging to the orders Cryptostigmata and Mesostigmata. However, when the microdistribution patterns of individual species populations are considered, 'wet' and 'dry' associations are notoriously difficult to define for the ranges of these populations often overlap in a mosaic arrangement. Only in extreme conditions, can 'indicator' species be defined, as Haarløv (1960) showed in a study of the microarthropod fauna of grassland soils in Jaegersborg Park, Copenhagen, Denmark. He could define a 'wet' association for a pond margin numerically dominated by the collembolan *Isotomurus palustris,* and a 'dry' association indicated by the presence of the cryptostigmatid *Passalozetes perforatus* on ant hills, but his results indicate a considerable amount of intergradation of populations between these two extremes. 'Indicator' species, particularly among the macrofauna, are perhaps more common in the soils of chalk grassland, good examples of which occur in the Chiltern Hills of southern England. Conspicuous among this fauna are the isopod *Armadillidium vulgare,* the millipede *Glomeris marginata,* snails belonging to the genera *Cepaea* and *Hygromia,* harvestmen belonging to the family Trogulidae, and carabid beetles. However, many of these groups are indicators of the chalky condition of the soil rather than of grassland vegetation, for they also occur in woodland, such as beech stands growing on chalk, where the mull-type soil profile often resembles that developed under grass on chalky sites.

   Much of the upland moorland and heath in Britain supports a mixed vegetation consisting of *Calluna vulgaris, Eriophorum vaginatum, Empetrum nigrum, Vaccinium,* and *Sphagnum,* covering blanket bog peat, and occurring side by side with tracts of grassland maintained by the activities of grazing sheep. These grasslands are present on brown earth limestone sites, and also on alluvial clay and sandy drift, the former supporting a variety of grass species, such as *Festuca ovina, Agrostis tenuis, Anthoxanthum odoratum, Sesleria caerulia,* and *Helictotrichon pubescens,* while the latter is dominated by *Nardus stricta* and *Deschampsia flexuosa.* In wetter peaty soil, clumps of *Juncus* are often conspicuous. These variations in vegetational pattern appear to have a marked effect on the density and species composition of the soil fauna. For example, populations of Lumbricidae, which form a conspicuous component of the fauna on limestone grassland sites, are barely in evidence on the podsolized and peaty sites of *Nardus* grassland and mixed moorland. Enchytraeid populations, on the other hand, flourish better in soils developed from alluvial drift or with a high peat content, than in the brown earth developed on limestone grassland sites. Interesting differences also occur between the various microarthropod groups on these sites. The Collembola, for example, attain their highest densities in limestone grassland, whereas the Acari are more numerous in soils under *Nardus* and mixed moor vegetation. These observations are summarized in Table 12.6.

TABLE 12.6. Densities per square metre of soil organisms on a Pennine moorland at Moor House (modified after Cragg, 1961)[1].

Group	Limestone grassland	*Juncus* moor	*Nardus* grassland	Mixed moor	Bare peat
Acari (x 10^3)	45·3	43·0	77·8	65·8	–
Collembola (x 10^3)	77·9	38·9	55·9	42·3	–
Enchytraeidae (x 10^3)	10-25	130-290	37-200	?	12-50
Lumbricidae	389	?	< 12	<1	–
Nematoda (x 10^6)	1·8-2·9	1·4-6·5	0·8-5·7	0·5-2·3	≤0·04
Short-palped Tipulidae larvae	–	1250	?	317	–
Long-palped Tipulidae larvae	49	111-168	?	41-68	–

[1]Data for Acari and Collembola taken from Block (1965) and Hale (1966) respectively.

In interpreting these data in terms of biological activity, it is important to remember that density estimates based on numbers give a less accurate reflection of this activity than biomass estimates. Thus, in these upland sites, the largest contribution to the total faunal biomass is made by the annelids: the Lumbricidae in limestone grassland, the Enchytraeidae in the remainder, and it is perhaps not surprising that estimations of carbon/nitrogen ratios and total soil respiration (Cragg, 1961) strongly point to the limestone grassland as the site of greatest biological activity.

The Fauna of Woodland and Forest Soils

The highly organic soils developed under woodland and forest vegetation in temperate regions support a diversified fauna which varies in its species composition from site to site. Variations in the character of the fauna are most closely related to variations in the character of the soil profile, and it is with this relationship that we are now concerned.

The two main types of organic profile developed under woody vegetation are the mull and the mor (see chapter 2). Essentially, these profiles are the end products of the interaction of a number of factors, such as the kind of tree species present, the character of the ground vegetation, and the parent material. One of the first, and still one of the most comprehensive, surveys of the soil fauna of a variety of woodland sites was carried out by Bornebusch (1930), and his findings are summarized in Table 12.7. More recent work has indicated that Bornebusch's estimates of density and biomass are too low, particularly those

TABLE 12.7. Biomass, expressed as g/m^2 and numbers/m^2 (in parentheses) of various groups of soil animals in five forest sites (from Bornebusch, 1930).

Tree species	Oak	Beech		Spruce	
Humus type	Mull	Mull	Mor	Mull	Mor
Lumbricidae	61·0 (122)	53·1 (177)	5·4 (81)	5·1 (101)	0·9 (18)
Gastropoda	5·3 (68)	4·9 (105)	3·2 (52)	0·2 (4)	0·1 (2)
Enchytraeidae	0·7 (342)	1·1 (533)	1·6 (782)	0·02 (42)	0·1 (258)
Isopoda	0·3 (283)	0·1 (149)	0·05 (53)	0·0 (1)	− (0)
Diplopoda	4·7 (110)	7·5 (177)	1·1 (39)	0·4 (10)	0·1 (2)
Acari	0·1 (967)	0·2 (3206)	0·3 (6161)	0·4 (7337)	0·6 (7828)
Collembola	0·1 (493)	0·1 (1198)	0·2 (5114)	0·1 (2210)	0·1 (1702)
Diptera	3·1 (271)	1·5 (232)	7·0 (1076)	1·5 (757)	4·3 (336)
Elateridae	0·2 (12)	0·2 (12)	3·5 (232)	0·9 (59)	3·7 (249)
Other insects	0·5 (129)	0·6 (222)	0·5 (194)	1·3 (54)	1·1 (86)
Carnivorous arthropods	0·8 (181)	1·5 (178)	1·1 (379)	0·9 (215)	1·1 (231)
Totals	76·8 (2978)	70·8 (6189)	23·9 (14 163)	10·8 (10 790)	12·1 (10 712)

relating to the Collembola and Acari which should be increased by a factor of 5 and 10, respectively, to give a more realistic picture. However, the general conclusions regarding the relative distribution of the more important groups of soil animals still retain their validity, and we can summarize these briefly as follows:

1. Looking broadly at the estimates for total biomass and total numbers for the various sites, it is apparent that there is an inverse relationship between the number of animals and their biomass. The most fertile soils are those of the mull type, under oak and beech, and these support the greatest weight of animals and also the lowest numbers. This is due to the fact that earthworms make a contribution somewhat in excess of 80 per cent to the total animal biomass in these sites. In contrast, the earthworm fauna is poorly developed in mor humus sites, which tend to be too acid for the majority of species. An exception to this is provided by the mor humus profile developed under beech, which has a richer earthworm fauna than other mor profiles, due principally to the presence of acid-tolerant *Dendrobaena octaedra* and *Lumbricus rubellus*. The large number of animals generally present in mor sites is a reflection of the suitability of such sites for the microarthropod Acari, Collembola, and insect larvae. Many of these microarthropods are fungal feeders and find abundant nutriment in the rather acid and unincorporated 'fermentation' layer of the mor profile. Population densities of Acari and Collembola in mor profiles often exceed $100\ 000/m^2$ (Table 12.8).

2. Carnivorous arthropods, such as the centipedes, spiders, pseudoscorpions, opiliones, and staphylinid and carabid beetles, are generally better represented, in terms of numbers and biomass, in mor profiles than in mull, and, in this respect, parallel the populations of microarthropod Collembola, Acari, and small insect larvae on which many of these predators feed. It is probable that the

distribution of these predators is governed more by the distribution of prey animals than by the type of organic material or ground vegetation. However, it is equally probable that the figures quoted in Table 12.7 for predator populations in mull sites are considerable underestimates, for they take no account of some of the larger-sized groups which are not susceptible to the sampling and

TABLE 12.8. Densities/m^2 of soil arthropods in various forest sites.

Tree Species	Humus types			Animal Groups	Authority
	Mull	Moder	Mor		
Oak	2446			Arachnida Collembola Insecta Crustacea Myriapoda	Bornebusch (1930)
Oak	9100			Acari Collembola and 'other arthropods'	Edwards and Heath (1963)
Oak		70 000- 180 000		Acari: Cryptostigmata	Lebrun (1965a)
Spruce			11 816	Acari Collembola Insecta Myriapoda	Bornebusch (1930)
Spruce			154 600	Total arthropods	Evans (1951)
Beech			17 852	Acari Collembola Diptera	Bornebusch (1930)
Spruce			834 500	Total arthropods	Murphy (1953)
Hemlock			176 250- 410 500	Acari: Cryptostigmata	Wallwork (1959)

extraction methods used. For example, centipedes of the genus *Lithobius* are commonly found in beech mull sites in England, although they tend to aggregate during the daytime under bark and in rotting wood of fallen trees. Further, the predatory activities of vertebrates, such as moles and insectivorous birds, must be taken into account when estimating the intensity of predation in mull sites.

3. If we compare the numbers of Enchytraeidae with the more recent density estimates provided in Table 5.3, page 66, it is obvious that Bornebusch's counts are considerable underestimates. To obtain representative samples of these animals, it is necessary to employ a wet funnel extractor (see chapter 14) rather than the dry funnel used by Bornebusch. Nevertheless, his data show that these worms are abundant in mull and mor soils under beech, and occur in lower numbers in soils under spruce.

4. The soil fauna, as a whole, is most poorly developed in the thin mor profile developed under *Polytrichum* in beech stands (not included in the table). Here, the effects of forest clearing are evident: the compacted soil is dry and exposed to wind action. The opening of the forest canopy permits the development of moss vegetation which apparently inhibits the formation of a mull type of humus profile, particularly in sites exposed to wind, for leaves of tree species are blown away before they have a chance to decompose. In such localities, the most important groups of animals, in numerical terms, are the microarthropod Collembola and Acari, Diptera larvae, and staphylinid beetles. Lumbricid earthworms provide the largest single contribution to the total biomass, although this family is represented exclusively by the acid-tolerant *Dendrobaena octaedra* which is often found associated with growths of moss. Generally speaking, poor sites of this type do not support large populations of Lumbricidae, Myriapoda, and Isopoda, the majority of which are susceptible to the dry conditions prevailing there.

5. From the functional aspect, it is clear that small-sized detritivores, such as *Dendrobaena* and the microarthropods, compensate for the absence of the large-sized, detritivorous Lumbricidae, Isopoda, Myriapoda, and Gastropoda in mor profiles (Macfadyen, 1963b). Many of these larger animals burrow actively in the soil, distributing organic material through the A horizon, whereas the microarthropods are mainly confined to the surface layers where they live in the small spaces between soil particles. In the absence of the larger detritivores, litter material tends to accumulate in definite layers above the mineral soil, and a strongly structured mor profile is produced.

The Fauna of Grassland and Forest Soils Compared

Direct and simultaneous comparisons between the soil fauna of grassland and woodland are few, but such data that are available suggest that the highly organic surface layers developed under woody vegetation support a more varied, but metabolically less active, fauna than the grassland habitat. This may well be a reflection of the amount of protection afforded by the vegetation in the two types of locality. Microarthropods, in particular, are often more richly represented, in terms of numbers of species and numbers of individuals, in the sheltered soils of woodland than in grassland soils exposed to strong fluctuations in temperature and relative humidity and the erosive effects of wind action. In a comparative study of the soil arthropod fauna under a mature oak woodland and a *Brachypodium* grassland, Lions (1965) recorded average monthly densities of 1635 and 454 respectively for the two sites, working with a sample unit size of 1300 cm^3. Lebrun (1965b) collected 89 species of Cryptostigmatid mite from an oak forest floor, compared with 53 from a neighbouring grassland, in Belgium. However, faunal distinctions between the broad 'grassland' and 'forest' categories are difficult to sustain because of the considerable amount of environmental variability occurring within each type. For example, the last-mentioned study included a comparison with the soil fauna of a poplar habitat which yielded fewer species of Cryptostigmata (48) than either the oak forest or the grassland, and, to judge from its species composition, represented a faunal transition between these two. Again, if we compare the density estimates presented in Tables 12.5 and 12.8, it is evident that microarthropod populations of similar orders of magnitude occur under grassland and woodland. It would, perhaps, be unwise to take this particular comparison further, in view of the variety of sampling and extraction techniques used by the authors cited.

On the other hand, when we are considering the contribution made by the soil fauna to the processes of organic decay, it is with the amount of protoplasm, the biomass, and the rate of metabolism that we are primarily concerned. Some tentative estimates of biomass and metabolism for the fauna of a number of different sites are presented in Table 12.9. In compiling these data, Macfadyen (1963b) made the distinction between true herbivores, such as nematodes, molluscs, and holometabolous insects, the larger detritivorous lumbricids, isopods, and diplopods, the smaller detritivorous nematodes, enchytraeids, mites, and collembolans, and the predatory spiders, harvestmen, centipedes, mites, and insects. Although it must be borne in mind that these estimates are only very approximate, they provide a basis for broad comparisons of community structure and activity in localities which differ from each other in the general character of the vegetation and the type of organic profile. They also emphasize the point that grassland soils tend to support a much greater faunal biomass and a much higher rate of energy turnover than woodland soils. Within the latter, biomass estimates are usually higher in the mull type than the mor, although there is no clear distinction between these two categories as far as their overall metabolic characteristics are concerned, for it is clear that the activities of the larger detritivores predominate over those of the smaller in mull soils, whereas the reverse is the case in the mor. The meadow grassland presents an interesting example of a 'managed' system treated with fertilizers (Macfadyen, 1961), in which the contribution to total metabolism made by small-sized detritivores, particularly nematodes, enchytraeids, and collembolans, and their predators, collectively overshadows that made by the larger lumbricids, isopods, and diplopods. A comparison between this system and the upland limestone grassland suggests that management practice can promote the activities of small detritivores to an appreciable extent, with a resultant marked increase in the total rate of energy turnover. Forest practice, on the other hand, must be designed to increase the metabolic contribution made by the larger detritivores.

It should be noted that one very important trophic level has not been included in the scheme presented in Table 12.9, namely, the true decomposer, the bacteria, and fungi. Direct measurements of biomass and metabolism for these organisms are difficult to make, and the kinds of microbiological techniques involved produce estimates which are not directly comparable with those obtained for soil animals (see below). A crude approximation of microbiological activity can be obtained, however, by determining the difference between total soil metabolism, estimated by measuring carbon dioxide production by a

TABLE 12.9. Biomass (g/m²) and metabolism (kcal/m²/yr) of soil invertebrates in various grassland and woodland sites (after Macfadyen, 1963b).

	Meadow grassland		Limestone grassland		Oak mull		Beech mor		Spruce mor	
	g/m²	kcal/ m²/yr	g/m²	kcal/ m²/yr	g/m²	kcal/ m²/yr	g/m²	kcal/ m²/yr	g/m²	kcal/ m²/yr
Herbivores	17·4	253·9	36·5	153·8	11·2	118·4	16·2	157·5	11·3	128·3
Large detritivores	137·5	311·7	137·0	333·0	66·0	128·5	6·6	17·0	1·0	2·1
Small detritivores	25·0	448·0	16·3	104·2	1·8	114·6	3·0	222·9	1·6	113·5
Predators	9·6	124·7	1·3	8·3	0·9	22·2	1·1	93·5	1·2	145·9
Totals	189·5	1138·3	191·1	599·3	79·9	383·7	26·9	490·9	15·1	389·8

block of soil, and the proportion of this total attributable to animal activity. Such approximations indicate that the activities of these decomposers contribute 80-90 per cent of the total soil metabolism. Thus, there is a considerable discrepancy between the respective contributions to total metabolism of soil animals and the microflora, but this should not obscure the fact that these two biological components of the soil community form an integrated and complementary system. As was noted in chapter 1, many of the small-sized detritivores, such as the mites and Collembola, feed on fungi and bacteria, contributing not only to the dispersal of spores, but also to the development of healthy and vigorous colonies of these micro-organisms. In addition, the physical fragmentation of litter material which occurs as a result of the feeding activities of the detritivores exposes fresh sites for bacterial and fungal infection. The most suitable sites for fungi are found among the moist, rather acidic, highly organic layers of the forest floor, whereas bacteria predominate in the better drained mineral grassland soils.

The Effect of Pesticides on the Character of the Soil Fauna

In the preceding pages, we have been concerned with the character of the soil fauna which develops more or less naturally under a variety of vegetational types. The gradual change in faunal composition that occurs as one kind of vegetational association gives way to another has been a recurring theme. On the other hand, Man's interference in a natural system often produces drastic and rapid changes in the faunal and floral character. Ploughing, clearing, and burning often cause a reduction in the abundance and species diversity of the soil fauna, but any decreased biological activity which may result from this reduction can be compensated for by the addition of inorganic fertilizers. Potentially, a more serious problem is posed, however, by the use of toxic chemical compounds designed to eliminate pests of cultivated crops. As we noted in chapter 10, these pesticides may persist in the soil, pass along food chains, and eventually be assimilated, in harmful or lethal concentrations, into the bodies of vertebrates. They undoubtedly affect organisms other than those at which they are specifically directed, and ecologists are becoming increasingly interested in the total impact of pesticides in ecosystems. The pesticide problem is a complex and controversial one, and it is difficult to do justice to all aspects in what can only be a brief survey. Further, although considerable progress has been made, much more basic information is required before the problem can be placed in its true perspective.

Chemical compounds applied by Man to the soil in order to control pests may be classified in various ways. Thus, the phytotoxic weed-killers, or herbicides, and fungicides can be distinguished, by the nature of their biological effect, from fumigants and insecticides. As a general rule, phytotoxic chemicals do not appear to have marked effects on the soil fauna, except in occasional instances. For example, of several herbicides tested on the soil fauna by Edwards (1965) only one, simazine, produced reductions in numbers of predatory mites, hemiedaphic Collembola and, to a lesser extent, of detritivorous mites, earthworms, enchytraeids and insect larvae. Fumigants, such as metham sodium, DD, and formaldehyde, which can be applied as surface treatments or as injections, have severe effects and will kill all soil animals within their immediate vicinity. Thus, surface fumigation can produce a kill to a depth of 15 cm, although eggs and diapausing stages evidently can survive this treatment. Insecticides, which are probably the most widely used pesticides in many localities, are much more variable in their effects on the soil fauna than are the herbicides or fumigants.

Insecticides in common use at the present time are of various kinds, although there are two particular categories which command most attention, the chlorinated hydrocarbons and the organophosphates. The chlorinated hydrocarbons, such as DDT, lindane (BHC), aldrin, dieldrin, and heptachlor, are noted for their persistence, and efforts are being made to curtail severely the use of these toxic compounds. Most of the chlorinated hydrocarbons cause reductions in predatory mite populations, with the result that populations of Collembola, released from predation pressure, increase in size; this disturbance of the predator-prey balance can be readily observed after applications of DDT and BHC (Sheals, 1956). Aldrin and its derivative, dieldrin, on the other hand, appear to have little effect on predatory mites, although they cause marked reductions in numbers of detritivorous mites, Collembola and insect larvae (Edwards *et al.*, 1967). In general, the chlorinated hydrocarbons have little or no effect on earthworms, enchytraeids, and nematodes, although heptachlor is exceptional in this respect and can cause severe reductions in these populations.

Because of their much lower degree of persistence in the soil, the organophosphate and carbamate pesticides are generally preferred. Compounds such as parathion, sevin, and diazinon cause general reductions in numbers of soil animals, whereas chlorfenvinphos apparently upsets the predator-prey balance in a manner similar to that produced by DDT and BHC, by reducing the predatory mite population and allowing the numbers of prey species, such as Collembola and detritivorous mites, to increase (Edwards, *et al.*, 1968). These effects are usually transitory, and recovery is more rapid than that occurring after the use of organochlorine pesticides.

References

Balogh, J. (1958) *Lebensgemeinschaften der Landtiere,* Akademie-Verlag, Berlin.

Bellinger, P. F. (1954) 'Studies on the soil fauna with special reference to the Collembola', *Bull Conn. agric. Exp. Stan.,* **583**, 1-67.

Block, W. C. (1965) 'Distribution of soil mites (Acarina) on the Moor House National Nature Reserve, Westmorland, with notes on their numerical abundance', *Pedobiologia,* **5**, 244-51.

Bornebusch, C. H. (1930) 'The fauna of forest soil', *Forst. ForsVaes. Danm.,* **11**, 1-224.

Cragg, J. B. (1961) 'Some aspects of the ecology of moorland animals', *J. Anim. Ecol.,* **30**, 205-34.

Davis, B. N. K. (1963) 'A study of microarthropod communities in mineral soils near Corby, Northants', *J. Anim. Ecol.,* **32**, 49-71.

Dhillon, B. S. and Gibson, N. H. E. (1962) 'A study of the Acarina and Collembola of agricultural soils. I. Numbers and distribution in undisturbed grassland', *Pedobiologia*, **1**, 189-209.

Edwards, C. A. (1965) 'Effects of pesticide residues on soil invertebrates and plants' in *Ecology and the Industrial Society*, Vth Symp. Brit. Ecol. Soc., 239-61.

Edwards, C. A. and Heath, G. W. (1963) 'The role of soil animals in breakdown of leaf material' in Doeksen, J. and Drift, J. van der, eds., *Soil organisms*, 76-84.

Edwards, C. A., Dennis, E. B., and Empson, D. W. (1967) 'Pesticides and the soil fauna: effects of aldrin and DDT in an arable field', *Ann. appl. Biol.*, **60**, 11-22.

Edwards, C. A., Thompson, A. R. and Beynon, K. I. (1968) 'Some effects of chlorfenvinphos, an organophosphorus insecticide, on populations of soil animals', *Rev. Ecol. Biol. Sol.*, **5**, 199-224.

Evans, G. O. (1951) 'Investigation on the fauna of forest humus layers' in Forestry Commission, *Rep. Forest. Res. Lond.* (1950), 110-13.

Fager, E. W. (1957) 'Determination and analysis of recurrent groups', *Ecology*, **38**, 586-95.

Ghilarov, M. S. (1968) 'Soil stratum of terrestrial biocenoses', *Pedobiologia*, **8**, 82-96.

Haarløv, N. (1960) 'Microarthropods from Danish soils. Ecology, Phenology', *Oikos*, suppl. 3, 1-176.

Hairston, N. G. and Byers, G. W. (1954) 'The soil arthropods of a field in southern Michigan: a study in community ecology', *Contrib. Lab. Vert. Biol. Univ. Mich.*, **64**, 1-37.

Hale, W. G. (1966) 'A population study of moorland Collembola', *Pedobiologia*, **6**, 65-99.

Ibarra, E. L., Wallwork, J. A., and Rodriguez, J. G. (1965) 'Ecological studies of mites found in sheep and cattle pastures. I. Distribution patterns of oribatid mites', *Ann. ent. Soc. Amer.*, **58**, 153-9.

Lebrun, P. (1965a) 'Contribution à l'étude écologique des oribates de la litiere dans une forêt de movenne-Belgique', *Mém. Inst. r. Sc. nat. Belg.*, **153**, 1-96.

Lebrun, P. (1965b) 'Quelques caracteristiques des communautés d'oribates dans trois biocenoses de Moyenne-Belgique', *Oikos*, **16**, 100-8.

Lions, J-C. (1965) 'Contribution à l'étude écologique des peuplements arthropodiens et des acariens oribates du sol dans la chaîne de la Trévaresse (Bouches-du-Rhône)', *Annls Fac. Sci. Marseille*, **38**, 121-47.

Macfadyen, A. (1952) 'The small arthropods of a *Molinia* fen at Cothill', *J. Anim. Ecol.*, **21**, 87-117.

Macfadyen, A. (1961) 'Metabolism of soil invertebrates in relation to soil fertility', *Ann. appl. Biol.*, **49**, 216-19.

Macfadyen, A. (1963a) *Animal ecology. Aims and methods* (second edn), Pitman, London. xxiv + 344 pp.

Macfadyen, A. (1963b) 'The contribution of the microfauna to total soil metabolism' in Doeksen, J. and Drift, J. van der, eds., *Soil organisms*, 3-17.

Mountford, M. D. (1962) 'An index of similarity and its application to classificatory problems' in Murphy, P. W., ed., *Progress in soil zoology*, 43-50.

Murphy, P. W. (1953) 'The biology of forest soils with special reference to the mesofauna or meiofauna', *J. Soil Sci.*, **4**, 155-93.

Renkonen, O. (1938) 'Statistisch-ökologische Untersuchungen über die terrestrische Käferwelt der finnischen Bruchmoore', *Suomal. eläin-ja kasvit. Seur. van Julk.*, **6**, 1-226.

Reynoldson, T. B. (1955) 'Observations on the earthworms of North Wales', *NWest. Nat.*, **3**, 291-304.

Salt, G., Hollick, F. S. J., Raw, F., and Brian, M. V. (1948) 'The arthropod population of pasture soil', *J. Anim. Ecol.*, **17**, 139-50.

Satchell, J. E. (1967) 'Lumbricidae' in Burges, N. A. and Raw, F., eds., *Soil biology* 259-322.

Sheals, J. G. (1956) 'Soil population studies. I- The effects of cultivation and treatment with insecticides', *Bull. ent. Res.* **47**, 803-33.

Sheals, J. G. (1957) 'The Collembola and Acarina of uncultivated soil', *J. Anim. Ecol.,* **26**, 125-34.

Sørensen, T. (1948) 'A method of stabilizing groups of equivalent amplitude in plant sociology based on the similarity of species content and its application to analyses of the vegetation on Danish commons', *Biol. Skr.,* **5**, 1-34.

Svendsen, J. A. (1957) 'The distribution of Lumbricidae in an area of Pennine moorland', *J. Anim. Ecol.,* **26**, 411-21.

Wallwork, J. A. (1959) 'The distribution and dynamics of some forest soil mites', *Ecology,* **40**, 557-63.

Wallwork, J. A. and Rodriguez, J. G. (1961) 'Ecological studies on oribatid mites with particular reference to their role as intermediate hosts of anoplocephalid cestodes', *J. econ. Ent.,* **54**, 701-5.

Weis-Fogh, T. (1948) 'Ecological investigations on mites and collemboles in the soil', *Natura jutl.',* **1**, 135-270.

Wood, T. G. (1966) 'The fauna of grassland soils with special reference to Acari and Collembola', *Proc. N.Z. ecol. Soc.,* **13**, 79-85.

13. The functioning of the soil community

In the previous chapter, metabolic rates of populations of soil animals were discussed in general terms. We now turn to a more detailed review of the energetics of soil populations emphasizing, where appropriate, the probable significance of metabolism in relation to the general activities of the whole community.

The Functional Character of the Community

Every community structure is built on a broad base of organisms called 'primary producers', and every community activity is powered by the activities of these organisms. Primary producers are mostly green plants which trap solar energy and manufacture complex organic materials by photosynthesis. The energy incorporated into the sugars produced may be bound in starch and cellulose, or released by the oxidation of the carbohydrate to participate in protein synthesis, or liberated as heat during respiration. In the soil community, these producers are largely represented by herbaceous and woody green plants rooted in the soil, with aerial parts extending for appreciable distances above its surface. Part of this vegetable material and energy store is channelled to the soil as litter which accumulates on the surface when the aerial parts die back or are discarded.

In many communities, the green plant producers are eaten by herbivorous animals, termed 'primary consumers', which are preyed upon by carnivores, or 'secondary consumers'. Other carnivores, preying on these secondary consumers, are termed 'tertiary consumers', the whole sequence being described as a herbivore/carnivore food chain. Herbivores and carnivores are subject to the attentions of parasites, so that a parasite food chain can also be defined. Finally, as plants and animals die, their bodies are consumed by detritivorous animals or decomposed by micro-organisms, so that organic material is broken down and the contained energy released, redistributed, or dissipated.

There are few true herbivores among the soil fauna, unless we consider the fungivorous microarthropods and enchytraeids to be such, or extend our definition of a soil animal to include surface-active forms, such as the molluscs and phytophagous insects; in any event, the detritivore food chain takes on a special significance. Important detritivores include the earthworms, enchytraeids, millipedes, certain insect larvae, collembolans, and several large groups of mites. The primary effect of these animals appears to be to promote a physical rather than a chemical change in the organic material ingested. Chemical decomposition occurs mainly through the activities of soil fungi and bacteria, although the presence of the soil fauna is necessary for the establishment of vigorous populations of these microflora.

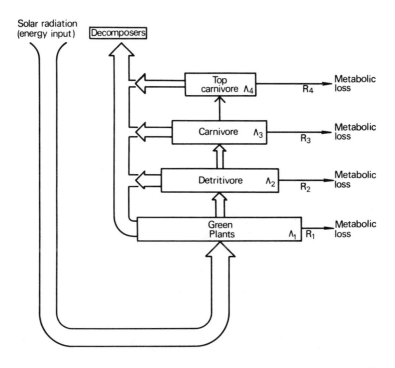

FIGURE 13.1. The detritivore/decomposer/carnivore energy pyramid.

The various feeding, or trophic, levels can be arranged in a linear sequence, and since the transfer of energy between two successive trophic levels obeys the laws of thermodynamics and is never 100 per cent efficient, there will be a progressive diminution in the energy content along the food chain. In its dynamic aspect, the trophic structure of the community can be described in terms of an energy pyramid, the broad base of which is the standing crop energy of the primary producers, and the apex is the energy content of the top carnivore level. This functional interpretation of community structure, developed by Lindeman (1942), is illustrated in Fig. 13.1. The energy content of the various trophic levels is generally designated by the Greek capital letter lambda (Λ), and the individual levels are identified numerically, so that Λ_1 denotes the energy content of the primary producers, Λ_2 that of the herbivores or detritivores, Λ_3 that of the carnivores, etc. The significance of this view of community structure will be discussed later in this chapter, but one important point may be emphasized at this stage, namely, that all the energy entering the community ultimately becomes dispersed as heat due to the metabolic activities of soil organisms; it does not cycle. Inorganic nutrients, on the other hand, continually recirculate through the plant/soil system, being bound up in organic

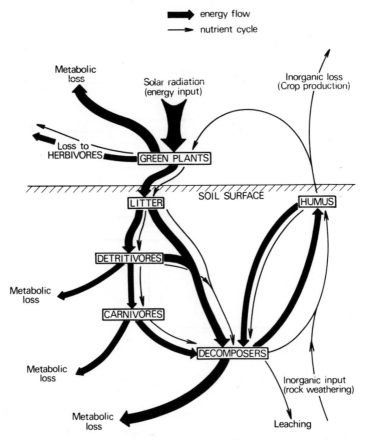

FIGURE 13.2. Energy flow and nutrient cycling in the soil ecosystem (heavy arrows = energy flow; light arrows = nutrient cycle).

complexes during photosynthesis and subsequently being released and becoming available to other plant rooting systems as these organic complexes are broken down in the soil. Figure 13.2 illustrates, in a simplified form, how energy flows and inorganic nutrients circulate in this system.

Primary Production

The first stage in the energy flow process is a transformation of solar energy into chemical energy by the photosynthetic activity of green plants. The amount of energy so transformed by these autotrophs represents but a small fraction, 1-5 per cent, of the amount available to them, the remainder being lost as heat. The amount of chemical energy stored in the tissues of these primary producers, per unit area per unit time, represents their gross primary production. Some of this energy will be used immediately, or subsequently, in respiration, and the balance, the net primary production, is the amount of energy available to the next trophic level. It has been estimated by Phillipson (1966) that net primary production is generally 80-90 per cent of the gross, although Macfadyen (1967) has pointed out that this ratio may vary widely and, although the above estimate may be applicable to temperate grasslands, it may be as low as 25 per cent in tropical forests.

The energy-rich organic material stored in green plants, over and above that used in respiration, has one of two possible fates. (a) It may be consumed by herbivorous animals living above the soil surface; the contained energy will either be incorporated into herbivore protoplasm or liberated as heat during respiration, or, if not assimilated, it will pass out of the body in the faeces. (b) It will pass into the soil ecosystem as litter, when the vegetation dies back. Clearly, the proportions of the net primary productivity flowing into these two alternative channels will vary from locality to locality and will be influenced, for example, by the intensity of grazing and harvesting in man-managed systems. However, even in such systems, where it would be expected that the amount of energy channelled into herbivores would be relatively high, Macfadyen (1963) has calculated that only two-sevenths of the gross primary productivity is so utilized, while one-seventh is dissipated during plant respiration; the remaining four-sevenths passes into the soil ecosystem as litter. This litter, together with the faeces and corpses of animals living above the soil surface, forms the energy base on which the detritivorous animals and microfloral decomposers in the soil operate.

The chemical degradation of energy-rich plant debris, which results from the feeding activities of soil organisms, is characterized by the liberation of energy and nutrients, as we have already noted. Before treating in more detail the pathways of energy flow, we will digress briefly to consider the cycling of inorganic nutrients, paying particular attention to carbon, nitrogen, phosphorus, and sulphur. The cycling of silicon will be omitted from this discussion, for, although there is evidence that this element does circulate to an appreciable extent in certain localities, for example, in grasslands, soil organisms play only a very minor role in this cycle. The following account is restricted to a rather generalized survey of the main characteristics of the nutrient cycles concerned. A more detailed review of this topic and, indeed, of the whole subject of community energetics in woodlands is given by Ovington (1962).

Nutrient Cycling

During photosynthesis, atmospheric *carbon*, in the form of carbon dioxide, is incorporated into sugars and subsequently may be converted into lignin, starch, or cellulose. Although some of this carbon is released again as carbon dioxide during plant respiration, or excreted in various organic forms through the root systems, the bulk enters the soil only when the vegetation dies. Here, carbon is assimilated into the bodies of detritivores and decomposers, as these organisms break down the complex organic material. This assimilated carbon may be incorporated into a variety of compounds as it travels through the soil community, but ultimately will be released to the atmospheric pool as carbon dioxide by the respiratory activities of soil organisms.

Nitrogen passes into the soil ecosystem in a variety of ways, the most important of which is via dead organic material. Some nitrogenous organic compounds, for example, amino acids, can be assimilated by plant roots, but much organic nitrogen is in a form which is not readily available to plants and, consequently, must be converted to inorganic forms before it can be utilized. This conversion is a two-stage process, the first step being the mineralization of organic nitrogen into inorganic ammonium salts, and the second, the nitrification of these salts into nitrites and nitrates. Nitrites cannot be utilized by plants for these compounds are toxic, but they are oxidized rapidly in the soil to form nitrates. The great bulk of the soil nitrogen available to growing plants is in the form of nitrate. A variety of heterotrophic micro-organisms, bacteria, and fungi, promote the mineralization process, but nitrification is carried out principally by autotrophic bacteria such as *Nitrosomonas* and *Nitrobacter.* Nitrogen also enters the soil from the atmospheric pool, dissolved in rainwater as ammonium and nitrate ions, or by a process of biological fixation carried out by certain blue-green algae and bacteria. This fixation process is extremely important, for it provides a supply of organic nitrogen to compensate for the loss incurred by leaching of the soluble inorganic nitrate. The principal groups of micro-organisms promoting fixation are bacteria of the genus *Rhizobium* which form a symbiotic association with the roots of leguminous plants, and the free-living bacteria *Azotobacter* and *Clostridium.* The activities of these fixers are countered, to some extent, by those of another group of bacteria which include members of the genera *Pseudomonas* and *Micrococcus,* and also certain fungi, which denitrify soil nitrate, liberating nitrogen, nitrous oxide, and oxygen. In this way, nitrogen leaves the soil and re-enters the atmospheric pool. Denitrification is more common in anaerobic conditions than in well-oxygenated soils.

Phosphorus and sulphur. The cycling of these two elements resembles that of nitrogen, in that all three nutrients occur in the soil in available and unavailable forms. Dead organic material usually contains appreciable amounts of phosphorus and sulphur bound up in complexes. In certain cases, for example, when sulphur is combined into simple organic compounds such as amino acids, the element may be directly available to the root systems of higher plants, but, as a general rule, the complexes in which these elements occur must be mineralized to yield orthophosphate and sulphates, respectively, before they can become available. Bacteria and fungi are important agents in these mineralization processes but, as in the nitrogen cycle, the activities of certain groups of these micro-organisms may inhibit, rather than promote, the availability of the element concerned. The analogues of the denitrifyers in the sulphur cycle are sulphate-reducing bacteria which channel sulphur into toxic sulphides under anaerobic conditions. Bacteria and fungi also compete with plants for the available nitrogen, phosphorus, and sulphur in the soil, and these elements may be immobilized in the microfloral protoplasm in unavailable inorganic or organic compounds.

This brief survey of the cycling of the more important nutrients of the plant/soil system emphasizes the considerable importance of the microfloral components, the bacteria and the fungi. Theirs is the principal influence on the mineralization process. The activities of the soil fauna are of secondary importance in this respect, although the lumbricids and the pill millipede *Glomeris marginata* have been shown to increase the soluble nitrogen fraction in the soil by their feeding (Heath, 1965; Bocock, 1963).

Energetics of the Detritivore/Decomposer Food Chain

Although it is easy enough to describe in theory the functioning of any community in terms of simple linear food chains, with herbivore feeding on primary producer, carnivore feeding on herbivore, etc., in practice, the interrelationships between populations are so complex that they can be considered more accurately as a web, rather than a chain. An example of such a web is provided in Fig. 13.3, and it can be seen from this simplified illustration that energy does not flow directly from one trophic level to the next, but meanders and recirculates within the various trophic levels.

As noted earlier, 80-90 per cent of the energy bound up in litter and available to the soil community is captured by microfloral decomposers. The remainder is unequally apportioned among the various taxonomic groups of the soil fauna, notably the detritivorous earthworms, enchytraeids, millipedes, insect larvae, collembolans, mites, and nematodes. There are formidable technical difficulties involved in making accurate assessments of the extent to which the available energy is shared among these groups, for many of the parameters involved cannot be investigated successfully under natural conditions. To provide an adequate description of the energy flow through a population, it is necessary to know the population density, biomass, age class composition, feeding and assimilation rates, and respiration rate. The picture is further complicated by the fluctuations in density and biomass which occur under natural conditions, and which influence the total metabolic contribution. Feeding, assimilation, and respiration rates vary as the environmental conditions vary, and also as the age structure of the population changes. The effects of all of these variables must be taken into consideration before any accurate estimate can be made of the contribution of individual species populations to the total flow of energy through the ecosystem. At the present time, work in this field has only just

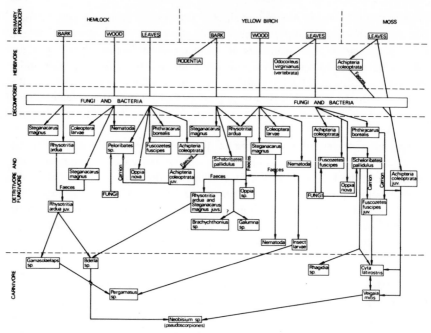

FIGURE 13.3. Part of the food web of a hemlock and yellow birch forest floor in northern Michigan, emphasizing the role of the Acari.

begun and the conclusions presented in this brief survey are, at the best, only tentative ones.

The energy budget of a population, reduced to its simplest terms, can conveniently be described by the equation:

$$I = R + Y$$

where I represents the energy assimilated with the food, R the energy used up in respiration, and Y the energy bound up in the protoplasm and available to organisms belonging to other trophic levels, i.e., the production of the population under consideration. Techniques are available which allow each of the three terms in the above equation to be estimated independently. Thus, an estimate for I can be obtained as the difference between the amount of food ingested and that egested per unit time per unit body weight. This can be done by subtracting the weight of faeces produced from the weight of food offered and consumed; the latter quantity can be estimated for detritivorous animals by presenting the food in the form of leaf discs of uniform thickness, known surface area and known weight, and subsequently assessing, by visual means, the total area of the discs consumed (Berthet, 1964). An alternative method, used by Engelmann (1961), makes a direct estimate of assimilation by measuring uptake of radioactive glycine C^{14} from labelled food material. The method allowed this author to estimate that populations of cryptostigmatid mites in a grassland soil assimilated food at a rate equivalent to 8 per cent of their body weight per day. The amount of production (Y) can be estimated by making successive determinations of biomass. In the case of the larger soil animals, these determinations present few problems, but direct weighings of microarthropods are often difficult and subject to error. Sensitive microbalances can be used to weigh the larger-sized Acari and Collembola, but this technique is unsatisfactory for many of the mites, such as members of the genera *Oppia, Suctobelba, Brachychthonius,* and *Scheloribates,* which are less than half a millimetre long. In an attempt to solve this problem, Engelmann (1961) defined a relationship between surface area and dry weight, and since measurements of length and width of even the smallest mites are easy to make, this approach provides a convenient way to estimate biomass. However, it assumes that most of the metabolically active body protoplasm is located in, or attached to, the cuticular exoskeleton, an assumption which may not be entirely valid (Wallwork, 1967).

Estimates of biomass and assimilation can be converted into calorific equivalents, for the purposes of the energy budget, by burning protoplasm and food material, respectively, in a bomb calorimeter. The amounts of material involved are often small, and various types of microbombs have been developed (see, for example, Slobodkin and Richman, 1960; Phillipson, 1964) to accommodate small samples. Golley (1961) published a list of calorific values for a range of biological materials, and Engelmann (1961) used equivalents of 5000 cal/g for arthropod protoplasm, and 4000 cal/g for fungal food, to estimate that a standing crop biomass of 54 mg of Cryptostigmata represented 270 cal of energy, and that the annual flow of energy into this standing crop due to assimilation of food was 2058 cal.

The final term in the energy budget equation, R, the energy used in respiration, can be estimated indirectly or directly. Direct measurements of oxygen uptake by small soil animals, such as mites, involve the detection of volume changes of considerably less than a microlitre (μl) per unit time. Of the various types of microrespirometer devised to solve this problem, the most successful to date are those employing the Warburg (Zinkler, 1966) and Cartesian Diver (Linderström-Lang, 1943; Holter, 1943) principles. Macfadyen (1961) has also described an electrolytic microrespirometer which can be used to detect volume changes in the order of a few microlitres. Despite these technical advances, the respiration rates of many small animals are too low to be susceptible to direct measurement, and an indirect method has to be used. Engelmann (1961), for example, obtained indirect estimates of respiration for small Cryptostigmata by using the regression equation:

$$\text{Log respiration } (\mu \text{l } 10^{-3}) = 0.85 \ (\log \text{ weight in } \mu\text{g}) + 0.44.$$

By combining estimates obtained in this way with direct measurements, corrected for field temperature conditions, he calculated that this component of a grassland soil fauna utilized 96 per cent of the energy assimilated during a year in respiratory activity. As a result of his studies, this author was able to construct the energy balance sheet depicted in Fig. 13.4, making the assumption that the populations considered were in a steady state so that the standing crop biomass was completely replaced each year. The fact that this budget does not entirely balance is a reflection of the fact that each parameter was estimated independently, and the errors involved are not, consequently, eliminated.

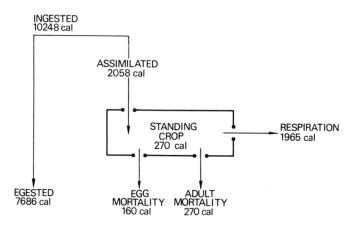

FIGURE 13.4. Yearly energy budget for the cryptostigmatid mite populations of a square metre of old grassland in Michigan (from Engelmann, 1961).

Another assumption made, which is, perhaps, questionable in view of more recent work, is that the relationship between log respiration and log body weight is linear. Berthet (1963), also working with Cryptostigmata, found that this linear relationship held within the limits 5-15°C, but at higher temperatures oxygen consumption was lower than expected, and the relationship between oxygen consumption, body weight, and temperature could be described by the equation:

$$Y = 18 \cdot 059 + 0 \cdot 7W - 0 \cdot 487Z,$$

where Y = log oxygen consumed/individual/day in $10^{-3}\,mm^3$,

   W = log body weight in μg,

$$Z = \frac{1}{T_{abs}} \cdot 10^4.$$

Probably the most significant point to note in the energy budget presented in Fig. 13.4 is the very large proportion of the assimilated energy that is expended in respiratory activity. Soil arthropods, in general, appear to be very poor converters of the energy content of the food they assimilate. Gere (1956) postulated that detritivores have an efficiency of the order of 2·3 per cent in this respect; Bocock (1963) reported that male and female *Glomeris* 'marginata converted 0·45 per cent and 0·29 per cent of consumed ash litter into body tissue; a similar order of efficiency for the isopod *Armadillidium vulgare* has been quoted (Saito, 1967). As Healey (1967b) has pointed out, since the major part of the assimilated energy is dissipated in respiration, the energy budget equation: $I = R + Y$ is considerably simplified, for an estimate of R will provide a good index of the flow of energy into a particular population. A reservation must be applied here, however, for rapidly reproducing organisms, such as the Protozoa, are more efficient converters than soil arthropods, and will store a greater proportion of the assimilated energy, leaving relatively less to be dissipated during respiration. Heal (1967) has estimated that 63 per cent of the total energy assimilated by soil amoebae is utilized for growth, and Healey (1967a) reported that annual secondary production in the collembolan *Onychiurus procampatus* amounted to about 46 per cent of the total energy flow through the population. In the arthropods, as in other animals, it can be expected that juvenile growing stages and gravid adult females channel appreciable amounts of assimilated energy into the production of new protoplasm. Accurate estimates of assimilation, in these cases, must be derived either from direct measurement (see above) or from a knowledge not only of the respiratory rate, but also of the rate of production of biomass.

On the other hand, if it can be established that the respiration rate multiplied by the standing crop biomass provides a guide to the proportion of the total available energy that is 'captured' by a particular population or taxonomic group, we can compare the metabolic contribution of the various groups, on this basis, to the total flow of energy per unit time into a given trophic level. The respiratory rates of several detritivores have been determined under experimental conditions, and although the results, shown in Table 13.1, are not always directly comparable, it is clear that there are marked differences between the different groups. For example, the metabolic activity per unit weight of Collembola and Enchytraeidae appears to be at least twice that of the cryptostigmatid mites and Isopoda. It will be noted that several of the estimates presented in the table are expressed as ranges, and these reflect differences in respiration rates of different age classes or sexes. Thus, younger Enchytraeidae, at 20°C, are metabolically more active than older ones (O'Connor, 1963), and Phillipson and Watson (1965) noted that much of the seasonal variation in respiratory activity of adults of the isopod *Oniscus asellus* was related to seasonal variations in reproductive activity, with peak rates coinciding with the greater metabolic activity associated with gonad development (Fig. 13.5).

The application of laboratory findings, such as those presented in Table 13.1, to field populations is, to say the least, difficult, when it is realized that the metabolic rate of an individual poikilothermous animal will vary as the environmental temperature varies, and will also depend on its stage of develop-

TABLE 13.1. Respiration rates, based on live weights, of some representatives of the soil fauna under experimental conditions (compiled from various sources).

Faunal group	Temp. °C	Respiration rate $\mu l\ O_2$/mg/day	Authority
A. Detritivores			
Lumbricidae:			
Allolobophora	15	1·8	see Satchell, 1967
Eisenia	15	3·0	see Satchell, 1967
Enchytraeidae:			
Hemihenlea	20	3·24-18·36	O'Connor, 1963
Cognettia	20	8·16-23·76	O'Connor, 1963
Achaeta	20	6·12-18·96	O'Connor, 1963
Isopoda:			
Oniscus asellus	16	4·99-5·33	Phillipson and Watson, 1965
Oniscus	22	5·14	Edney and Spencer, 1955
Porcellio	22	5·3	Edney and Spencer, 1955
Armadillidium	22	4·85	Edney and Spencer, 1955
Collembola:			
Onychiurus			
procampatus	15	7·68-24·0	Healey, 1967b
Cryptostigmata:			
Parachipteria			
willmanni	15	4·51	Berthet, 1963
B. Carnivores			
Opiliones:			
Mitopus morio	16	15·0-19·1	Phillipson, 1962
Oligolophus			
tridens	16	22·6-33·0	Phillipson, 1962

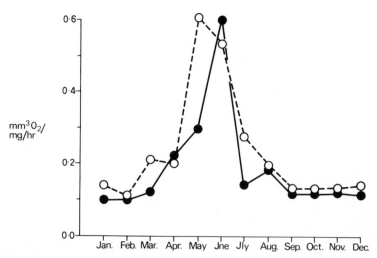

FIGURE 13.5. Seasonal differences in the mean respiratory rate per unit weight of individuals of *Oniscus asellus* which exceed 20 mg live weight. (Open circles = females; solid circles = males.) (From Phillipson and Watson, 1965.)

ment and physiological state. This point has been stressed by Phillipson (1966), and is illustrated by the estimates of respiratory rates for the opilionids *Mitopus morio* and *Oligolophus tridens* given in Table 13.1; the lower estimate, in each case, represents the rate of oxygen consumption during the day, and the higher figure is the rate during the night. It will be noted that the discrepancy between these two rates is greater in the more nocturnal *O. tridens* than in *M. morio*. Newell (1967) measured oxygen consumption of three species of slug during 'active' and 'quiescent' phases and noted considerable differences in some cases. By determining the durations of these two phases in the 24-hour period, he was able to show that estimates of actual oxygen consumption were appreciably lower than those calculated by assuming a constant respiration rate (Table 13.2).

TABLE 13.2. Estimates of oxygen consumption for three species of slug during inactive and active phases (from Newell, in press).

Species	Respiration rate $(mm^3 O_2/100\ mg/day$ at $10°C)$			Estimated total rate assuming constant consumption
	Inactive	Active	Total	
Agriolimax reticulatus	871·2	1171·8	2043·0	2923·2
Arion hortensis	322·2	600·0	922·2	1414·8
Milax budapestensis	280·8	1300·8	1581·6	2788·8

In order to estimate an annual respiration rate for an entire population under natural conditions, it is necessary, first of all, to construct a temperature/ metabolism curve, by measuring oxygen consumption at several different temperatures in the laboratory over a 24-hour period, and taking account of variations in activity during this period. Several such curves may be required if the rate varies with the stage in development, sex, or breeding condition of the individual. Second, the temperature conditions in the natural environment throughout the year must be determined: these are usually expressed as monthly mean temperatures. Third, the age class composition of the population must be determined weekly, monthly, or seasonally, depending on the length of the life cycle. With this information, an estimate can then be made of the total annual respiration rate for the whole population, using the temperature/metabolism curves as a basis for calculating the rate of respiration month by month and summating over the 12-month period. Allowance must be made for the variations in age class composition of the population through the year; this can be done if temperature/metabolism curves are available for each of the stages in the life cycle, and if the proportions of the various stages in the population are determined throughout the year. When the various populations within a trophic level are considered in this way, a general picture of the distribution of energy at that level can be obtained.

In view of the technical problems and time-consuming measurements involved, it is not surprising that only the broad outlines of this picture have so far been drawn, and, frequently, even these must be based on certain assumptions. For example, Engelmann (1961) estimated an annual respiration rate for soil Cryptostigmata by equating this to 4 months of full activity (at 25°C) in the laboratory. Berthet (1963) estimated the contribution made by forest soil Cryptostigmata to total soil metabolism by calculating that the yearly total consumption of oxygen (4·5 litres O_2/m^2) corresponded to the complete combustion of 5·5 g of cellulose. Assuming an average yearly leaf-fall of 300 g of dry leaf material which was completely decomposed, the Cryptostigmata utilized 5·5/300 x 100 = 1·8 per cent of the total available energy. This is undoubtedly an underestimate of the effect of this particular group, for it is based on measurements of the respiratory rates of adults only. If account is taken of the contribution of the metabolically more active juvenile stages, which, according to Berthet (1963), may utilize as much as 70 per cent of the total available energy, the total contribution made by the group as a whole may be as high as 5 per cent. It appears likely that the other main group of soil microarthropods, the Collembola, make a contribution to total soil metabolism of the same order of magnitude; Macfadyen's (1963) estimates of 13-15 per cent for the proportion of the total available energy channelled into grassland populations of Collembola are probably too high, owing to their being based on overestimates of biomass (see Hale, 1967).

It will be realized that the metabolic contribution made by any particular taxonomic group will vary with the biomass present, and, since this will vary with the locality, the relative importance of the group in litter breakdown and energy utilization will vary from place to place. However, it is probable that groups such as the Isopoda compensate for a low metabolic rate with a high biomass in certain sites, whereas the relatively low biomass of Collembola, Nematoda, and Enchytraeidae may be offset by their relatively high metabolic rates. The low biomass of cryptostigmatid mites, coupled with a relatively low metabolic rate, indicate that the contribution of this group to total soil metabolism, and, therefore, to the chemical decomposition of litter material, is unlikely to be large. As noted earlier, the principal effect of this group of soil animals appears to be to promote the activities of bacteria and fungi whose direct contribution to total metabolism completely dominates that of all other groups of soil organisms combined. In grassland soils, the large biomass of lumbricids may qualify this group for a major metabolic role among the detritivores, although Satchell (1967) has calculated that woodland populations of *Lumbricus terrestris* in the English Lake District are responsible for the release of only 8-10 per cent of the total energy input to the community. This compares with an estimated contribution of 11 per cent for the enchytraeids of a moder coniferous soil (O'Connor, 1967). It is evident that the high biomass of the lumbricids may be considerably offset by their relatively low metabolic rate, and their direct contribution to the release of energy may be no greater than that of other smaller soil animals; in moder and mor woodland soils it may be considerably less.

Energetics of the Detritivore/Carnivore Food Chain

The energy stored in the protoplasm of the detritivore is not locked up there indefinitely. Ultimately, it is made available to decomposer organisms, when the detritivore dies, or to carnivores, when the detritivore is preyed upon by the latter. In order to complete our picture of the energy flow through the soil community, we need to know what proportions of the energy made available by the detritivores are utilized by other trophic levels.

It is sometimes difficult to identify the carnivore in the soil community, for animals, such as the lithobiomorph centipedes, which are usually considered as predators may also become detritivorous as the occasion demands (chapter 6). To attempt to determine rates of predation under natural conditions then becomes a formidable task, and it is not surprising that little progress has been made in this direction to date. Simple predator/prey systems can be set up in the laboratory, but there is no reason to believe that these even remotely approach the natural situation where a particular species population of detritivore may be subject to the attentions of a variety of predators. The intensity of predation is influenced by a number of factors, each of which may be influenced by other factors. For example, prey density or the number of moribund or diseased animals in the prey population may determine the extent to which this population is exploited by predators, and the amount of available food may determine not only the size of the prey population, but also whether this population is healthy or moribund. As yet, we know very little about the conditions under which there is maximum exploitation of the available resources by predator populations. It is very unlikely that a predator utilizes all of the food material available to it, and before we can evaluate the role of this trophic level in the energetics of the soil community, we need to have some information about assimilation efficiencies, and the uses to which the assimilated energy is put, i.e., how much is used in respiration and how much in the production of new tissue. The latter energy may become available to other carnivores or to decomposers, thus, we need to know whether or not there is more than one carnivore level operating in the system. Despite the formidable nature of these questions, there are some grounds for believing that the entire system is not quite so complex as it would seem to be at first sight.

The fact that energy is continually entering and leaving a particular trophic level in measurable quantities emphasizes the dynamic character of the ecosystem. Following Lindeman's (1942) interpretation, introduced earlier in this chapter, the standing crop energy of any given trophic level (n) can be designated as Λ_n, and the contribution of energy per unit time from a lower trophic level (Λ_{n-1}) to Λ_n is designated λ_n. The latter quantity represents the rate at which energy is flowing from one trophic level to a higher one. The significance of these quantities can best be expressed by quoting from Phillipson (1966):

> The trophic-dynamic formulation poses a number of important questions. Λ_n, as already stated, represents the energy content of a standing crop of a trophic level; we might ask if Λ_n/Λ_{n-1} is a constant. For example, does Λ_2/Λ_1 in a tropical forest equal Λ_2/Λ_1 in the open ocean? Or, in a desert, does Λ_2/Λ_1 equal Λ_3/Λ_2? More important still is the fact that λ_n represents the net production of a trophic level, and as such is a measure of the energy available to the next highest trophic level. How efficiently is energy transferred between trophic levels? Is $\lambda_n/\lambda_{n-1} \ldots$ a constant? Answers to questions such as these are important not only from the academic viewpoint of discovering what basic principles, if any, underlie the functioning of ecosystems, but also as a means of suggesting to man how he might turn the potential productivity of ecosystems to his own use.

It is with the last question, the efficiency with which energy is transferred from one trophic level to the next, that we are particularly concerned here. Slobodkin (1962) approached this by considering the constancy of the ratio of productivities of a species and of its predators; this ratio he termed 'ecological efficiency'. This has been defined in a variety of ways by different authors, and a schematic comparison of 20 common usages has been given by Kozlovsky (1968). Using an 'artificial' laboratory ecosystem, with *Chlamydomonas reinhardi* as producer, *Daphnia pulex* as herbivore, and the experimenter, who removed numbers of *Daphnia* from time to time, as the 'carnivore', Slobodkin was able to demonstrate that population size and production of *Daphnia* were proportional to food consumed, other factors being equal. However, when predation intensity was high (more than 25 per cent) abundant food was less efficiently exploited by *Daphnia* than were lower levels of food supply, because predation reduced numbers to a point at which the population could not consume all the available food. This situation does not provide maximum benefit to the predator which is not able to exploit to the full, the food of the prey. Maximum benefit is attained when predation intensity is such that the remaining prey is able to consume all of the available food. The ecological efficiency of this system can then be defined as:

$$\frac{\text{Calories ingested by carnivore}}{\text{Calories ingested by herbivore}} \times 100$$

The quantities required for this estimate were measured, and the maximum ecological efficiency for this system was determined as 13 per cent, expressed as a function of the intensity of predation. In a second series of experiments using the food chain: *Artemia*/*Hydra*/Man, this maximum was about 7 per cent (Fig. 13.6). Slobodkin (1962) suggested that these findings indicated that ecological efficiency, i.e., λ_n/λ_{n-1}, 'may either be constant or may only take a narrow range of values in nature since the taxonomic and ecological differences between *Daphnia* and *Hydra* may be as significant as the differences between any two field situations'. He concluded that this range is probably of the order of 5-20 per cent. The ecological efficiency of the Cryptostigmata populations studied by Engelmann (1961) can be estimated from the energy budget presented in Fig.

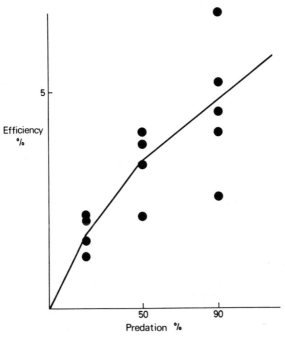

FIGURE 13.6. The ecological efficiency of *Hydra oligactis* populations as a function of the intensity of predation (from Slobodkin, 1962).

13.4; this efficiency can be determined from the ratio mortality:ingestion, assuming that all mortality is due to predation, giving a value of:

$$\frac{160 + 270}{10\ 248} \times 100 = 4 \cdot 2\%$$

Any attempt to apply this experimental approach to entire trophic levels in field situations, requires a detailed knowledge of feeding habits, food webs, assimilation, and respiratory rates. Although precise information regarding these functions in the soil ecosystem is, at best, fragmentary, Engelmann (1961) obtained an approximation to the ecological efficiency of the 'herbivore' level ('detritivore', in the sense used in this book), by making certain assumptions. In the first instance, he restricted his analysis to the ecologically important arthropod Acari, Collembola, Protura, Symphyla, Pauropoda, and Japygida, of

17

which the acarine Mesostigmata and certain groups of Prostigmata represented the carnivore level, the remainder the 'herbivore' level. The japygids could not be established with certainty as carnivores, and efficiencies were calculated (a) with these animals ignored, (b) with them considered as carnivores, and (c) with them considered as 'herbivores'. Second, since ingestion rates for these various groups were not known, the ecological efficiency of the 'herbivores' was defined as:

$$\frac{\text{Respiration cal of carnivores}/\% \text{ assimilation by carnivores}}{\dfrac{\text{Respiration cals of herbivores}}{\% \text{ assimilation by herbivores}} \times \dfrac{\text{Respiration cals of carnivores}}{\% \text{ assimilation by carnivores}}} \times 100$$

Respiration values were obtained by using the regression equation (see page 235) which provided the following estimates:

(a) Herbivore respiration, with japygids omitted or considered as carnivores, amounted to 2045·19 cal.

(b) Herbivore respiration, with japygids included as herbivores, amounted to 2343·97 cal.

(c) Carnivore respiration, with japygids omitted or considered as herbivores, amounted to 477·33 cal.

(d) Carnivore respiration, with japygids included as carnivores, amounted to 776·10 cal.

Assimilation rates were not directly measurable for most groups, and, to make an approximation of these, Engelmann utilized the results of Richman (1958) on *Daphnia* which indicated that these rates may vary between 14 and 32 per cent, depending on food supply. He selected the two extreme values (14 per cent and 32 per cent) and also an intermediate rate of 25 per cent assimilation, applying these both to the herbivore and carnivore categories. Thus, instead of computing a single ecological efficiency, the 3 x 3 x 3 permutation of (a) three possible levels of assimilation rate for carnivores, (b) three possible assimilation levels for herbivores, and (c) three possible definitions of the herbivore and carnivore categories, i.e., without japygids, with japygids as carnivores, and with japygids as herbivores, gave 27 possible estimates of efficiency (Table 13.3). The range of these estimates is 8·5-45·4 per cent. Engelmann calculated that the upper limit of this range was too high, for it required an energy flow into the carnivore level greater than that which could be produced by the herbivores during the course of a year, and concluded that a reasonable range of efficiency for the herbivore level was between 8 per cent and 30 per cent. Another important assumption made in this entire analysis is that all the carnivores fed on the herbivores, and not on other carnivores, i.e., there are no secondary carnivores. Much more precise investigation of feeding habits and the energetics of the carnivore level is required before the validity of these assumptions can be tested. The little information that is available concerning respiration rates of carnivores suggests that these are somewhat higher than those of the most active detritivores (Table 13.1), but that considerable intraspecific

TABLE 13.3. Ecological efficiency of the herbivores of an old field (from Engelmann, 1961).

Assimilation %		Efficiency %		
Carnivore	Herbivore	Without *Japex*	*Japex* as carnivore	*Japex* as herbivore
	32	18·9	27·5	16·9
32	25	15·4	22·9	13·7
	14	9·6	14·7	8·5
	32	23·0	32·7	20·7
25	25	18·9	27·5	16·9
	14	12·0	18·1	10·6
	32	32·9	45·4	30·1
14	25	28·1	39·4	25·5
	14	18·9	27·5	16·9

variability occurs, particularly during different stages in the life cycle (Phillipson, 1966). Thus, in the case of the opilionid *Leiobunum rotundum*, high oxygen consumption by young females reflects increased metabolic activity occurring during egg production, while a high respiratory rate among senescent adults may be attributed to an inability, on the part of these animals, to convert the energy assimilated into new protoplasm. With Phillipson (1966), we may conclude: '... if respiratory data are to be used in conjunction with population data to calculate population metabolism, then it is essential that measurements of metabolic activity be made on all life stages of a single species, throughout the course of a year.' This applies with equal force to assessments of assimilation rates and ecological efficiencies.

References

Berthet, P. (1963) 'Mesure de la consommation d'oxygène des oribatides (Acariens) de la litière des forêts' in Doeksen, J. and Drift, J. van der, eds., *Soil organisms*, 18-31.

Berthet, P. (1964) 'L'activité des oribates d'une chênaie', *Mém. Inst. r. Sc. nat. Belg.*, 152, 1-152.

Bocock, K. L. (1963) 'The digestion and assimilation of food by *Glomeris*' in Doeksen, J. and Drift, J. van der, eds., *Soil organisms*, 85-91.

Edney, E. B. and Spencer, J. O. (1955) 'Cutaneous respiration in woodlice', *J. exp. Biol.*, 32, 256-69.

Engelmann, M. D. (1961) 'The role of soil arthropods in the energetics of an old field community', *Ecol. Monogr.*, 31, 221-38.

Gere, G. (1956) 'The examination of the feeding biology and humicative function of Diplopoda and Isopoda', *Acta biol. hung.*, 6, 257-71.

Golley, F. B. (1961) 'Energy values of ecological materials', *Ecology*, 42, 581-84.

Hale, W. G. (1967) 'Collembola' in Burges, N. A. and Raw, F., eds., *Soil biology*, 397-411.

Heal, O. W. (1967) *Paper presented to the Symposium on Methods of Study in Soil Ecology*, UNESCO-IBP, Paris, 1967.

Healey, I. N. (1967a) 'The energy flow through a population of soil Collembola' in Petrusewicz, K., ed., *Secondary productivity of terrestrial ecosystems*, 695-708.

Healey, I. N. (1967b) 'The population metabolism of *Onychiurus procampatus* Gisin (Collembola)' in Graff, O. and Satchell, J. E., eds., *Progress in soil biology*, 127-37.

Heath, G. W. (1965) 'The part played by animals in soil formation' in Hallsworth, E. G. and Crawford, D. V., eds., *Experimental pedology*, 236-43.

Holter, H. (1943) 'Technique of the Cartesian diver', *C. R. Trav. Carlsberg, Sér. chim.*, **24**, 399-478.

Kozlovsky, D. G. (1968) 'A critical evaluation of the trophic level concept. I. Ecological efficiencies', *Ecology*, **49**, 48-60.

Lindeman, R. L. (1942) 'Trophic-dynamic aspect of ecology', *Ecology*, **23**, 399-418.

Linderström-Lang, K. (1943) 'On the theory of the cartesian diver microrespirometer', *C. R. Trav. Carlsberg, Sér. chim*, **24**, 333-98.

Macfadyen, A. (1961) 'A new system for continuous respirometry of small air breathing invertebrates in near-natural conditions', *J. exp. Biol.*, **38**, 323-41.

Macfadyen, A. (1963) 'The contribution of the microfauna to total soil metabolism' in Doeksen, J. and Drift, J. van der, eds., *Soil organisms*, 3-17.

Macfadyen, A. (1967) *Paper presented to the Symposium on Methods of Study in Soil Ecology*, UNESCO-IBP, Paris, 1967.

Newell, P. F. (1967) *Paper presented to the Symposium on Methods of Study in Soil Ecology*, UNESCO-IBP, Paris, 1967.

O'Connor, F. B. (1963) 'Oxygen consumption and population metabolism of some populations of Enchytraeidae from North Wales' in Doeksen, J. and Drift, J. van der, eds., *Soil organisms*, 32-48.

O'Connor, F. B. (1967) 'The Enchytraeidae' in Burges, N. A. and Raw, F., eds., *Soil biology*, 213-57.

Ovington, J. D. (1962) 'Quantitative ecology and the woodland ecosystem concept' in Cragg, J. B., ed., *Advances in ecological research*, **1**, 103-92.

Phillipson, J. (1962) 'Respirometry and the study of energy turnover in natural systems with particular reference to harvestspiders (Phalangiida)', *Oikos*, **13**, 311-22.

Phillipson, J. (1964) 'A miniature bomb calorimeter for small biological samples', *Oikos*, **15**, 130-9.

Phillipson, J. (1966) *Ecological energetics*, Institute of Biology, London; St Martins Press, New York.

Phillipson, J. and Watson, J. (1965) 'Respiratory metabolism of the terrestrial isopod *Oniscus asellus* L', *Oikos*, **16**, 78-87.

Richman, S. (1958) 'The transformation of energy by *Daphnia pulex*', *Ecol. Monogr.*, **28**, 273-91.

Saito, S. (1967). *Paper presented to the Symposium on Methods of Study in Soil Ecology*, UNESCO-IBP, Paris, 1967.

Satchell, J. E. (1967) 'Lumbricidae' in Burges, N. A. and Raw, F., eds., *Soil biology*, 259-322.

Slobodkin, L. B. (1962) 'Energy in animal ecology' in Cragg, J. B., ed., *Advances in ecological research*, **1**, 69-101.

Slobodkin, L. B. and Richman, S. (1960) 'The availability of a miniature bomb calorimeter for ecology', *Ecology*, **41**, 784.

Wallwork, J. A. (1967) 'Acari' in Burges, N. A. and Raw, F., eds., *Soil biology*, 363-95.

Zinkler, D. (1966) 'Vergleichende Untersuchungen zur Atmungsphysiologie von Collembolen und anderen Bodenkleinarthropoden', *Z. vergl. Physiol.*, **52**, 99-144.

14. Collection, preservation, and identification of soil animals

Soil animals are both easy and difficult to collect. This ecosystem is so rich in animal life that even casual sorting, under a binocular microscope, will reveal a varied assemblage of forms. However, it is more difficult to obtain samples of this fauna that are representative of the population sizes present, for to do this requires that the animals be separated from the solid material of the soil. This final chapter is concerned with some of the problems of extracting, preserving, and identifying some of the more common groups of soil animals.

Extraction Techniques

An exhaustive account of the many different kinds of extraction methods in use at the present time is unnecessary, for comprehensive accounts are available elsewhere (Macfadyen, 1961, 1962a and b; Murphy, 1962a; Southwood, 1966). Here, we will be concerned with outlining the procedures used in the simpler and more general methods, and these can be divided into two broad categories: the mechanical and the behavioural.

Mechanical Methods

The techniques included within this category are passive, in the sense that they do not utilize the behaviour of the animals concerned, and, therefore, will extract inactive as well as active stages. Further, they do not discriminate between animals that are dead at the time of sampling and those that are alive, which may lead to overestimates of population size and underestimates of mortality. Under this heading are included sieving, washing, and flotation methods.

Sieving methods are usually employed when the size of the animals under study is appreciably different from that of the soil particles, for example, the separation of earthworms from friable mineral soil. The selectivity of this 'dry' sieving method depends on the mesh size used, and it is often possible to separate out several different size groupings of animals by using a number of sieves of differing mesh sizes assembled in a series. Wet sieving is often more efficient than the dry method, particularly for medium- and small-sized litter-dwelling animals other than arthropods, and a simple apparatus useful for collecting enchytraeids and small molluscs is illustrated in Fig. 14.1. Leaf litter is supported on a coarse mesh (1 cm), and the whole apparatus filled with water.

The litter may be gently stirred or continuously agitated, and the animals become detached and collect on the fine cloth covering the lower grid. The whole apparatus can be drained after about half an hour of this treatment, the litter removed and the animals lifted out on the fine cloth for identification and counting. Although satisfactory for leaf litter extractions, this method is not efficient for finely particulate material, such as humus and mineral soil, for these small particles pass through the upper sieve and clog the lower one. This prevents rapid drainage and also obscures the animals collected.

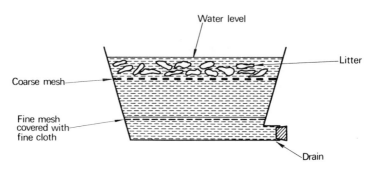

FIGURE 14.1. Wet sieving apparatus for collecting molluscs and enchytraeids from leaf litter (after Southwood, 1966).

Microarthropods cannot usually be extracted satisfactorily with sieving methods, for the fraction in which they accumulate frequently contains large amounts of plant debris and mineral soil particles. The separation of these three components can be achieved by a 'flotation' technique consisting, essentially, of two operations. First, the mineral soil is separated from the organic matter (animals + plant debris) by making use of the different specific gravities of these two fractions. Second, the microarthropods are separated from plant material by differential wetting, the plant material being wetted by water whereas the waxy arthropod cuticle is not. The full sequence of steps is as follows:

(a) The soil core is broken up thoroughly, either by freezing and thawing or by jets of water, and washed through a set of sieves which remove the larger soil particles. The microarthropods wash down and collect, along with small soil particles and fragments of plant debris, in the filtrate 'settling can'.

(b) The contents of the settling can are then poured into another can, called a 'Ladell' can (Fig. 14.2a) which is fitted with a fine phosphor-bronze gauze.

(c) The mineral and organic material collects on the fine gauze, and, when all the water has drained through, a plug is inserted into the drain hole and the drainage tank removed.

(d) A concentrated solution of magnesium sulphate is then fed into the Ladell through the drain plug (Fig. 14.2b). This will cause the organic material to float away from the gauze, leaving the denser mineral particles behind. Any organic material which adheres to the gauze can be freed by bubbling air through for a few minutes, and will collect on the surface of the magnesium sulphate solution, as a 'float'.

(e) The float is then decanted off by raising the level of the magnesium sulphate in the Ladell; this is conveniently done by using a reservoir which can be raised or lowered to fill or drain the Ladell, as shown in Fig. 14.2b.

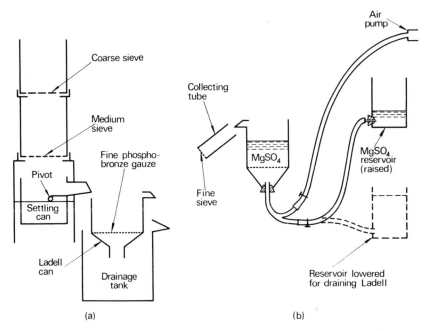

FIGURE 14.2. (a) Soil washing apparatus; (b) Ladell flotation apparatus (see text for details of operation) (from Southwood, 1966, and Salt and Hollick, 1944).

(f) The float is then passed through a filter which retains the solid plant and animal material. In highly mineral soils, for which this technique is, perhaps, the most appropriate, there may be very little plant debris, and the animals can be detected easily in this residue. However, if there is an appreciable amount of plant debris present, a second, and different, flotation process will be required.

(g) In this case, the residue collected after filtration is washed into a beaker or flask with a jet of water. Since the subsequent separation will depend for its success on the plant material being completely waterlogged, it is useful to boil the suspension at this stage.

(h) After the suspension has cooled, xylene or benzene is added, and the mixture stirred or shaken thoroughly. If good separation has been achieved, the microarthropods will collect in the upper hydrocarbon layer, or at the interface between this and the water, and the plant material will sink to the bottom of the water layer.

(i) The upper layer containing the animals is then decanted, filtered, and the residue examined or stored in preservative (70 per cent alcohol + glycerin) for future study.

The flotation method is, perhaps, the most widely used of the mechanical techniques, for it will extract simultaneously a variety of animal groups. Other, more selective, methods in use include centrifuge procedures for Protozoa and microarthropods, and sedimentation and elutriation techniques based on the different settling rates of animals and soil particles. Elutriation is a modified type of sedimentation, in which the settling occurs against an opposing current of water. These methods have been found particularly useful for collecting nematodes, but are much less efficient for microarthropods, many of which settle at the same rate as the soil particles.

Perhaps one of the greatest disadvantages of the mechanical extraction techniques is the considerable amount of work involved and time consumed in operating them. Therefore, it is not surprising that many soil zoologists prefer to use behavioural techniques, in which the animals do most of the work.

Behavioural Methods

These methods utilize the behavioural responses of the animals, such that they will leave the soil after being subjected to the appropriate stimulus, for example, heat, illumination, desiccation. Since these methods rely on animal activity, they will not extract eggs or resting stages in representative numbers. Further, as different animals react differently to the same stimulus, the efficiency with which the various groups are extracted from a single soil core will vary with the group. It is unlikely that the extraction will be 100 per cent efficient for any group, consequently, population estimates based on these methods will tend to be underestimates.

The most popular kind of dry behavioural extractor is the Berlese-Tullgren funnel, which has been modified in various ways to improve its efficiency (see Macfadyen, 1961; Murphy, 1962b) (Fig. 14.3). The soil or litter sample is placed on a wire gauze in the mouth of a steep-sided funnel and heated from above by an ordinary lamp bulb, an infrared bulb, or a heating coil. As the surface of the sample becomes heated and desiccated, the animals move down and eventually are driven out of the bottom of the sample, and fall down the funnel into a collecting vial placed below the apparatus. For its successful operation, this method requires that steep gradients of temperature and relative humidity are set up, and maintained, between the soil sample and the atmosphere in the funnel immediately beneath it. Thus, the collecting vial should contain water or some aqueous preservative, such as picric acid, which will increase the relative humidity within the funnel as it evaporates. The temperature gradient can also be increased by surrounding the lower part of the funnel with a cold-water circulating system. It is also important to ensure that the heating of the soil sample is gradual, otherwise many animals, particularly immature stages, will succumb before they are able to escape. The soil sample should be disturbed as little as possible when being placed in the extractor. If the sample is in the form of a plug, it should be inverted in the extractor, so that the animals can leave it rapidly and easily through the larger surface channels. One annoying feature of

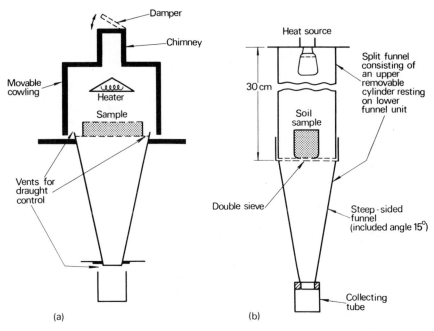

FIGURE 14.3. Two types of funnel extractor: (a) Macfadyen's controlled-draught funnel for macroarthropods; (b) Murphy's split-funnel for microarthropods (from Macfadyen, 1962b, and Murphy, 1962b).

the dry funnel, which occurs particularly when wet soil is being used, is condensation of water on the inner walls of the funnel which may imprison small animals and prevent them from falling into the collecting vial. Much of this condensation can be avoided by using a long funnel with sharply angled sides. It is also obvious that the inner surface of the funnel must be as smooth as possible to prevent debris and organisms accumulating there; spiders are often a particular problem in this respect, and the funnels should be inspected regularly for their webs which form effective barriers between the soil sample and the collecting vial.

The problems inherent in the funnel apparatus, described above, are not always capable of easy solution; it is particularly difficult to control the gradients along it, and it is virtually impossible to construct a funnel which is perfectly smooth on the inside. Recently, a dry 'bowl' extractor has been developed

(Kempson *et al.*, 1963) which does not require the use of a funnel and yet is able to maintain high temperature and relative humidity gradients. Each extractor is a two-tiered bowl unit (Fig. 14.4), the floor of the upper tier being a removable plastic grid on which are placed two sheets of cotton fillet net; the soil or litter sample is placed in the upper tier, and an aqueous solution of picric acid is placed beneath it in the lower bowl. When assembled, the two tiers are held together by

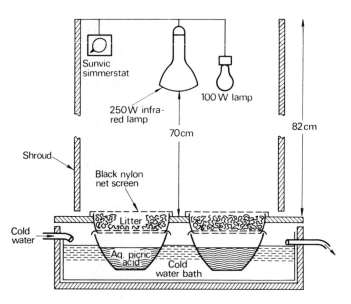

FIGURE 14.4. The dry bowl extractor developed by Kempson *et al.* (1963).

means of a strong elastic band which passes underneath the lower bowl and clips on the sides of the upper one. This extractor unit is then set into an insulated baffle mounted above a coldwater bath, so that the lower collecting bowl is surrounded by circulating cold water, and the upper surface of the soil sample is level with the upper surface of the baffle, as shown in Fig. 14.4. A black nylon net lid may be placed over the top of each extractor to prevent animals from escaping upwards. A shrouded box is placed on top of the baffle, and the sample is heated by pulses from an infrared lamp which can be controlled by means of a Simmerstat switch. An ordinary lamp bulb is included in the circuit, and this switches on when the infrared bulb is off, thus ensuring that the sample is constantly illuminated. Extraction usually takes about one week with this apparatus, although the time will vary with the amount and type of soil sample used. The method has produced excellent results for microarthropods, for which the efficiency varies from 90 to 100 per cent, but is less efficient for nematodes (2 per cent), enchytraeids (11 per cent), snails (21 per cent), and larvae of Coleoptera, Diptera, and Lepidoptera (40-60 per cent), which are very susceptible to desiccation and cannot escape quickly enough from dry extractors. In these cases, wet funnel methods are more suitable.

A great deal of work has been done on comparing these various extraction methods with each other and with 'standard' counts from handsorted samples (see, for example, Macfadyen, 1955, 1962a; Müller and Naglitsch, 1957; Müller, 1962, Satchell and Nelson, 1962; Wood, 1965). It is, perhaps, safe to conclude from these studies that no one method emerges as the best for all groups of the soil fauna in all types of soil, although flotation methods often provide higher counts than funnel methods for mineral soils, considering the arthropods as a whole. However, as pointed out earlier in this chapter, the flotation methods may produce overestimates due to the fact that a distinction is not easily made between animals alive and those dead at the time of sampling. Considering individual groups of the soil fauna, on the other hand, it is possible to make certain generalizations:

(a) The controlled-draught funnel extractor (Fig. 14.3a) appears to be distinctly more efficient than the conventional Tullgren funnel for the recovery of macroarthropods. Macfadyen (1955, 1962b) found this method significantly better, to the extent of between 1 and 7 per cent, for beetle larvae, most myriapods (excluding Symphyla), isopods, pseudoscorpions, and spiders.

(b) Certain groups of cryptostigmatid mites are extracted more efficiently by the Tullgren funnel than by the flotation methods. Satchell and Nelson (1962) noted that this was the case with all stages of *Nothrus silvestris*, nymphs and larvae of *Tectocepheus* spp., and adults of *Brachychthonius* sp. and *Steganacarus magnus* from a moder woodland site. These authors also found that there was no significant difference between the efficiencies of the two methods with regard to most other groups of Cryptostigmata in this soil type, including adults of *Oppia* sp., *Suctobelba* sp., and *Tectocepheus* sp. When this is the case, the funnel method would be recommended in view of its ease of operation and time-saving characteristics.

(c) Funnel methods appear to be quite unsuitable for such groups of mites as the minute Scutacaridae and the Astigmata, for these forms are relatively inactive and, in the latter, are represented by inert hypopial stages. Satchell and Nelson (1962) found that the flotation method was significantly better at the 0·1 and 1 per cent probability level respectively for these groups inhabiting a moder woodland soil.

(d) Small and rather delicate microarthropods, such as Pauropoda, Collembola, and Symphyla, may be seriously damaged during the conventional flotation extraction, and yet may not be satisfactorily recovered by Tullgren funnel methods, particularly when the soil sample contains large amounts of clay and a low content of organic matter. For such cases, von Törne (1962) devised an elutriation and sieving method. Edwards and Dennis (1962) described a modified flotation method for the extraction of Symphyla from organic soils (Fig. 14.5) in which the soil sample is spread over the surface of a saturated solution of sodium chloride in the flotation vessel; the addition of Calgon, or sodium hexametaphosphate, helps to break up the soil particles and allows a more even dispersion. Air is bubbled through the suspension, the animals float to the surface and can be decanted by raising the level of the sodium chloride in the flotation vessel. The 'float' is collected on a sieve, washed into a beaker to which benzene is added, and the final separation of animal and plant material carried out in the conventional way. Although designed for the collection of Symphyla, this method may also be suitable for a wide variety of soil microarthropods.

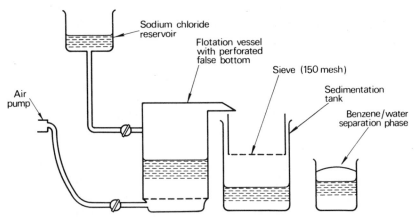

FIGURE 14.5. Modified flotation apparatus for extracting Symphyla from soil (from Edwards and Dennis, 1962).

Clearly, the kind of 'dry' extraction method selected in any particular study will depend, to a large extent, on the composition of the fauna and the aims of the investigation. As a general rule, however, flotation methods operate most efficiently for mineral soils with a low organic content, whereas funnel extractors are more suited to highly organic soils.

In the wet extractor technique, of which the Baermann funnel (Fig. 14.6a) is a simple example, the soil sample is kept moist, or saturated, with water and heated gently to drive out the animals. It may be necessary to contain the sample in a muslin bag, although it is often sufficient to place the soil openly in a sieve mounted in the mouth of the filter funnel which is flooded with water. Heating from above will cause enchytraeids and nematodes to leave the sample, pass through the sieve and collect in the neck of the funnel from whence they may be recovered by releasing the stopcock. A modification of this method, useful for collecting Enchytraeidae, has been developed by Nielsen (1952); the soil sample is placed over a bed of coarse gravel, in a perforated canister, and covered with a layer of sand or fine gravel in which is embedded a tubular glass coil through which cold water circulates. The canister is placed in a warm water bath (Fig. 14.6b) so that the soil sample is constantly perfused with saturated air; the enchytraeids are driven upwards into the cooler sand from which they can be separated by flotation.

All of the techniques outlined above, and these are but a few of those described or reviewed in the papers edited by Murphy (1962a), are designed to treat soil samples brought into the laboratory. The collection of animals in the

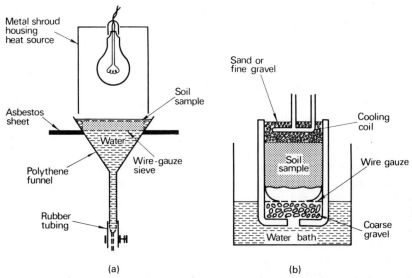

FIGURE 14.6. Wet extractors used for the collection of Enchytraeidae: (a) modified Baermann funnel; (b) the Nielsen extractor (from O'Connor, 1962).

field requires very different methods, which are more often relative than absolute (Southwood, 1966). Within this category, are included a variety of pitfall traps suitable for collecting surface-dwelling insects, isopods, spiders, Collembola, and myriapods; suction traps (Taylor, 1962), sticky traps, and sweeping and brushing machines (Chant, 1962) are also useful for these groups. The application of chemical substances, such as formalin and potassium permanganate, to the soil surface has been used to drive out earthworms and geophilomorph centipedes, but with these, as with many other field methods, it is difficult to relate the numbers collected to the natural population density. There are two reasons for this: first, baited traps may attract animals from sites remote from the actual trap, and thus the effective area sampled is an unknown quantity; second an animal's susceptibility to trapping may vary with its age, reproductive condition, and its diurnal or seasonal activity pattern, so that the size of the collection may be more an indication of the activity of the population than of its size. The first of these two difficulties may be met, in part, by combining grid sampling with marking techniques to determine the mobility of the animals; the second requires that the results of sequential sampling be interpreted in the light of information about the behaviour and phenology of the animals concerned.

Soil Sectioning

An important step forward in the study of the soil fauna was marked by the development of a soil sectioning technique by Haarløv and Weis-Fogh (1955). In contrast to the methods described above, this technique allows observations to be made of soil animals in their natural surroundings, and although it is not widely used at the present time to obtain estimates of population densities, it has considerable potential in this context. Briefly, the procedure is as follows. Cylindrical soil cores, 10 cm in diameter and 5-10 cm deep, are taken from the field and cooled to $-10°C$ in the laboratory. From these cores, smaller cylinders can be cut, using a heated sampler 10 mm in diameter, and these cylinders, which are 30-50 mm long, are then immersed in 40 per cent formaldehyde solution at 70°C for about an hour. This treatment dissolves the ice and fixes any soil animals present. The cylinders are then slowly immersed in 2 per cent agar solution for about one hour, after which time they can be removed to 96 per cent alcohol for hardening. Sections of this hardened material can be cut with a razor blade, and the authors report that good serial sections, 0·75 mm thick, can be cut from sandy soils and even thinner sections (0·1 mm thick) from organic soils. The sections are then passed through glycerol-alcohol mixtures to glycerol and mounted in glycerol-gelatin.

Microscopic examination of the sections so obtained can provide information on the spatial distribution of soil animals in a profile and also on the extent, size, and distribution of soil cavities. With data of this kind, it is possible to express population densities of soil animals in terms of the amount of available living space, i.e., the area of the walls of inhabitable soil cavities. This is surely more realistic than density estimates based on numbers per unit weight or volume of soil. Considering the Collembola and mites together, Haarløv (1955) estimated a density of 1 animal per 100 mm^2 within the depth range 0-4 cm in the soil of a Danish woodland plantation, using this technique.

Preservation

Once a sampling and extraction programme is in full operation, animals accumulate faster than they can be identified. This can often create problems, for example, in the case of lumbricids and molluscs, in which identification is easier with living specimens than with preserved material. However, more often than not, it becomes a practical necessity to preserve collections until a later date when they can be examined at leisure, or sent to an appropriate specialist in the taxonomy of the group. Preservation in 70-80 per cent alcohol, to which a small amount (up to 5 per cent) of glycerol may be added to prevent drying out, is recommended for most soil arthropods and for molluscs, although the latter should be dehydrated in a graded series of alcohols before final storage.

Earthworms and nematodes may be preserved satisfactorily in 5 per cent and 10 per cent solutions, respectively, of formalin. Some authors prefer to use aqueous picric acid as a preservative for microarthropod Collembola and mites, and, since this fluid can be incorporated in a behavioural extraction technique (see above), collections can be removed to storage as rapidly as they are processed.

It is a common practice to preserve at least a representative sample of some of the smaller soil animals as semipermanent or permanent mounts on glass microslides. In this way, quick access is obtained to identified specimens for comparison with subsequent collections. However, if material is to be sent to a specialist for identification, it is usually better to send preserved material stored in glass vials, in preference to microscope preparations. Semipermanent slide preparations of nematodes can be made using lactophenol, a mountant which also clears the specimens. Used in a 1:1 combination with polyvinyl alcohol, lactophenol is also a suitable mountant for astigmatid and prostigmatid mites, and for Symphyla. For hard-bodied mesostigmatid and cryptostigmatid mites a gum chloral mountant is often used. Hoyer's medium is one such mountant and consists of the following ingredients:

Distilled water	50 g
Gum arabic (clear crystals)	30 g
Chloral hydrate	200 g
Glycerol	20 g

These constituents are mixed at room temperature and the resulting solution filtered through bolting silk before use. Gum chloral mountants will clear the specimens to some extent, but, in the case of deeply coloured or dark specimens, it is advisable to clear them first in warm concentrated lactic acid before mounting. These mountants have the advantage over resins that preserved, or living, specimens can be mounted directly without prior dehydration. In addition, the refractive index of the mountant is sufficiently different from that of the mites, so staining is usually not necessary; this is not the case with balsam and other resin mountants. However, gum chloral does not always harden satisfactorily, particularly in the tropics, and slides must be ringed to prevent excessive liquefaction of the mountant. On the other hand, when these mountants do harden, they may crystallize or shrink and thereby distort or crush the specimen. This disadvantage may be overcome, in part, by using a raised coverslip or cavity slide, although this often precludes the use of the oil immersion technique for microscopic detail.

Permanent slide preparations are rarely completely satisfactory, except in a general way for routine comparisons, and many workers prefer to study microarthropods as temporary preparations. One such simple and convenient method utilizes a cavity slide on which a coverslip is positioned in such a way that only a small part of the depression is covered. A drop of lactic acid, lactophenol, or glycerol is then introduced with a pipette beneath the projecting edge of the coverslip to fill that part of the cavity below this edge. Cleared specimens can then be inserted in the fluid beneath the coverslip and manipulated into position with a fine needle. Subsequent reorientation of the specimen can be achieved by moving the coverslip slightly or by the use of a needle. This method has the advantage of being rapid, and specimens can be returned to storage directly after examination. Indeed, this is desirable, for prolonged immersion in lactic acid renders the microarthropod cuticle brittle, with the result that specimens may fragment or lose their appendages and setae.

Identification of Soil Animals

It would be inappropriate to conclude this book without drawing attention to one of the most daunting tasks confronting the soil ecologist, namely, the identification of the animals he collects. The determination of genus and species, even family, in many groups of the soil fauna remains the province of the specialist taxonomist, who is, himself, a rather rare animal. This is unfortunate, for inaccurate or imprecise identifications detract considerably from the value of any ecological investigation. The ideal solution is for the ecologist to become his own taxonomist. However, it may take several years to become familiar enough with one group of soil animals to undertake detailed identifications with confidence, and few dedicated ecologists are prepared to sacrifice this amount of time. On the other hand, there is no reason why even the beginning student should not be able to sort his collections accurately into major groupings; preliminary investigations of a general character often require no more than this, and, even if more detailed identifications are required, it will be easier to enlist the cooperation of a specialist, if the collections are well organized and adequately sorted. Comprehensive keys to the identification of major groups of soil animals have been provided in Kevan's *Soil Zoology* and Dunger's *Tiere im Boden,* and the 'How to Know' series of handbooks, particularly the work by Chu (1949) on the immature insects, can also be recommended for identification to the family level. Once an initial familiarity with a particular group has been gained, more detailed identifications can be undertaken using the keys referred to in the appropriate chapters of this book.

References

Chant, D. A. (1962) 'A brushing method for collecting mites and small insects from leaves' in Murphy, P. W., ed., *Progress in soil zoology,* 222-5.

Chu, H. F. (1949) *How to know the immature insects,* Brown, Dubuque. 234 pp.

Edwards, C. A. and Dennis, E. B. (1962) 'The sampling and extraction of Symphyla from soil' in Murphy, P. W., ed., *Progress in soil zoology,* 300-4.

Haarløv, N. (1955) 'Vertical distribution of mites and Collembola in relation to soil structure' in Kevan, D. K. McE., ed., *Soil zoology,* 167-79.

Haarløv, N. and Weis-Fogh, T. (1955) 'A microscopical technique for studying the undisturbed texture of soils' in Kevan, D. K. McE., ed., *Soil zoology,* 429-32.

Kempson, D., Lloyd, M., and Ghelardi, R. (1963) 'A new extractor for woodland litter', *Pedobiologia,* 3, 1-21.

Macfadyen, A. (1955) 'A comparison of methods for the extraction of soil arthropods' in Kevan, D. K. McE., ed., *Soil zoology*, 315-32.

Macfadyen, A. (1961) 'Improved funnel-type extractors for soil arthropods', *J. Anim. Ecol.,* 30, 171-84.

Macfadyen, A. (1962a) 'Soil arthropod sampling' in Cragg, J. B., ed., *Advances in ecological research,* 1, 1-34.

Macfadyen, A. (1962b) 'Control of humidity in three funnel-type extractors for soil arthropods' in Murphy, P. W., ed., *Progress in soil zoology*, 158-68.

Müller, G. (1962) 'A centrifugal-flotation extraction technique and its comparison with two funnel extractors' in Murphy, P. W., ed., *Progress in soil zoology*, 207-11.

Müller, G. and Naglitsch, F. (1957) 'Vergleichende Prüfung bodenzoologischer Auslese-methoden für Kleinarthropoden', *Zool. Jb. (Syst.)*, 85, 177-210.

Murphy, P. W. (1962a) *Progress in soil zoology. Papers from a colloquium on research methods organized by the Soil Zoology Committee of the International Society of Soil Science, Rothamsted, 1958*, Butterworths, London. xviii + 398 pp.

Murphy, P. W. (1962b) 'A split-funnel extractor—a modified Tullgren funnel' in Murphy, P. W., ed., *Progress in soil zoology*, 174-8.

Nielsen, C. O. (1952) 'Studies on Enchytraeidae. 1. A technique for extracting En-chytraeidae from soil samples', *Oikos*, 4, 187-96.

O'Connor, F. B. (1962) 'The extraction of Enchytraeidae from soil' in Murphy, P. W., ed., *Progress in soil zoology*, 279-85.

Salt, G. and Hollick, F. S. J. (1944) 'Studies of wireworm populations', *Ann. appl. Biol.* 31, 52-64.

Satchell, J. E. and Nelson, J. M. (1962) 'A comparison of the Tullgren-funnel and flotation methods of extracting Acarina from woodland soil' in Murphy, P. W., ed., *Progress in soil zoology*, 212-16.

Southwood, T. R. E. (1966) *Ecological methods*, Methuen, London, xviii + 391 pp.

Taylor, L. R. (1962) 'Suction methods for sampling arthropods at and above ground level' in Murphy, P. W., ed., *Progress in soil zoology*, 217-21.

Törne, E. von (1962) 'An elutriation and sieving apparatus for extracting micro-Arthropoda from soil', in Murphy, P. W., ed., *Progress in soil zoology*, 204-6.

Wood, T. G. (1965) 'Comparison of a funnel and a flotation method for extracting Acari and Collembola from moorland soil', *Pedobiologia*, 5, 131-9.

Author Index

Abaturov, B. D. 187, 190
Agrell, I., 145, 147
Andrewartha, H. G., 191, 203, 205
Anglade, P., 91, 92, 101
Armsby, A., 187, 188, 190
Arnold, M. K., 9, 22
Arthur, D. R., 65, 74
Ashby, M., 12, 22
Axtell, R. C., 173, 175, 200, 201, 205

Baker, E. W., 159, 167, 175
Balduf, W. V., 113, 116, 125
Balogh, J., 159, 175, 210, 225
Banage, W. B., 54, 55, 57, 202, 205
Banerjee, B., 99, 101
Bartsevich, V. V., 126
Beier, M., 155, 156, 157, 158, 178, 199, 201, 206
Bellinger, P. F., 133, 146, 147, 212, 225
Berg, C. O., 206
Berthet, P., 234, 236, 238, 240, 245
Bessard, A., 32, 36
Bétrémieux, R., 6, 22, 29, 36
Betts, M., 181, 190
Beynon, K., 226
Bhattacharyya, S. K., 167, 176
Birch, L. C., 191, 203, 205
Block, W. C., 169, 170, 171, 172, 176, 203, 205, 218, 225
Bloomfield, C., 27, 36
Blower, J. G., 94, 97, 98, 99, 101
Bocock, K. L., 31, 32, 36, 37, 100, 101, 118, 125, 233, 237, 245
Bornebusch, C. H., 218, 219, 220, 225
Boyd, J. M., 59, 74
Brady, N. C., 22
Brauns, A., 116, 125
Brereton, J. LeG., 84, 86, 87, 88, 101, 192, 195, 201, 205
Brian, M. V., 123, 124, 125, 226
Bristowe, W. S., 152, 176
Britt, N. W., 144, 145, 147

Browning, E., 155, 176
Buckman, H. O., 22
Burges, N. A., 8, 9, 10, 11, 22
Burgess, A. F., 113, 125
Bursell, E., 82, 101
Byers, G. W., 216, 226

Cernosvitov, L., 59, 74
Chadwick, M. J., 19, 22, 120, 125, 186, 190
Chant, D., 255, 258
Cherrett, J. M., 151, 152, 153, 176
Chitty, D., 203, 205
Christensen, B., 66, 75
Christiansen, K., 42, 44, 132, 134, 135, 141, 143, 147
Chu, H. F., 258
Clark, L. R., 191, 205
Cloudsley-Thompson, J. L., 19, 22, 84, 85, 89, 90, 101, 120, 125, 150, 151, 176, 186, 190, 198, 205
Coaker, T. H., 108, 125, 200, 205
Cook, E. F., 168, 169, 172, 174, 179, 192, 193, 194, 195, 202, 207
Cooper, B. A., 193, 205
Cragg, J. B., 59, 74, 197, 205, 218, 225
Cranbrook, Earl of, 187, 190
Crossley, D. A., 9, 22, 31, 36
Crowcroft, P., 189, 190
Crump, L. M., 57
Cutler, D. W., 49, 57

D'Aguilar, J., 32, 36
Davidson, J., 112, 125
Davis, B. N. K., 216, 225
Delany, M. J., 108, 125
Delkeskamp, K., 115, 125
Den Boer, P. J., 85, 101
Dennis, E. B., 226, 253, 254, 258
Deschiens, R., 201, 205, 206
Dhillon, B. S., 132, 135, 140, 146, 147, 171, 176, 216, 226

Donner, J., 55, 56, 57
Drift, J. van der, 30, 37, 39, 44, 70, 73, 74, 84, 86, 99, 100, 101, 102, 111, 113, 114, 115, 118, 125, 132, 134, 147, 151, 164, 171, 176, 193, 205
Duddington, C. L., 55, 57, 201, 205
Dudich, E., 102
Duffey, E., 151, 152, 153, 176
Dunger, W., 33, 37, 86, 87, 99, 100, 102, 141, 147, 258

Eason, E. H., 93, 102, 201, 205
Edney, E. B., 80, 81, 82, 83, 84, 85, 102, 198, 205, 238, 245
Edwards, C. A., 90, 91, 92, 102, 110, 111, 125, 220, 224, 225, 226, 253, 254, 258
Empson, D. W., 226
Engelmann, M. D., 128, 147, 234, 235, 236, 240, 243, 244, 245
Evans, A. C., 59, 61, 63, 64, 74, 75
Evans, G. O., 155, 159, 170, 171, 176, 220, 226
Evans, W. D., 7, 22

Fager, E. W., 210, 226
Filipponi, A., 173, 176
Forsslund, K. H., 132, 147, 174, 176
Franz, H., 100, 102
Freeman, B. E., 118, 120, 125

Gabbutt, P. D., 151, 152, 153, 156, 157, 176
Gasdorf, E. C., 156, 176
Geier, P. W., 205
Gentry, J. B., 123, 126
Gerard, B. M., 59, 61, 64, 75, 195, 197, 205
Gere, G., 99, 100, 102, 237, 245
Ghabbour, S., 58, 75
Ghelardi, R., 258
Ghilarov, M. S., 33, 37, 208, 226
Gibson, N. H. E., 132, 135, 140, 146, 147, 171, 176, 216, 226
Gilbert, O. J., 31, 37
Gisin, H., 42, 44, 132, 147
Glasgow, J. P., 132, 146, 147
Godfrey, G., 189, 190
Godfrey, R., 156, 176
Golley, F. B., 123, 126, 235, 245
Goodey, T., 50, 55, 57

Goodnight, C. J., 156, 176
Grandjean, F., 159, 168, 177, 193, 205
Greenslade, P. J. M., 108, 126
Guild, W. J. McL., 32, 37, 61, 63, 64, 75

Haarløv, N., 134, 146, 147, 148, 170, 171, 177, 212, 216, 217, 226, 256, 258
Hairston, N. G., 203, 205, 216, 226
Hale, W. G., 132, 133, 143, 144, 145, 146, 147, 148, 218, 226, 245
Handley, W. R. C., 8, 22, 34, 37
Harding, D. J. L., 170, 177
Harris, W. V., 106, 126
Hartenstein, R., 167, 169, 177
Hatchett, S. P., 80, 87, 102, 192, 205
Hayes, A. J., 19, 22
Hayes, W. P., 112, 126
Heal, O. W., 46, 47, 48, 49, 50, 57, 237, 245
Healey, I. N., 143, 148, 237, 238, 245
Heath, G. W., 9, 22, 32, 37, 65, 75, 110, 111, 125, 220, 226, 233, 246
Hénin, S., 6, 22, 29, 36
Hollick, F. S. J., 226, 249, 259
Holt, S. J., 123, 126
Holter, H., 235, 246
Hughes, R. D., 108, 126, 200, 205
Hughes, T. E., 159, 177
Huhta, V., 68, 75, 146, 148
Hunter, P. J., 71, 72, 73, 74, 75, 197, 199, 203, 205
Hurlbutt, H., 173, 177, 200, 205
Hurley, D. E., 78, 79, 102

Ibarra, E. L., 210, 226

Jacks, G. V., 6, 22
Jacot, A. P., 40, 45, 174, 177
Jalil, M., 169, 170, 177, 178
Janetschek, H., 134, 148
Janus, H., 70, 75
Jongerius, A., 33, 37

Karpachevsky, L. O., 118, 126
Karppinen, E., 75, 148, 162, 163, 164, 177
Kaston, B. J., 151, 177
Kemner, N. A., 115, 126
Kempson, D., 252, 258

Kern, P., 113, 126
Kessler-Geschiere, A. M., 151, 152, 179
Kevan, D. K. McE., 40, 44, 45, 104, 123, 126, 141, 142, 143, 146, 149, 258
Khalaf el Duweini, 58, 75
Kirmiz, J. P., 186, 190
Klima, J., 42, 45
Knight, C., 133, 148
Knutson, L. V., 202, 206
Kozlovsky, D. G., 242, 246
Krantz, G. W., 173, 179
Kubiena, W. L., 34, 35, 37
Kuenen, D. J., 85, 102
Kühnelt, W., 11, 22, 79, 102, 104, 117, 121, 126, 128, 137, 138, 140, 148, 174, 177

LaFollette, J. R., 73, 75
Lamy, L., 205
Lawrence, R. F., 50, 57, 77, 78, 79, 90, 102, 150, 177
Lebrun, P., 164, 169, 170, 171, 173, 177, 220, 221, 226
Lee, A. K., 186, 190
Leitenberger, L., 100, 102
Lewis, H. C., 73, 75
Lewis, J. G. E., 94, 95, 96, 102, 202, 206
Lindeman, R. L., 229, 241, 246
Linderström-Lang, K., 235, 246
Lions, J. C., 221, 226
Ljungström, P. O., 58, 75
Lloyd, M., 258
Locket, G. H., 151, 177
Long, I. F., 18, 22
Lozek, V., 70, 71, 75
Lüscher, M., 105, 106, 126
Lyon, T. L., 19, 22

Macfayden, A., 17, 22, 132, 148, 171, 172, 177, 208, 216, 221, 222, 223, 226, 231, 235, 240, 246, 247, 250, 251, 253, 258, 259
Macfarlane, D., 175
MacMillen, R. E., 186, 190
Madge, D. S., 15, 19, 22, 31, 37, 58, 75, 164, 165, 166, 177
Manton, S. M., 95, 96, 102, 103
Maynard, E. A., 132, 148
Mellanby, K., 187, 188, 190

Michael, A. D., 169, 178
Michelbacher, A. E., 92, 103
Mihelcic, F., 100, 103
Millidge, A. F., 151, 177
Milne, A., 204, 206
Milne, S., 132, 145, 148
Misonne, X., 185, 190
Mitchell, B., 108, 126
Morris, P., 188, 190
Morris, R. F., 191, 205, 206
Mountford, M. D., 210, 213, 226
Moursi, A., 137, 148
Müller, G., 253, 259
Müller, P. E., 29, 37
Murdoch, W. W., 114, 126
Murphy, D. H., 133, 148
Murphy, P. W., 39, 45, 170, 174, 178, 220, 226, 247, 250, 251, 255, 259

Nadvornyj, V. G., 110, 126
Naglitsch, F., 253, 259
Nelson, J. M., 253, 259
Newell, I. M., 174, 178
Newell, P. F., 73, 74, 75, 239, 246
Nicholson, A. J., 203, 206
Nielsen, C. O., 52, 53, 54, 55, 57, 66, 67, 68, 75, 197, 206, 254, 255, 259
Niering, W. A., 80, 103
Noble-Nesbitt, J., 130, 138, 139, 148
Noordam, D., 172, 178
Nooteboom, H. P., 85, 102
Nørgaard, E., 152, 178
Nosek, J., 127, 128, 148
Nurminen, M., 75, 148

O'Connor, F. B., 66, 67, 68, 69, 75, 203, 206, 237, 238, 240, 246, 255, 259
Odum, E. P., 123, 126
Ögel, S., 138, 148
Oliver, J. H., 202, 206
Oppermann, J., 189, 190
Ovington, J. D., 231, 246

Palmén, E., 80, 103
Paris, O. H., 83, 84, 85, 86, 87, 88, 103, 192, 197, 199, 202, 203, 206
Park, D., 8, 22
Parkin, E. A., 109, 126
Pauly, F., 168, 169, 178, 193, 206
Peachey, J. E., 66, 67, 75
Penney, M. M., 114, 126

Perel, T. S., 126
Peters, B. G., 51, 57
Peterson, A., 119, 126
Phillipson, J., 154, 178, 231, 235, 237, 238, 239, 242, 245, 246
Pitelka, F. A., 86, 87, 88, 103, 192, 195, 206
Pontin, A. J., 123, 126
Poole, T. B., 132, 134, 135, 142, 146, 148
Pryor, M. E., 134, 148

Quick, H. E., 70, 75
Quilliam, T. A., 187, 190

Rajski, A., 164, 178
Raw, F., 99, 103, 107, 109, 117, 126, 128, 149, 189, 190, 200, 206, 226
Reed, C. A., 187, 190
Reid, D. M., 78, 103
Reinecke, A. J., 58, 75
Renkonen, O., 212, 213, 226
Ressl, F., 155, 156, 157, 158, 178, 199, 201, 206
Reynoldson, T. B., 59, 75, 195, 206, 216, 226
Richman, S., 235, 244, 246
Riha, G., 174, 178
Ritcher, P. O., 109, 110, 111, 112, 126
Rockett, C. L., 55, 57, 168, 169, 172, 178, 192, 193, 199, 206
Rodriguez, J. G., 15, 23, 55, 57, 164, 173, 178, 179, 181, 190, 200, 206, 207, 212, 226, 227
Rohde, C. J., 173, 178
Roubaud, E., 201, 206
Rudd, R. L., 181, 182, 190
Ruppel, H., 130, 137, 149
Russell, E. J., 1, 11, 13, 22, 27, 29, 33, 34, 35, 36, 37
Russell, E. W., 22, 37

Saito, S., 237, 246
Salt, G., 216, 226, 249, 259
Salter, D. D., 200, 205
Sandon, H., 57
Sankey, J. H. P., 153, 154, 178
Satchell, J. E., 32, 37, 59, 60, 61, 62, 63, 64, 65, 75, 76, 192, 193, 203, 204, 206, 216, 226, 238, 240, 246, 253, 259

Savoury, T. H., 151, 153, 178
Schaller, F., 132, 133, 149
Schönborn, W., 57
Schmidt-Nielsen, B., 186, 190
Schmidt-Nielsen, K., 185, 186, 190
Schuster, R., 108, 126, 168, 174, 175, 178
Sengbusch, H. G., 169, 178
Sharma, G. D., 141, 142, 143, 146, 149
Sheals, J. G., 159, 162, 171, 176, 178, 200, 206, 216, 225, 227
Singer, G., 173, 179
Singh, B. N., 49, 57
Singh, M. P., 201, 206
Sitnikova, L. G., 168, 169, 179
Slobodkin, L. B., 191, 205, 206, 235, 242, 243, 246
Smith, F. E., 205
Soehnle, H., 190
Sørensen, T., 210, 211, 212, 227
South, A., 73, 76
Southern, H. N., 187, 190
Southwood, T. R. E., 191, 196, 206, 247, 248, 249, 255, 259
Spencer, J., 83, 102, 238, 245
Springett, J. A., 66, 76
Starling, J. H., 89, 90, 103
Stebaev, I. V., 11, 22
Stephenson, J. W., 206
Stöckli, A., 54, 57
Stout, J. D., 46, 47, 48, 49, 50, 57
Strenzke, K., 42, 45, 132, 149, 162, 179
Struble, G. H., 115, 126
Sturm, H., 130, 149
Svendsen, J. A., 60, 76, 216, 227

Taberly, G., 168, 179
Tarras-Wahlberg, N., 15, 23, 42, 45, 164, 179
Taylor, L. R., 255, 259
Thiele, H. U., 99, 103
Thomas, D. C., 73, 76
Thompson, A. R., 226
Todd, V., 153, 154, 179
Törne, E. von, 133, 144, 149, 253, 259
Toye, S. A., 98, 103
Tuxen, S. L., 128, 149

Vaart-Vlieger, S. H. van der, 172, 178

Vachon, M., 156, 176
Valpas, A., 75, 148
Vautrin, E., 205
Verhoeff, K. W., 89, 92, 93, 96, 98, 103
Vlijm, L., 151, 152, 179
Volz, P., 54, 57
Voronov, N. P., 188, 190

Wade, C. F., 57, 173, 178, 206
Wadsworth, J. T., 115, 126
Wallwork, J. A., 10, 15, 23, 158, 159, 164, 166, 168, 171, 172, 173, 174, 175, 179, 181, 190, 201, 202, 206, 212, 220, 226, 227, 235, 246
Wallwork, J. H., 200, 207
Warburg, M. R., 82, 85, 86, 103
Waters, R. A. S., 64, 76
Watson, J., 237, 238, 246
Watt, K. E. F., 191, 207
Webb, G. C., 104, 126
Weber, P. W., 73, 76

Weis-Fogh, T., 132, 149, 216, 217, 227, 256, 258
Wells, C. N., 57, 178, 206
Wharton, G. W., 159, 167, 175, 179
Wheeler, W. M., 122, 126
Wieser, W., 88, 89, 103
Willem, V., 143, 149
Williams, D. A., 108, 125, 200, 205
Williams, G., 113, 126, 154, 179
Williams, T. D., 193, 207
Winslow, R. D., 193, 207
Witkamp, M., 9, 22, 31, 36
Wittich, W., 9, 10, 23
Wood, T. G., 134, 149, 216, 227, 253, 259
Woodring, J. P., 55, 57, 168, 169, 172, 174, 178, 179, 192, 193, 194, 195, 199, 202, 206, 207

Yalden, D. W., 187, 190

Zinkler, D., 136, 137, 149, 235, 246

General Index

Abax ater, 113
  parallelus, 113
Abida secale, 70
Ablattaria laevigata, 116
Abrasive effect of water, 4-5
  of wind, 4
Abundance, 209-210
Acanthocerinae, 109, 110
Acari, 39, 150, 159, 193, 216, 218,
  219, 220, 221, 234, 235, 243,
  244; *see also* Mites
Acarid mites, 162, 167, 200
Acerella remyi, 128
Acerentomon carpaticum, 128
  doderoi, 128
  gallicum, 128
Acerentulus confinis, 128
  danicus, 128-129, 130
  minimus, 128
Achaeta, 66
  bohemica, 67
  camerani, 67
  eiseni, 67, 69, 70
Achatina, 73
Achipteria coleoptrata, 163
Acicula parcelineata, 70
  polita, 71
Acomys, 184
Acrobeles, 54
  ciliatus, 52
  vexilliger, 52
Acrobeloides, 54
Adela viridella, 125
Adoristes ovatus, 163, 174
Aegeriidae, 125
Aeolosomatidae, 58
Agamidae, 181
Agelenidae, 151
Agonum, 114
Agriolimax laevis, 70
  reticulatus, 71, 72, 73, 74, 197, 199
Agriotes, 110, 202
  lineatus, 110

Agriotes—cont.
  obscurus, 110
  sputator, 110
Aldrin, 225
Aleochara, 108
  bilineata, 115, 202
  curtula, 115
  intricata, 115
Alloeocoela, 50
Allolobophora caliginosa, 59, 60, 61,
  62, 63, 64, 65, 197, 216
  chlorotica, 59, 60, 61, 62, 63, 64,
  65, 197, 202, 216
  longa, 59, 60, 63, 65
  nocturna, 59, 60, 61, 62, 63
  rosea, 62, 65
Alopia clathrata, 71
Amblygamasus septentrionalis, 167
Ameronothridae, 168
Amoebae, 46, 47, 49, 237
Amphibia, 183, 189
Amphimallon solstitialis, 110, 111
  majalis, 112
Amphipoda, 78, 79, 80
Amphisbaenidae, 184
Amphitrema flavum, 48
Anabiosis in nematodes, 198
  in rotifers, 56
  in snails, 198
  in tardigrades, 101
Anachipteria, 210
Anamorphic development in centi-
  pedes, 93, 95
  in millipedes, 98
Anatonchus, 55
Androctonus australis, 150
Anguidae, 184
Anisopodidae, 117
Anisus, 70
Annelids, 11, 35, 41, 58-70, 192
Anoetidae, 167, 202
Anomala, 111
  binotata, 111

Anomala—cont.
    nigropicta, 111
Anomma, 122
Antarcticola meyeri, 168
Ant nests, 121
    beetle fauna of, 110, 112
    collembolan fauna of, 132
    millipede fauna of, 97
    mite fauna of, 217
Ants, 43, 121-124; *see also* Formica,
    Formicidae
    emigration of, 204
    harvester, 121, 122, 123, 199
Aphelenchoides parietinus, 52
Aphids, 40
Aphodiinae, 109
Aphodius, 112
Apocheiridium ferum, 156
Apoda, 183
Aporcelaimus, 55
Arable soil; *see also* Cultivated soil
    distribution of slugs in, 71, 72, 73,
        197
    wireworm fauna of, 110
Arachnida, 42, 150-175
Araneida, 39, 150; *see also* Spiders
Arcella, 47
Archeboreoiulus pallidus, 97
Arenivaga, 198
Arion ater, 74
    hortensis, 71, 72, 74, 197, 199
    intermedius, 70
    subfuscus, 70, 73
Armadillidium vulgare, 22, 80, 81,
    82-86, 87, 88, 96, 192, 195,
    197, 202, 203, 217, 237
Armadillo albomarginatus, 86
Armillaria mellea, 8
Army worms, 116
Arrhopalites, 131
Artemia, 242
Arthropleona, 131, 136-141
Arthropoda, 77
Artiocotylus, 50, 77
Ascomycetes, 189
Asilidae, 112, 116
Astigmata (Astigmatid mites), 159,
    160, 253
    distribution of, 159
    life cycles of, 167
    population dynamics of, 171
    preservation of, 257

Atheta fungi, 115
Athous haemorrhoidalis, 111
    niger, 110
    subfuscus, 111
Atmobios, 41
Atta, 110
Attii, 123
Autogneta willmanni, 169
Autotrophs, 230, 231
Azonal soils, 25
Azotobacter, 232

Bacillus, 143
Bacteria as decomposers, 8, 33, 222,
    224, 233
    as gut symbionts, 109, 143
    as food for Collembola, 143
    as food for mites, 175
    role in biological fixation, 232-233
Badger, 181
Baermann funnel, 254, 255
Balaustium, 174
Balea perversa, 70
Bark lice, 104
Batrisodes, 41
Bdellidae, 167, 174, 199
Bdelloidea, 55-56
Bees, 120
Belba, 164, 175, 193
    geniculosa, 165, 166
Bellinger's coefficient, 212
Bembidion, 114
    lampros, 108, 200
Berlese-Tullgren funnel, 250, 251, 253
BHC, 181, 225
Bibio marci, 118, 119
Bibionidae, 34, 116, 189
Bimastos eiseni, 34, 59, 60, 61
Biological concentrators, 181
Bipalium kewense, 50
Blackbird, 181
Blaniulus guttulatus, 97
Blanket bog, 182, 217-218
Blatella germanica, 82
Blepharisma, 48
Blue-green algae, 232
Bodo, 46
Bomb calorimeter, 235
Borboridae, 117
Bostrichidae, 109
Box mites, 174
Brachycera, 116, 117

Brachychthonius, 163, 194, 235, 253
Brachydesmus superus, 96-98
Brachygeophilus truncorum, 94
Breviceps, 183
Bristle tails, 104, 127
Brown earth (Braunerde), 26, 27, 36
    mollusc populations in, 73
Bryobia praetiosa, 162
Bryocamptus pygmaeus, 79
Bunonema, 54
    reticulatum, 52
Burying beetles, 109

Cabbage root fly, 117, 200
Caddis flies, 104
Caecilidae, 183
Caecilioides, 71, 74
    acicula, 71
    petitiana, 71
Calcicoles, 71, 97
Calcification, 25, 26
Calliphoridae, 117
Caloglyphus mycophagus, 173
Calosoma sycophanta, 113
Calotermes, 104-106
Camisia horridus, 168
    lapponica, 163
    scabra, 163
    segnis, 168
    spinifer, 169
Camisiidae, 162, 163
Campodea, 154
    augens, 128
    fragilis, 128
Campodeidae, 127
Camponotus, 121, 123
Cannibalism in centipedes, 201
    in Collembola, 143
    in isopods, 201
    in mites, 201
    in pseudoscorpions, 158, 201
    in termites, 106
Cantharoidea, 107
Canthon, 110
Cape Golden Mole, 187
Capillary water, 18, 19
Carabid beetles, 43, 106, 107, 108,
    112, 113-115, 154, 199, 200,
    217, 219
    activity patterns of, 16-17, 112-115
    as food for centipedes, 95
    diapause in, 114, 115

Carabid beetles—*cont.*
    distribution patterns of, 108
    feeding habits of, 108
    life history of, 113-115
    of grassland, 108
    of woodland, 108
Carabodes, 162, 174
    labyrinthicus, 165
    marginatus, 170
Carabus arvensis, 113
    auratus, 113
    cancellatus, 113
    convexus, 113
    glabratus, 113
    granulatus, 113
    monilis, 113
    nemoralis, 113, 115
    problematicus, 113
    violaceus, 113
Carbamate pesticides, 225
Carbonation, 6
Carbon cycle, 231-232
Cardisoma rotundum, 80
Carnivores, 40, 43, 141, 219, 229,
    241-245
Carpenter bee, 120
Carrion, 99, 108, 109, 142, 175
    beetles, 108, 115-116
    flies, 117
Carrot beetle, 110
    fly, 117
Cartesian diver, 235
Carychium minimum, 70
    tridentatum, 70
Castes, in ants, 123-124
    in termites, 104-105
Cataglyphis, 121
Catajapyx confusus, 128
Cave cricket, 183
Caves, Collembola of, 42, 132
    Diplura of, 128
    millipedes of, 97
Cellulase, 33, 74, 106
Centipedes, 43, 44, 89, 93-96, 219,
    220; *see also* Chilopoda
    distribution of, 93-94
    feeding habits of, 94-95, 197
    life history of, 95-96
Centropyxidae, 46, 49
Centropyxis, 46, 48
Centrurus, 150
Cepaea, 71, 217

Cepaea—cont.
  hortensis, 71
  nemoralis, 74
Cephalobus, 51, 54
Cepheidae, 168
Cepheus, 162, 174
  palmicinctum, 169
Cerambycidae, 109
Ceratopogonidae, 116, 117
Ceratoppia bipilis, 169, 174
Ceratozetes cisalpinus, 168, 169, 172,
    192, 193, 194, 195, 202
  gracilis, 169, 174
  jeweli, 168, 169, 192, 193
Cetonia aurata, 110
Cetoniinae, 109
Ceutophilus, 183
Chaetonotus, 57
Chafer beetles, 110
Chalcididae, 120
Chamobates cuspidatus, 170
  incisus, 169
Cheiridium museorum, 155
Chelifer cancroides, 155-156, 158
Chelonethi, 39, 150, 155-159; *see also*
    Pseudoscorpions
Chemical weathering, 6-7
Chernes cimicoides, 155, 156
Chernozem, 26-27
Chestnut soil, 26
Cheyletidae, 174
Chilodonella gouraudi, 48
Chiloplacus, 54
Chilopoda, 39, 89, 93-96, 216; *see also*
    Centipedes
Chironomidae, 116, 117
Chlamydomonas reinhardi, 242
Chlordane, 181
Chlorfenvinphos, 225
Choanolaimus, 55
Chondrina avenacea, 71
  clienta, 71
  tatrica, 71
Chromadorida, 50, 51
Chromatoiulus projectus, 99
Chrysochloridae, 187
Chrysochloris, capensis, 187
Chrysomelidae, 40
Chthonius ischnocheles, 155-157
  tetrachelatus, 155
Cicadas, 104
Cicindelidae, 108

Ciliates, 46-49
Cilliba, 173
Citellus leucurus, 184
Clausilia dubia, 70
  grimmeri, 71
  parvula, 70
Clay minerals, 3
Clearwings, 125
Clegs, 116
Cleroidea, 108
Click beetles, 108; *see also* Elateridae
Climatic factors, 196-199, 203-204
Clivina, 107
Clostridium, 232
Clubionidae, 151
C:N ratio, 9, 10, 175, 218
Coccinellidae, 40, 41
Cochlodina commutata, 70
Coenobita brevimanus, 80
  perlatus, 80
Cognettia, 66, 67
  cognetti, 67, 69, 70
  glandulosa, 67
  sphagnetorum, 67
Coleoptera, 40, 41, 43, 44, 106-116,
    217
  as food for moles, 189
  as hosts for phoretic mites, 162
  distribution and feeding habits of,
    108-110
  extraction of, 252-253
  life cycles and population biology
    of, 111-116
  soil-dwelling, 106, 107, 108
Collembola, 10, 32, 33, 35, 39, 41, 42,
    43, 127, 130-147, 192-193,
    199-200, 203, 212, 216-221,
    224-225, 243
  as food for beetles, 108
  as food for mites, 173-174
  as food for pseudoscorpions, 157
  effect of pesticides on, 225
  extraction of, 253-254
  feeding habits of, 141-143, 228,
    233
  grassland populations of, 217-218
  hemiedaphic, 42, 225
  metabolic activity of, 136-137,
    237-238, 240
  mouthparts of, 141
  preservation of, 257
  woodland populations of, 220, 256

Colpoda steinii, 46, 48
Concretions, 7
Coniosporium, 8
Controlled-draught funnel extractor, 251, 253
Copepoda, 41, 78, 79
Coprinae, 109, 110, 111
Coprophages, 43
Cordyceps, 112
Coreids, 40
Corymbites, 110
Corythion, 46
Cotalpa lanigera, 110, 111
Crane flies, 116
Craters of the Moon, 1
Crayfish, 80
Crematogaster, 121
Crickets, 104
Crotoniidae, 168
Crumb-formation, by cementing, 11-12, 32-33
   by electrochemical bonding, 11, 12
   role of earthworms in, 65-66
   role of molluscs in, 74
Crustacea, 78-89
Cryptostigmata, 21, 42, 43, 150, 159, 160-166, 168-175, 196, 199, 202, 210, 212, 234-236
   as food for titmice, 181
   extraction of, 253
   feeding habits of, 174-175
   metabolic activity of, 236, 237, 240
   of grassland, 217, 221, 234
   of woodland, 220, 221
   population regulation, 203
   preservation of, 257
   respiration rates of, 238, 240
   vertical migrations of, 164, 181
Cucujoidea, 107
Cultivated crop pests, 52, 73-74, 109-110, 117-118, 125, 131
Cultivated soil; *see also* Arable soil
   astigmatid mites in, 159
   centipedes of, 94
   cryptostigmatid mites of, 163
   decapod densities in, 80
   earthworm populations in, 61
   moles in, 187
   mollusc populations in, 71-74
   nematodes in, 53
   symphylid distribution in, 91
Cunaxidae, 167, 174

Curculionidae, 108
Cutworms, 104, 125, 201
Cyclorrhapha, 117-118
Cylindroiulus boleti, 99
   britannicus, 98
   meinerti, 99
   nitidus, 99
   parisiorum, 98
   punctatus, 96-99
   teutonicus, 100
Cylisticus convexus, 82, 87, 192
Cypridopsis, 79

Dactylella bembicoides, 201
   ellipsospora, 201
Dactylochelifer latreillei, 155
Damaeobelba minutissima, 168
Damaeus boreus, 169
   clavipes, 169, 170, 172
   onustus, 163, 165, 168, 169, 170
Dance flies, 116
Daphnia pulex, 242
Daudebardia, 71
DD, 225
DDT, 181, 182, 200, 225
Decapoda, 78, 80
Decomposers, 7-11, 31-35, 222, 229, 232-234, 241
Decomposition rates, 9, 10
Deer, 182
Delayed expression, 181
Delima ornata, 70
Dendrobaena, 34, 59, 62, 221
   octaedra, 59, 60, 64, 65, 219
   rubida, 59, 60
   subrubicunda, 60, 63
Denitrification, 232
Density-independent effects, 203-204
Density-related effects, 203-204
Dermaptera, 41, 104
Deroceras laeve, 70
Desert arachnids, 150, 158, 159
   insects, 198
   mammals, 184, 185, 186
Detritivores (detritus-feeders), 40, 43, 221, 224, 228-231, 233-245; *see also* Saprophages
Deutovum, 168
Diapause, 114-115, 143
Diapterobates humeralis, 164
Diazinon, 225
Dictyoptera, 104

Dicyrtoma, 147
  fusca, 144
  minuta, 136
Dieldrin, 181, 225
Difflugia, 48
Difflugiella, 46
Digamasellidae, 164
Diplogaster, 51, 54
Diplopoda, 34, 39, 89, 90, 96-100, 216, 222; *see also* Millipedes
  distribution of, 96-98
  egg-laying habits of, 98, 192, 193
  feeding habits of, 99-100
  reproduction and population biology of, 98-99
Diplura, 39, 127-128
Dipodomys, 44, 184, 185
Diptera, 40, 41, 43, 116-120
  as hosts for mites, 162
  extraction of, 252
  of grassland soil, 216
  of mor profiles, 221
Discus perspectivus, 71
Dolichopodidae, 118, 119
Dorylaimus, 51, 52, 55
Dorylus, 122, 123
Dorymyrmex, 121
Driver ants, 122
Drought, 197-198
Dung, 59-60, 109, 110, 162, 173, 181
  as food for beetles, 109
  as food for dipterans, 117
  collembolan fauna of, 137
  mite fauna of, 162
Dung beetles, 108; *see also* Scarabaeidae
Dung flies, 117
Dutch Elm disease, 182
Dynastinae, 109-110
Dyschirius, 107

Earthworms, 31, 32, 33, 58-70; *see also* Lumbricidae
  as detritivores, 10, 228, 233
  as food for moles, 189
  effect of pesticides on, 182, 224-225
  extraction of, 247-248, 255
  in forest soil, 219, 221
  in grassland soil, 216-217
  population regulation, 202-203
  preservation of, 257

Earwigs, 104
Echiniscus (*Bryodelphax*) *parvulus,* 101
  (*Echiniscus*) *blumi,* 101
Eciton, 122
Ecological efficiency, 242-245
  valence, 162, 163
Eelworms, 52
Eisenia foetida, 65
  rosea, 59, 60, 61; *see also Allolobophora rosea*
Elateridae, 107, 108, 110, 112
  as food for moles, 189
  as predators, 107
  life cycles of, 111
Electrochemical bonding, 11-12
Elephants, 182
Embioptera, 104
Emigration, 40, 105, 191, 196, 204
Empididae, 116, 119
Ena, 71
Enchodelus, 55
Enchytraeidae, 10, 39, 43, 44, 58, 66-70, 217, 222, 228, 233
  as food for mites, 173
  as food for pseudoscorpions, 157, 158
  effect of pesticides on, 225
  extraction of, 247, 248, 254, 255
  in forest soil, 66, 68, 69, 219, 220
  in grassland soil, 66, 68
  metabolic activity of, 237, 238, 240
  moorland populations of, 66, 68, 218
  mortality in, 197
  population regulation in, 203
Enchytraeus, 66, 67
  albidus, 195
Energy budget, 234-245
  pyramid, 229
Enoplida, 50, 51
Entomobrya, 133, 135, 137, 142, 217
Entomobryidae, 130, 131
Eosentomon armatum, 129, 130
  spinosum, 128
  transitorium, 128
Epigeon, 41, 42
Epimorphic development, 93, 95
Eremaeidae, 173
Erioischia brassicae, 108, 115, 117, 200

Erosion, 4-6, 180, 182, 190, 221
Erythraeidae, 155, 174
Eucobresia diaphana, 71
　nivalis, 70
Eudrilus eugeniae, 58
Euedaphon, 41, 42
Eugamasus cornutus, 167
Euglypha, 46
Euomophalia strigella, 71
Eupelops, 162, 164, 175, 210
Euphthiracaridae, 174
Eurypauropus, 90
Euzetes globulus, 165, 166, 169
Evaporative cooling, 83, 166
Extraction techniques, 247-256

Fannia canicularis, 119
Feather-winged beetles, 108
Fecundity, 192-195
Fenland soil, collembolans of, 132-133
　life cycles of *Tipula* in, 118-120
　mites of, 171
　moles in, 188
Fermentation layer, 14, 30, 134, 219
Feronia oblongopunctatus, 113
　madida, 108
Fertility, 195-196
Field capacity, 18, 19
Flagellates, 46, 49
　as intestinal symbionts, 106, 109
Flotation extractors, 248, 249, 250, 253, 254
Folsomia, 135, 142, 147
　brevicaudata, 133
　candida, 138, 142
　quadrioculata, 142
　similis, 142
Food chain, 228-245
　supply, 202-203
　web, 234
Forest soil, 25-27, 29, 31, 36, 218-224
　activity of staphylinids in, 115, 221
　Amphipoda of, 78
　Collembola of, 132-135, 146, 219-221
　Copepoda of, 79
　Diptera of, 116-118, 219-221
　earthworms in, 59, 63, 64, 219, 221
　Enchytraeidae in, 66-70, 219
　harvestmen in, 153
　isopods in, 84, 219, 221

Forest soil—*cont.*
　lithobiomorphs in, 93
　millipedes in, 96-98
　mites of, 159, 162-164, 171, 174, 219, 224
　moles in, 187
　molluscs of, 70-71, 219, 221
　myriapods in, 219-221
　nematodes in, 54
　Ostracoda in, 79
　pauropods in, 90
　Protozoa in, 46-49
　spiders of, 151
　symphylids in, 90
　wireworms in, 110, 111
Forficula, 41
Formaldehyde (formalin), as a fumigant, 225
　for earthworm extraction, 255
Formica, 110
　polyctena, 123
　rufa, 121
Formicidae, 121; *see also* Ants
Fortresses, 188
Frequency, 209-210
Fridericia, 66-67
Friesea, 133, 141, 142, 143, 217
　mirabilis, 133, 135, 147
Frit fly, 117
Frogs, 183
Frontonia, 48
Fruticicola fruticum, 71
Fumigants, 225
Fungi, 8, 32, 33, 55, 99, 106, 109, 112, 117, 123, 130, 133, 142, 159, 173-175, 195, 201, 202, 222, 229, 232, 235, 240
Fungus gnats, 116
Funnel extractors, 250-253, 255
Fuscozetes fuscipes, 165
Fuscuropoda marginata, 173
Fusicoccum, 8

Galeodes arabs, 150
Galumna, 162, 164
　confusa, 169, 172, 193
　curvum, 210
　elimata, 169, 174
　longipluma, 169
　nervosa, 169
　parva, 169, 172, 193, 194
　virginiensis, 210

Gamasolaelaps, 173
Gamasolaelaptidae, 166
Garden slugs, 71-74
Gastropoda, 70-74, 219, 221
Gastrotricha, 55, 57
Gecarcoidea lalandei, 80
Gelechiidae, 125
Geobionts, 41
Geograpsus crinipes, 80
  grayii, 80
Geomys, 184
Geophiles, 40-41
Geophilomorpha, 93-95, 255
Geophilus carpophagus, 94
  electricus, 94
  insculptus, 94
Geotrupinae, 109-110
Gerbils, 184
Ghost moths, 125
Glacial drift, 5, 6
Glaciers, 5
Glandina, 74
Glaphyrinae, 109
Gleisol, 29
Gleization, 26, 28-29
Glomeridae, 98
Glomeris connexa, 100
  hexasticha, 99
  marginata, 32, 93, 96, 98, 99, 100,
    118, 192, 217, 233, 237
Glossoscolecidae, 58
Gnaphosidae, 151
Goldsmith beetle, 110
Gomphiocephalus hodgsoni, 134
Gophers, 184
Gopher tortoise, 183
Grapeleaf beetle, 110
Grassland soil, 25-26, 35-36, 215-218,
    221-224
  Amphipoda in, 79
  carabid beetles in, 16, 108
  centipedes in, 93-94, 216
  Collembola in, 132, 134-135,
    146-147, 216-218
  Diptera in, 216
  earthworm fauna of, 59-66, 216,
    218
  enchytraeid fauna of, 66, 68, 218
  harvestmen in, 217
  Hemiptera in, 216, 217
  isopods in, 83-88, 195, 197,
    203-204, 217

Grassland soil—*cont.*
  millipedes in, 96-97, 216, 217
  mites in, 159, 166, 171, 216-218,
    234-235
  moles in, 187-190
  molluscs in, 71, 217
  nematodes in, 53, 54, 218
  pauropods in, 217
  Protozoa in, 48, 49
  proturans in, 128, 217
  scarabaeids of, 110
  silicon cycling in, 36, 231
  spiders in, 151-152
  symphylids in, 90-91, 216, 217
  tipulids in, 218
  Thysanoptera in, 216
  Thysanura in, 127, 216, 217
Gravity, 5
Ground beetles, 106
  squirrels, 184
  water, 18, 19
Gymnophiona, 183

Habrotrocha, 56
Hahnia helveola, 151
Hammock-web spiders, 151
Harvester ants, 121-123
Harvestmen, 43, 153-155
HCH, 92
Heathland, 26, 35, 54, 217
Heleopora, 46, 49
Helicella itala, 71
  neglecta, 71
  obvia, 71
  striata, 71
  unifasciata, 71
Helicigona cingulella, 70
  rossmässleri, 71
Helix aspersa, 73
  desertorum, 198
  pomatia, 71
Hemiedaphon, 41, 42
Hemilepistus reaumuri, 44, 82, 84, 86,
    199
Heminothrus paolianus, 163
  thori, 162, 163
Hemiptera, 104, 216, 217
Henlea, 66, 67
Hepialidae, 125
Heptachlor, 181, 225
Herbicides, 224-225

Herbivores, 43-44, 74, 228-231, 233-234, 242-245; *see also* Phytophages
Hermannia scabra, 169, 170
Hermit crabs, 80
Heterocypris brevicaudata, 79
Heterodera, 51, 52, 55
  rostochiensis, 52
Heteromorphic males, 167
Heteroptera, 40
Hippodamia convergens, 40, 41
Histeridae, 107, 112
Histiosoma murchiei, 202
Hodotermes, 106
Holcomyrmex, 121
Horse flies, 116
House flies, 117
Hover flies, 117
Hoyer's mountant, 257
Humerobates, 162
  rostrolamellatus, 165, 166
Humus, 8-14, 27-36, 55, 70, 100, 106, 109, 118, 134, 175, 230
Hyalinia, 70
Hyalosphenia, 47-48
Hydra, 242-243
Hydrolysis, 6
Hydrozetidae, 162
Hygromia, 217
Hygroscopic coefficient, 18, 19
  water, 19
Hymenoptera, 120-124
Hyperiodrilus africanus, 58
Hyphomycetes, 200, 201
Hypochthonius rufulus, 165, 169, 170
Hypogastrura bengtssoni, 137
  denticulata, 144, 145, 146
  purpurescens, 142
Hypopial stage (hypopus), 159, 162, 167, 253
Hypsibius (*Diphascon*) *scoticus,* 101
  (*Hypsibius*) *convergens,* 101
  dujardini, 101
  pallidulus, 101
  (*Isohypsibius*) *franzi,* 101
  tuberculatus, 101

Ichneumonidae, 43, 202
Igneous rocks, 2
Iguanidae, 181
Immigration, 40, 191, 196, 204

Incurvariidae, 125
Indicator species, 217
Insecta, 39, 43, 104-125
Insecticides (Pesticides), 92, 181-182, 224-225
Insectivora, 39, 187
Interspecific competition, 204
Intraspecific competition, 202-204
Intrazonal soils, 25
Iotonchus, 55
Iphigena, 71
Isobates varicornis, 98
Isognomostoma, 71
Isopoda, 35, 39, 41, 42, 44, 78, 80-88, 192-193, 195
  desert-dwelling, 44, 82-84, 86, 199
  extraction of, 253
  feeding habits of, 201-203
  metabolic activity of, 237-238
  nocturnal activity of, 84-86, 197
  of grassland, 217
  of woodland, 219, 221-222
Isoptera, 104-106
Isotoma, 135, 142
  antennalis, 133
  grandiceps, 142
  infuscata, 144
  klovstadi, 134
  olivacea, 144
  saltans, 136
  sensibilis, 133, 144, 147
  viridis, 136, 142
Isotomidae, 131
Isotomiella minor, 147
Isotomina thermophila, 137
Isotomurus palustris, 144, 217
Isotope labelling, 196
Iulidae, 44, 98
Iuliformia, 96
Iulus, 93
  scandinavius, 96, 98, 100

Japanese beetle, 110
Japygidae, 127-128, 243, 244
Japyx, 128, 245
Javelina, 182
Jerboa, 186

Kangaroo-rat, 44, 184, 185, 186
Kempson bowl extractor, 251, 252
Kommetjies, 58

Lacertidae, 181
Lace wings, 104
Laciniaria biplicata, 71
  nitidosa, 70
Ladell apparatus, 248, 249
Ladybirds, 40
Lamprochernes nodosus, 155
Lampyridae, 108
Land crabs, 80
Lasius brunneus, 121
  flavus, 121
Laterite, 26, 28
Laterization, 26, 27-28
Leaf-cutters, 125
Leatherjackets, 116
Lebensformtypen, 42
Leiobunum blackwalli, 154
  rotundum, 245
Leiurus quinquestriatus, 150
Lepidocyrtus lanuginosus, 137, 144
Lepidoptera, 40, 43, 124-125
Lepismachilis y-signata, 127
Leptohylemyia coarctata, 117
Lichens, 6, 7, 21
Life forms, 42, 135, 140
  tables, 191
Light, 21-22
Ligia oceanica, 82, 83
Ligiidae, 81, 83
Ligyrus gibbosus, 110, 111
  relictus, 111, 112
Limax flavus, 73
  maximus, 73, 74
  tenellus, 70
Limnaea, 70
Limnozetidae, 162
Lindane, 225
Linyphiidae, 151, 152, 153
Liochthonius, 175
Liodes, 162, 168
Liodidae, 168
Lithobiomorpha, 93, 95, 241
Lithobius, 154
  crassipes, 94
  duboscqui, 94
  forficatus, 94, 95
  variegatus, 93, 94, 95
Lizards, 181, 183-184
Lophodermium, 8
Lucanidae, 108
Lucerne flea, 131

Lumbricidae, 35, 39, 43, 44, 59, 189, 212, 216, 218, 219, 221, 222, 225, 233
  British, 59
  cocoon production in, 63, 193
  deep-burrowing, 35, 61
  fecundity of, 195
  feeding activity of, 65-66, 192-193
  horizontal distribution of, 59-61
  metabolic activity of, 238, 240
  moorland populations of, 218
  mortality in, 197
  population sizes of, 62-64
  reproduction in, 64-65
  role in crumb-formation, 13, 65
  role in mineralization, 65
  surface-burrowing, 61
  vertical distribution of, 61, 62
Lumbricillus, 66
  lineatus, 195
Lumbricus castaneus, 60, 61, 63, 199
  festivus, 60
  rubellus, 59, 60, 61, 63, 64, 199, 219
  terrestris, 59, 60, 61, 62, 63, 64, 189, 216, 240
Lung fish, 181
Lycoria sociata, 118
Lycosidae, 151-152

Machilidae, 127
Machilis, 127
Macrobiotus intermedius, 101
  hufelandi, 101
Macrocheles muscaedomesticae, 200
Macrochelidae, 44, 159, 163, 173, 200
Macrofauna, 39, 41
Macrotrachela, 56
Mammalia, 184-190
March flies, 116
Marionina, 66
  cambrensis, 67, 69, 70
Marsupial mice, 184
Mecoptera, 104
Megabunus diadema, 154, 155
Megascolecidae, 58
Megascolides, 58
Meiofauna, 39
Meloidae, 108
Melolontha melolontha, 110, 111
Melolonthinae, 109
Meranoplus, 121

Mesocypris terrestris, 79
Mesofauna, 38, 39, 41
Mesostigmatid mites (Mesostigmata), 43, 147, 158, 159, 161, 162, 163, 164, 166-167, 170, 171, 173, 174, 199, 201, 244
Messor, 121
Metamorphic rocks, 2
Metasesarma aubryi, 80
Metrioppiidae, 168
Mettarrhizium anisopliae, 112
Mice, 189
Miconchus, 55
Microchaetidae, 58
Micrococcus, 232
Microfauna, 38, 39
Microflora, *see* Bacteria and Fungi
Microhyla, 183
Micro-organisms, 8, 10, 11
Microphytic feeders, 43
Microrespirometer, 235
Microtus, 184
Micryphantidae, 151
Milax budapestensis, 71, 72, 73, 197
Millipedes, 10, 32-33, 38, 43, 44, 97-100, 199, 228, 233; *see also* Diplopoda
Milnesium tardigradum, 101
Mineralization, 65, 232, 233
Minerals, 2-3
Minunthozetes semirufus, 169, 170
Miscellaneous feeders, 43, 55
Mites, 10, 15, 19, 21, 32, 33, 35, 38, 41, 42, 44, 147, 150, 159-175, 202, 210, 222; *see also* Acari
  as food for beetles, 108
  as food for moles, 189
  effects of pesticides on, 225
  energetics of, 234-238, 240, 243-244
  extraction of, 253
  fecundity of, 192-195
  feeding habits of, 43, 173-175
  fertility of, 196
  grassland populations of, 216, 217
  horizontal distribution of, 159-163
  humidity and temperature reactions of, 164-166
  life cycles of, 166-170
  moorland populations of, 218
  phoretic, 174
  population dynamics of, 170-173

Mites—*cont.*
  population regulation, 203
  predation by, 199-201
  preservation of, 257
  vertical distribution of, 163-164
  woodland populations of, 220, 221
Mitopus morio, 154-155, 238-239
Mniobia, 56
Moder soil, 34-35
  enchytraeids in, 67
  extraction of mites from, 253
  isopods of, 84
Mole crickets, 104
Mole-rats, 184
Moles, 186-190, 220
Mollusca, 32, 39, 42, 43, 70-74, 219, 247, 248
Monhystera, 51, 55
  vulgaris, 52
Mononchus, 51, 55
Moorland soil, 26, 27, 36, 217, 218
  collembolans in, 132-134, 144-147, 218
  earthworms in, 63, 218
  enchytraeids in, 68, 218
  mites in, 170, 171, 218
  spiders in, 151-153
  tipulids in, 117, 218
Mor and mull, 11, 29-31, 35, 36
  biochemical characteristics of, 34
  biological characteristics of, 31-34, 219, 221-223
  centipede fauna of, 94
  earthworm fauna of, 62-63
  isopods of, 84
  millipede fauna of, 98
  protozoan fauna of, 46-47
Mortality, 196-204
Moth flies, 116
Mountford's index, 213-215
Mull, *see* Mor
Musca domestica, 173
Muscidae, 117
Mutillidae, 120
Mycetophilidae, 43, 116, 117
Myriapoda, 11, 35, 41, 89-100, 220, 221
  as food for pseudoscorpions, 157
  as hosts for phoretic mites, 162
  as prey for moles, 189
  extraction of, 253
  mortality in, 197

Myrmecocystus, 121
Myrmica ruginodis, 121, 124
Myrmicinae, 121-123

Naegleria, 46
Naididae, 58
Nanhermannia, 164
  elegantula, 170
  nana, 165, 168, 169
Narrow-mouthed toad, 183
Nasal cooling device, 186
Natality, 192-196
Natural associations, 208-215
Neanura muscorum, 136
Nebela, 46-49
Nebria brevicollis, 108, 113, 114
Necrophages, 43
Necrophloeophagus longicornis, 94
Necrophorus, 116
  fossor, 116
  germanicus, 116
  humator, 116
  investigator, 116
  vespillo, 116
  vespilloides, 116
Neelidae, 131, 142
Nemastoma lugubre, 154
Nemastomatidae, 153
Nematocera, 116, 117
Nematoda, 39, 41, 43, 50-55, 153,
    200-201, 202, 203
  as food for mites, 162, 173, 175,
    199
  extraction of, 252
  moorland populations of, 218
  preservation of, 257
Nematophora, 99
Neobisium muscorum, 155-157
  sylvaticum, 155
Neostyriaca corynodes, 70
Neotoma, 184
Neuroptera, 104
Nielsen extractor, 255
Nitidulidae, 43, 108
Nitrobacter, 232
Nitrogen cycle, 232
Nitrosomonas, 232
Noctuidea, 104, 125
Nocturnalism, in carabid beetles, 17,
    108
  in desert rodents, 184

Nocturnalism—*cont.*
  in harvestmen, 154
  in isopods, 84-86
Nothrus, 163, 168
  palustris, 163
  pratensis, 163, 164
  silvestris, 162-164, 169
Notiophilus, 113
  palustris, 108
  rufipes, 108
  substriatus, 108
Notomys, 186
Notoryctes typhlops, 187
Nutrient cycling, 230-233

Ochrosol, 28
Octolasium cyaneum, 59-63, 216
  lacteum, 61
Odiellus palpinalis, 154
Odontotermes, 106
Oicomonas, 46
Oligochaetes, 58, 189
Oligolophus agrestis, 154
  tridens, 154, 238, 239
Oncopodura, 142
Oniscidae, 81, 82
Oniscus asellus, 80-84
  activity patterns of, 84, 197-198
  metabolic activity of, 82, 83, 237,
    238
Onychiuridae, 130, 131
Onychiurus, 133, 135, 142, 217
  armatus, 136, 137
  fimatus, 136
  furcifer, 144, 145
  granulosus, 137
  latus, 144, 145, 146
  procampatus, 143-146, 237, 238
  tricampatus, 144-146
Onychophora, 77-78
Ophyiulus pilosus, 96, 98
Opiliones, 39, 153-155, 238
Opisthopatus, 77, 78
  cinctipes, 78
Oppia, 163, 164, 169, 217, 235, 253
  nitens, 169
  nova, 164, 168, 169, 172, 193,
    194, 195, 210
  ornata, 163, 164
  quadricarinata, 170
  subpectinata, 170

Orchesella, 133, 135, 142
  cincta, 136
  flavescens, 136
Orchestia, 78
Orcula doliolum, 70, 71
Organo-chlorine pesticides, 181-182, 225
Organo-mineral complexes, 1, 11-13
Organo-phosphate pesticides, 225
Oribatella quadricornuta, 170
Oribatula tibialis, 174
Oribella castanea, 175
Oribotritia berlesei, 168
Orthogalumna terebrantis, 174
Orthoptera, 43, 44, 104
Oryctes, 112
Oscinella frit, 117
Ostracoda, 78, 79
Othius angustus, 108
  punctulatus, 108
Overlapping generations, in centipedes, 96
  in harvestmen, 154
  in isopods, 87
Oxidation, 6
Oxychilus inopinatus, 71
Oxypoda annularis, 115

Pagodulina pagodula 71
Pampas, 215
Paracentropyxis, 48
Parachipteria willmanni, 170, 238
Parapelops, 210
Parasites and parasitism, 43, 50, 112, 115, 120, 201-202
Parasitic mites, 159, 202
Parasitidae, 167
Parasitoids, 112, 202
Parasitus, 163, 173
Parathion, 225
Pardosa monticola, 151, 152
  nigriceps, 151, 152
  pullata, 151, 152
Parental care, 95
Parent material, 1-7
Passalidae, 108
Passalozetes perforatus, 217
Pasture soil, 211, 216
  Collembola in, 132, 134-135
  earthworms in, 59-60
  enchytraeids in, 66, 68
  mites in, 171
  moles in, 187

Pauropoda, 89-90, 243, 253
Pauropus huxleyi, 89
  silvaticus, 90
Peat soil, 25, 26, 28, 34, 36, 218
  earthworm fauna of, 59
  enchytraeid populations in, 66, 218
  moles in, 188
  nematodes in, 218
  wireworms in, 110
Pedalfers, 27
Pedocals, 27
Pelidnota punctata, 110
Pelobates, 183
Peloribates, 175
Pentatomids, 40
Pentazonia, 96
Pergalumna omniphagous, 55, 168, 169, 172, 175, 192, 193, 199
Pergamasus, 163, 173
  crassipes, 167
Peripatoides, 77
Peripatopsis, 50, 77, 78
  balfouri, 78
  capensis, 78
  moseleyi, 78
Peripatus, 77, 78
Pesticide, *see* Insecticide
Phalangiidae, 153
Phalangium opilio, 154, 155
Phascogale, 184
Pheidole, 121
Pheidologeton, 121
Pheretima, 58
Pheromones, 106
Philodina, 56
Philoscia muscorum, 81, 82, 84
Phoridae, 117
Phosphorus cycle, 232-233
Phosphuga atrata, 116
Photosynthesis, 228-231
Phryganella, 46
Phthiracaridae, 43, 55, 174
Phthiracarus anonymum, 168
  borealis, 164
  piger, 170
Phyllopertha horticola, 110, 111
Phyllophaga, 110, 111, 112
Phytophages (plant-feeders), 9, 43, 44, 55, 74, 91, 99, 106, 108, 109, 110, 117, 123, 125, 142, 174, 228-230, 234; *see also* Herbivores

Picris echioides, 88
Pigs, 182
Pirata piraticus, 152
Pisidium, 70
Pitfall traps, 255
Plagiopyxis, 46, 48
Planarians, 50
Platybunus triangularis, 154
Platyhelminthes, 50
Platyliodes, 162
Platynothrus peltifer, 162, 163, 165, 166, 169, 170, 171, 172, 173, 193, 210
Plectus, 51-54
  granulosus, 51
  rhizophilus, 52
Pleocoma, 112
Pleocominae, 109
Ploughing, effect on earthworm distribution, 61
  effect on slug distribution, 72, 73
Plusiocampa, 128
Podacarus auberti, 168
Podura aquatica, 130, 133, 138-139, 141
Poduridae, 131
Podzol, 36
Podzolization, 26-27, 30
Pogonomyrmex, 121, 122
  badius, 123
Polydesmidae, 96
Polydesmoidea, 44, 96
Polydesmus, 93
  angustus, 96, 98
  denticulatus, 98
Polymicrodon polydesmoides, 96, 97, 98
Polyxenus lagurus, 97
Ponera coarctata, 121
Ponerinae, 121, 122
Popillia japonica, 110, 111
Population regulation, 203-204
Porcellio dilatatus, 82
  scaber, 80-87, 192, 195, 201, 202
Porcellionidae, 80, 81, 82
Prairie soil, 26, 215
Precipitin test, 196
Predator/prey relationship, 200, 201, 241
Predators, 43, 49, 55, 57, 70, 74, 77, 94-95, 108, 117, 122-123, 128, 130, 141-142, 150-151, 154, 157-159, 162, 163, 173-175,

Predators—*cont.*
  184, 187-190, 191-201, 203-204, 219, 228-230, 241-245; *see also* Carnivore
Prelarva, 168
Primary consumers, 21, 44, 228
  producers, 44, 228
  production, 230-231
Prionchulus, 55
Prismatolaimus, 51, 54
  dolichurus, 52
Proctotrupidae, 120
Prodinychus, 174
Projapygidae, 127
Prostigmata (Prostigmatid mites), 43, 159, 161, 167, 171, 174, 244, 257
Protentomon, 128
Proteroiulus fuscus, 97, 98
Protopterus, 181
Protoribates lophotrichus, 169
Protozoa, 10, 38-39, 41, 43, 46-50, 237, 250
Protura, 39, 127-130, 143, 200, 243
Pselaphidae, 41, 43, 107, 108
Pseudachorutes, 142
Pseudechiniscus suillus, 101
Pseudergates, 105
Pseudomonas, 232
Pseudoscorpions, 43, 44, 155-159, 192, 197, 199, 201, 219, 253
Pseudosinella alba, 143
Pseudotracheae, 83
Psila rosae, 117
Psocoptera, 104
Psychodidae, 116
Pterostichus (= Feronia) minor, 114
  nigrita, 114
  trenuus, 114
Ptiliidae, 108
Puffin, 181
Pupilla, 71, 74
  sterri, 71
  triplicata, 71
Pyemotidae, 174
Pyramidula rupestris, 71

Quedius boops, 108
  lateralis, 115
Quotient of Similarity (Q/S), 210-212

Rabbits, 180
Rats, 184

Reduction, 6
Relative abundance, 209, 210, 212-213
Rendzina, 35
Renkonen's number, 212-213
Reptiles, 183-184
Reticulitermes, 104, 106
Rhabditella leptura, 200
Rhabditida, 50, 51
Rhabditis, 50, 51, 55
Rhagidiidae, 167
Rhagionidae, 116
Rhinoceros, 174, 182
Rhizobium, 232
Rhizoctonia solani, 8
Rhizoglyphus echinopus, 167
Rhizopods, 46
Rhodacarus, 164
Rhynchodemus terrestris, 50
Rhysotritia, 164
    ardua, 169
    duplicata, 170
Roaches, 104
Robber flies, 116
Robin, 181
Rocks, classification of, 2
Rodents, 184
Roncus lubricus, 156
Rostrozetes flavus, 169, 172, 193
Rotifera, 38-39, 41, 55-57
Rutelinae, 109, 111

Sand martin, 181
    minerals, 3
    roach, 198
    swimmers, 183
Sap-feeding beetles, 108
Saprophage, 43, 44, 221, 223; *see also*
    Detritivores
    beetles, 106, 108, 109
    Collembola, 142
    Diptera, 117
    earthworms, 10
    enchytraeids, 10
    isopods, 10, 88-89
    Lepidoptera, 125
    millipedes, 10, 99-100
    mites, 10, 174
    nematodes, 54
    symphylids, 91
Sarcophagidae, 117
Saturation deficit, 19-20, 139

Savannah, 215
Scapanus latimanus, 187
Scarabaeidae, 43, 107-112
Scarites, 107
Scatophagidae, 117
Scatopsidae, 117
Scavengers, 43
Scheloribates, 163
    laevigatus, 164, 168, 169, 172, 174, 175, 193, 195, 210
    parabilis, 169, 193
Schizophyllum sabulosum, 96, 98, 99
Sciara, 119, 154
Sciaridae, 116
Scincomorpha (skinks), 183
Sciomyzidae, 202
Scoliidae, 112, 120
Scolopendra, 93
    amazonica, 95, 96
Scolopendridae, 95
Scolopendromorpha, 93, 95, 96
Scolytidae, 109
Scorpions, 43, 78, 150
Scorpion flies, 104
Scutacaridae, 174, 253
Scutigera coleoptrata, 94
Scutigerella immaculata, 89-92
Scutigeromorpha, 93-95
Scydmaenidae, 43, 107, 108
Secondary consumer, 44, 228-229
    production, 237
Sedimentary rocks, 2
Selatosomus aeneus, 110
Sepsidae, 117
Serianus, 158
Serica brunnea, 110
Sesarma rotundatum, 80
Sevin, 225
Shearwater, 181
Sheep, 182
Shrews, 189
Sieving methods, 247-248
Silpha, 116
Silphidae, 107, 108, 112, 115-116
Silt minerals, 3
Simazine, 224
Sipalia circellaris, 115
Slow worms, 184
Slugs, 32, 33, 70-74, 197, 199
    accumulation of pesticides in, 181
    population regulation in, 203
    respiration rates of, 239

Sminthurides malmgreni, 133
Sminthurus fuscus, 136
  viridis, 131, 136
Snails, 70, 181
Snakes, 183, 184
Soil, azonal, 25
  classification of, 25-29
  mineral and organic composition of, 1-14
  sectioning, 256
  sedentary, 5, 6
  stages in development of, 13
  transported, 5, 6
Soil atmosphere, 20, 21
  community, 208
  ecosystem, 208
  moisture, 18-20
  temperature, 14-18
  water fauna, 41, 44, 52, 55, 57, 100, 101
Soil types, alkali, 26
  desert, 82, 184, 185, 199
  forest, 26, 218-224
  grassland, 26, 215-218, 221-224
  heath, 26, 217-218
  moor, 26, 217-218
  peat, 25, 26, 28, 34, 36, 218
  rendzina, 35
Soldier flies, 116
Solifugae, 150
Sørensen's quotient, 210-212
Spade-foot toad, 183
Spalax, 184
Spelaeodiscus tatricus, 71
Sphecidae, 121
Sphingidae, 125
Spiders, 43, 150-153, 219, 222, 251
  as food for beetles, 108
  as food for moles, 189
  extraction of, 255
  mortality in, 197
Spiny mice, 184
Spirostreptus, 97
Springtails, *see* Collembola
Stable flies, 117
Stag beetles, 108
Standing crop, 236, 237
Staphylinidae, 43, 106, 107, 112, 219, 221
  as food for centipedes, 95
  as predators, 108, 200, 202
  life history of, 115

Staphylinus chalcocephalus, 115
Steganacarus diaphanum, 169
  magnus, 163, 165, 170, 174, 253
Steppe, 71, 215
Sticky traps, 255
Stiletto flies, 117
Stratiomyidae, 116
Strigamia maritima, 94
Strongyloides papillosus, 50, 201
Stylommatophora, 70
Succinea, 70
Suction traps, 255
Suctobelba, 163, 164, 169, 175, 235
  subtrigona, 170
  trigona, 169
Sulphur cycle, 232-233
Sunspiders, 43, 150
Survival rates, 195
Symbiosis, 232
Symphyla, 43, 44, 90-92, 243, 253
Symphylella, 91, 92
Symphylellopsis, 91, 92
Symphypleona, 131
Synchronization of life cycles, 172-173
Synoecomorphs, 42
Syrphidae, 117

Tabanidae, 112, 116, 118
Tabanus, 119
Tachinidae, 112, 117, 202
Tachypodoiulus niger, 98
Talitridae, 78
Talitroides dorrieni, 78
Talorchestia, 78
Talpa, 44
  europeae, 187-190
  micrura, 187
Tardigrada, 39, 41, 100-101, 143
Tarsonemidae, 174
Tawny owls, 188
Tectocepheus velatus, 163, 170, 210
Temperature/metabolism curve, 239
Tenebrionidae, 108
Termites, 32, 35, 43, 104-106
Termitidae, 106
Terra rossa, 28
Tertiary consumer, 44, 154, 158, 228
Testacea, 46-49
Testacella, 74
Testudo polyphemus, 183

Tetracanthella brachyura, 133
    wahlgreni, 134
Tetradontophora bielanensis, 136
Tetragnathidae, 151
Tetramorium caespitum, 123
Thecamoebae, 46
Therevidae, 117
Theridiidae, 151
Thomomys, 184
Thrips, 40, 104, 174
Thrushes, 181
Thysanoptera, 40, 104
Thysanura, 104, 127
Ticks, 159
Tiger beetles, 106
Tipula, 41, 119, 120, 197
    fulvipennis, 118, 119
    luna, 118, 119, 120
    luteipennis, 118, 119
    maxima, 118
    oleracea, 118
    pruinosa, 118
    staegeri, 118, 119
    variicornis, 119
    vittata, 118, 119, 120
    unca, 118
Tipulidae, 34, 116, 117, 218
    as food for moles, 189-190
Titmice, 181
Toads, 183
Tomocerus, 133, 135, 141, 142
    flavus, 147
    longicornis, 136, 158
    minor, 144
    vulgaris, 136
Tortoises, 183
Toxochernes panzeri, 155
Trachytes, 163
Trichoceridae, 117
Trichoderma viride, 8
Trichoniscidae, 81
Trichoniscus pusillus, 80, 81, 84
Trichoptera, 104
Tricladida, 50
Trigonopyxis, 47
Trilobus, 55
Trinema, 46
Trinervitermes, 106
Tripyla, 51, 54
    setifera, 52
Troginae, 109
Troglomorphs, 42

Trogulidae, 153
Trombidiidae, 155, 174
Trophic levels, 229
Truncatellina claustralis, 71
    strobeli, 71
Tuber worms, 125
Tubificidae, 58
Tullbergia, 133, 217
    krausbaueri, 135, 144-147
Tullgren funnel, 250, 251
Tydeidae, 165
Tylenchida, 50, 51
Tylencholaimus, 55
    mirabilis, 52
Tylenchorhynchus martini, 199
Tylenchus, 51, 55
    filiformis, 52
    polyhypnus, 198
Typhiid wasps, 112, 120
Typhlops, 184
Typhlosaurus, 183

Urine/plasma osmotic ratio, 186
Urodeles, 183, 199
Uropodina, 173

Veigaia, 158, 173, 200
    mitis, 199
Velvet ants, 120
Venezillo arizonicus, 82, 83, 86
Vertebrates, 39, 44, 180-190
Vertigo alpestris, 70, 74
Vitraea, 74
Vitrina, 71, 74
Viviparity, 78, 166, 168, 192
Voles, 184

Wasps, 112, 120-121
Weathering agents, 3-7
Web spinners, 104
Wet funnel extractor, 220, 254, 255
Wet sieving, 247-248
Wheat bulb fly, 117
Wilsonema otophorum, 52
Wind action, 4
Wireworms, 110, 190
Wood-boring beetles, 43, 109
Woodland soil, 212, 218-224; *see also*
        Forest soil
    ants of, 121
    carabid beetles in, 108
    Collembola of, 256

Woodland soil—*cont.*
  lumbricids of, 240
  millipedes of, 96-98
  mites of, 159, 162, 171, 173, 256
  moles in, 188
  Nematocera in, 117
  spiders in, 151
  tardigrades in, 100-101
Woodlice, 10, 80; *see also* Isopoda

Xerophiles, 42, 133, 134, 162
Xerophytic plants, 188
Xylocopa, 120
Xylodrepa quadripunctata, 116

Xylophages, 43
  beetles, 107, 109, 174
  millipedes, 99
  termites, 106

Yeasts, 142

Zebrina detrita, 71
Zerconidae, 164
Zoochlorellae, 48
Zonal soils, 25
Zonites, 74
Zonitoides nitidus, 70, 74
Zygoribatula rostrata, 210

Printed by Spottiswoode, Ballantyne and Co. Ltd., London and Colchester